100 MATHS LESSONS

YEAR 6

Published by Scholastic Ltd,
Villiers House,
Clarendon Avenue,
Leamington Spa,
Warwickshire CV32 5PR

© **2000 Scholastic Ltd**
Text © **Jean Livingstone & Wally Nickels 2000**
2 3 4 5 6 7 8 9 0 1 2 3 4 5 6 7 8 9

SERIES CONSULTANT
Ann Montague-Smith

AUTHORS
Jean Livingstone & Wally Nickels

EDITORS
Angela Dewsbury
Steven Carruthers

ASSISTANT EDITOR
David Sandford

SERIES DESIGNER
Joy White

DESIGNERS
Paul Cheshire
Rachael Hammond

COVER PHOTOGRAPH
Kim Oliver

ILLUSTRATIONS
Ray and Corinne Burrows

British Library Cataloguing-in-Publication Data
A catalogue record for this book is available from the British Library.

ISBN 0-439-01698-3

The right of Jean Livingstone & Wally Nickels to be identified as the Authors of this work has been asserted by them in accordance with the Copyright, Designs and Patents Act 1988.

ACKNOWLEDGEMENTS

The publishers wish to thank:
Galt Educational and NES Arnold Educational Supplies for kindly loaning the equipment used on the front cover.
This publication contains material from *The National Numeracy Strategy* which was published by the **Department for Education and Employment**. © Crown copyright 1999. Reproduced with the permission of the Controller of Her Majesty's Stationery Office.

CONTENTS

INTRODUCTION

100 Maths Lessons is a series of year-specific teachers' resource books, for Reception to Year 6, that provide a core of support material for the teaching of mathematics within the National Numeracy Strategy *Framework for Teaching Mathematics* (March 1999) and within the structure of the 'dedicated mathematics lesson'. Each book offers three terms of medium-term planning grids, teaching objectives and lesson plans. At least 100 maths lessons are given in detail, with outlines for all the others needed to provide support for teachers for a whole year of maths teaching. Photocopiable activity pages and resources are included to support the learning. Regular assessment is built into the structure of the book, with assessment activity pages that can be kept as evidence of attainment.

Each *100 Maths Lessons* book provides support across all the mathematics topics and learning objectives specified for a particular year group. However, the pages of the books have been hole-punched and perforated, so that they can be removed and placed in teachers' own resource files where they can be interleaved with complementary materials from the school's existing schemes. This makes the integration of favourite material into this series very easy.

These books are intended as a support for the dedicated mathematics lesson for the school mathematics co-ordinator, teachers, and trainee teachers. The series of books can be used as the basis of planning, teaching and assessment for the whole school from Reception to Year 6. These resources can be adapted for use by the whole school for single-aged classes, mixed-age classes, single- and mixed-ability groups, and for team planning across a year or a key stage. There is sufficient detail in the differentiated group activities within the 100 lesson plans to offer guidance to classroom assistants working with a particular group.

The activities in this book are designed to encourage pupils to develop mental strategies, to use paper and pencil methods appropriately, and to use and apply their mathematics in realistic tasks within proper contexts.

The approach and content of the book dovetails into the work of Year 5. At times it specifically revises important aspects before extending into the learning objectives specified by the National Numeracy Strategy for Year 6. Each unit of work develops the mathematics for the children, providing the platform for a smooth entry into the work of KS3, where algebra (working with formula and equations), graphical work, 2-D and 3-D shape work and so on will feature. There is also an expectancy in the activities provided that children can organise their work, individually, in pairs or as a group.

By the time children reach Year 6 their ability range is wide. Differentiation is important and care has been taken to ensure that this is catered for in every lesson provided. Whenever it is relevant, the activities have been applied to real-life contexts and care has been taken to make them both interesting and realistic.

As suggested in the National Numeracy Strategy *Standards in Mathematics* booklet, solving problems is an essential element of mathematical education. *100 Maths Lessons* gives emphasis to children communicating and comparing their solutions, describing their reasoning and justifying their results.

The content of this book is also appropriate for, and adaptable to, the requirements of Primary 6–7 in Scottish schools. Teachers in schools which decide not to adopt the National Numeracy Strategy can choose activities from this book to match their own planning.

USING THIS BOOK

THE MATERIALS

This book provides at least 100 maths lesson plans for Year 6, and further activity ideas to support all other dedicated maths lessons required during the year. Each maths lesson plan contains ideas for developing pupils' oral and mental maths, a detailed explanation of the main part of the lesson, ideas for differentiated activities and suggestions for the plenary session. The book follows the Year 6 planning grid given in the National Numeracy Strategy *Framework for Teaching Mathematics* and so, for each teaching section, whether it covers one, two or three units of work, there are some detailed lessons plans and objectives and outline content for the other lessons. These materials should be regarded as a core for developing your own personalised folder for the year. More detail on planning and managing all aspects of the National Numeracy Strategy can be found in the *Framework for Teaching Mathematics*.

ADAPTING AND PERSONALISING THE MATERIALS

The materials are based on the 'Teaching Programme and planning grid' for Year 6 given in the National Numeracy Strategy *Framework for Teaching Mathematics*. What follows is a suggested method of using this **100 Maths Lessons** book to its full potential, but bear in mind that you may need to make adjustments to these materials in order to meet the learning needs of the pupils in your class.
- Separate the pages of the book and place them in an A4 ring binder.
- Check that the activities are of a suitable level for your pupils and agree with colleagues who teach lower years that the entry level is a good match. If not, you can use materials from the **100 Maths Lessons** book for the previous or subsequent years.
- Add your own favourite materials in the relevant places.
- If your school uses a published scheme, insert suitable teacher and pupil resources into your file to supplement these materials.

PREPARING A SCHEME OF WORK

All schools are required to write detailed schemes of work, and this series has been designed to facilitate this process. The termly 'Planning grids' given in these books are provided at the beginning of the work for each term and list all the learning objectives. For example, here is part of the grid for Term 1:

ORAL AND MENTAL STARTER Use known number facts and place value to consolidate mental addition, subtraction and multiplication strategies from previous year(s). Consolidate mental addition and subtraction of any two numbers less than 100. Derive quickly doubles of all whole numbers 1 to 100 (Year 5). Consolidate knowing by heart multiplication facts up to 10 × 10.		
UNIT	**TOPIC**	**OBJECTIVES: CHILDREN WILL BE TAUGHT TO**
1	Place value, ordering and rounding Understanding × and ÷	• Read and write whole numbers in figures and words and know what each digit represents (Year 5). • Order a set of integers less than 1 million (Year 5). • Consolidate rounding an integer to the nearest 10, 100 or 1000. • Use the vocabulary of estimation and approximation. • **Use appropriate operations to solve word problems involving numbers and quantities** based on 'real life' and money. • Develop calculator skills and use a calculator effectively.
2–3	Mental calculation strategies (× and ÷) Pencil and paper procedures	• Understand and use the relationships between the four operations, and the principles (not the names) of the arithmetic laws. • Use brackets. • Partition. • Develop calculator skills and use a calculator effectively. • Use known number facts and place value to consolidate mental multiplication. • Approximate first. Use informal pencil and paper methods to support, record or explain multiplications. • **Extend written methods to** multiplication of ThHTU × U (short multiplication).

ORGANISATION

The **Organisation chart** outlines the key activities for each part of each maths lesson and can be used as a weekly plan, but could be adjusted according to the needs of the class.

LESSON PLANS

After the **Organisation chart** comes a short section detailing which lessons are shown as full lesson plans and which are extensions of what has already been taught in a previous lesson. Some of these will be shown in grid form.

DETAILED LESSON PLANS

Each detailed lesson plan is written to the following headings:

Resources
Provides a list of what you need for that lesson.

Preparation
Outlines any advance preparation needed before the lesson begins, such as making resources or photocopying worksheets.

Learning outcomes
These are based on the objectives in the 'Teaching programme: Year 6' from the *Framework for Teaching Mathematics*. All the objectives are covered at least once in this book. Key objectives for Year 6 are highlighted in bold, as they are in the *Framework for Teaching Mathematics*. If a lesson does not cover an objective in its entirety, then only the portion that is intended to be covered is listed in the 'Learning outcomes' (or any of the grids provided).

The specific objectives for the **Oral and mental starter** and **Main teaching activity** are each listed separately.

Vocabulary
The National Numeracy Strategy *Mathematical Vocabulary* booklet has been used to provide the vocabulary lists, with additional words and phrases included where necessary. New or specific vocabulary to be used during the lesson is listed. Use this vocabulary with the children so that they have a chance to hear it and understand it. Encourage pupils to use the vocabulary orally when asking or answering questions, so that they develop understanding of its mathematical meaning.

Oral and mental starter
This is designed to occupy the first 5–10 minutes of the lesson, but the duration of the work is not critical. This section contains activity suggestions to develop oral and mental work. Where applicable, suggestions for differentiated questioning are included to show how all the children can benefit. The detail in the lesson plan will help you to: provide a variety of sequentially planned, short oral and mental activities throughout the week, use a good range of open and closed questions, encourage all children to take part and target differentiated questions to individuals, pairs or small groups.

Main teaching activity
This sets out what to do in the whole-class teaching session and should last for about 40 minutes. In some lessons, much of the time will be spent in whole-class, interactive teaching. In others, the whole-class session will be shorter, with differentiated activities for groups, pairs or individuals taking up most of the time. The detailed lesson plans will help you to organise this part of the lesson appropriately.

Differentiation
This section suggests activities for differentiated group, paired or individual work for the more able and less able children within the class. These activities will take the form of reinforcement, enrichment or extension, and many will provide challenges to encourage pupils to use and apply their mathematics.

Plenary
This session is a chance to bring the children together again for a 10 minute whole-class session at the end of the lesson. This offers opportunities to assess pupils' progress, summarise key facts learned, compare strategies used, make links to other topics and to plan for the next topic.

EXTENSION LESSON PLANS
These provide activities that extend those already covered. They are less detailed, as they are based on one of the previous lessons for that week.

OUTLINE LESSON PLANS
These contain brief descriptions, as grids, of further lessons. They extend the scope of the book to give sufficient material for a year's work. Since they develop work already introduced, there are no vocabulary suggestions as the same range of words will be needed as in the previous, related lesson(s).

WEEKLY PLANNING

The Organisation chart, which appears at the beginning of each unit or block of units of work, outlines the key activities for each part of each maths lesson, and can be used as a weekly plan. Follow it if you wish to use the ready-prepared plans:

	LEARNING OUTCOMES	ORAL AND MENTAL STARTER	MAIN TEACHING ACTIVITY	PLENARY
LESSON 1	• Read and write whole numbers in figures and words and know what each digit represents (Year 5). • Order a set of integers less than 1 million (Year 5). • Consolidate rounding an integer to the nearest 10, 100 or 1,000.	ABOUT US: Practising operations to 'hit' a target number using 'personal' numbers.	WHERE DOES IT LIVE? Positioning numbers to 1,000,000 on number lines.	Discussing where larger numbers are used in the world.
LESSON 2	• Read and write whole numbers in figures and words and know what each digit represents (Year 5). • Use the vocabulary of estimation and approximation. • Consolidate rounding an integer to the nearest 10, 100 or 1,000. • **Use appropriate operations to solve word problems involving numbers and quantities** based on 'real life' and money. • Develop calculator skills and use a calculator effectively.	BAG NUMBERS: Adding and finding the difference between two- or three-digit numbers.	WHAT THE PAPERS SAY: Using, estimating and rounding large numbers. Investigating car and house prices.	Discussing answers.
LESSON 3	• Read and write whole numbers in figures and words and know what each digit represents (Year 5). • Use the vocabulary of estimation and approximation. • Consolidate rounding an integer to the nearest 10, 100 or 1,000. • **Use appropriate operations to solve word problems involving numbers and quantities** based on 'real life' and money. • Develop calculator skills and use a calculator effectively.	BAG NUMBERS: Adding and finding the difference between two- or three-digit numbers and doubles of these numbers.	FOOTBALL CROWDS: Using, estimating and rounding larger numbers. Investigating football match attendances. Discussions centred on their findings.	
	ORAL AND MENTAL SKILLS Use known number facts and place value to consolidate mental addition, subtraction and multiplication strategies from previous year(s). Consolidate mental addition and subtraction of any two numbers less than 100. **Derive quickly** doubles of all whole numbers 1 to 100 (Year 5).			

If you prefer to plan your week using some of the lesson plans in the book with some activities you have chosen yourself, then make some photocopies of the blank 'Weekly planning chart' on page 11 of this book. You can then fill in the details of all the activities that you intend to use, those chosen from this book and those that you have taken from other sources.

MIXED-AGE CLASSES

If you have a mixed-age class, you will probably need to use the materials from more than one book in this series. You will find the blank 'Weekly planning chart' on page 11 a useful planning tool, as you can use it to combine planning from two or more books.

CLASSROOM ORGANISATION

WHOLE-CLASS TEACHING

During a whole-class session it is important that all the children can see you and any children participating at the front (together with the resources being used by you or them), and the board or flip chart, if used. In many classrooms space is at a premium, so it is worth spending time considering how the furniture can best be arranged for the various types of activities that are used.

GROUP WORK

Again, it is important that the pupils sit so that they can see you and, if used, the board or flip chart. Before the start of the lesson, plan which group you are going to spend most of your time with. References are made regarding this throughout the book. While the children are working in groups, you may wish to ask whole-class questions, or remind pupils of how much time is left to complete their task.

WORKING WITH OTHER ADULTS

If you have classroom helpers, brief them before the lesson starts on which group you would like them to work with, the purpose of the task, any vocabulary they should be helping to develop, and the type of questions they should be asking. Check that all the resources needed are available or, if not, that the helper knows where to find them. You may want to ask a classroom helper to work with just one or two pupils, perhaps those who are finding the work difficult, or pupils who have been absent to provide an opportunity for them to catch up on missed work. Whatever the reason, always ensure that the helper is well briefed before the lesson starts, and allow a few minutes after the lesson has finished to discuss any specific observations, queries or concerns that the helper would like to make.

CHILDREN WITH SPECIAL EDUCATIONAL NEEDS

Include children with special educational needs in the whole-class work. If you have a classroom helper or support assistant, ask them to sit beside the pupils with special needs to provide support. This could include repeating the questions quietly or encouraging them to use individual resources (such as a number line or a calculator when appropriate) to find the answer. During differentiated questioning, ensure that some questions are specifically focused for these pupils and encourage them to answer.

Pupils who are partially sighted or deaf will need to sit close to you, so take this into account when considering the layout of the classroom for maths lessons. Those with emotional or behaviour difficulties will benefit from the structure and routines of the daily maths lesson and, where possible, from the support of a helper who can encourage on-task working.

For children who are learning English as an additional language, speak more slowly, repeat instructions, and provide visual clues on worksheets or puzzle cards. For pupils who have an Individual Education Plan (IEP) that includes mathematics as an area of learning difficulty, use other books from this series to find activities of an appropriate level which can be linked to the work of the rest of the class.

PARENTS AND HOMEWORK

In order that mathematics homework can be used as an effective adjunct to the work in schools, it is important that parents appreciate that they have a role. With Year 6 children, homework may involve the participation of the parents but should also provide opportunities for the children to work without their assistance in order to build good study habits, and to build on their work at mathematics in school both in the lesson time and in extra-curricular clubs. They could help with number games and similar activities that occur throughout the year.

It is important that you share with parents the expectations for what most children in Year 6 should know, understand and be able to do. Without this knowledge, they will find it difficult to assess for themselves how their child is doing and how to help them. The

National Numeracy Strategy *At Home with Numeracy* booklet is a useful guide, providing background and ideas.

The homework provided by you may take the form of:

● a follow-up from a lesson, say a survey or finding where the mathematics being learned is used in the 'real world'
● learning number facts, eg through a game from your resource stock
● an investigation
● a worksheet.

Many of the activities in this book can be used or adapted for use as homework, while other useful materials can be found in the following Scholastic publications: *IMPACT Maths Homework* (Key Stage Two titles) and *Mental Maths Homework for 10 year olds/11 year olds* (by the IMPACT Project); *Quick Mental Maths for 10 year olds/11 year olds.*

RESOURCES

PHOTOCOPIABLE PAGES

The photocopiable pages in each section support the work and can be resource pages or activity sheets. They are marked with the photocopiable symbol:

Resource pages

These are sheets that have several applications and are used in various places in the book. They are given on pages 13 and 14: '1–100 square' and 'Answers to multiplication facts'. Each of the sheets can be made into sets of individual cards by photocopying on to card (enlarged if necessary), covering with self-adhesive plastic and then cutting them out.

Activity sheets

These are located at the end of the relevant units, and relate to specific activities. They may provide a resource, a game or a question sheet.

CLASSROOM EQUIPMENT

All the equipment used in this book will normally be found within any primary school. The following list shows what will be needed on a regular basis. Alternatives are suggested where they would be equally appropriate. Apart from a chalk board and chalk or flip chart and marker pens, you will also need:

● Base 10 apparatus: Dienes, MAB or Tillich Blocks
● large column boards covered with self-adhesive plastic
● pegboards and pegs
● interlocking cubes, Multilink and Centicubes
● dice: 1–6, 0–9, 1–9, 1–12
● shape apparatus: sets of 2–D and 3–D shapes
● drawing instruments: sharp pencils, cm and half cm rulers, 45° and 60° set squares, circular protractors with a 12cm diameter, compasses
● measuring equipment: metre rules, tape measures, various timers, stop clock, scales (bathroom and kitchen), measuring jugs, litre cubes
● calculators, including some with a 'sign change' key
● computers and software, including databases and Logo.

USING INFORMATION COMMUNICATION TECHNOLOGY

Make use of your favourite mathematical games software as a paired or small group activity. Some of the activities in this book use data handling software such as *Excel* (Microsoft Corporation), *Quattro Pro* (Corel Corporation) or any child-friendly software.

It is recommended that ICT lessons are used in order to give time for the children to develop the mathematical activities involved in using a computer.

ASSESSMENT

During the final week of each half term, an assessment period of two lessons is built into the planning. This gives you the opportunity to make medium-term assessments of the key objectives for Year 6, as listed in the National Numeracy Strategy. The aims of these assessments are to find out what progress each pupil has made, what he or she knows, understands and can do, whether they can apply and use the mathematics in context, and whether he or she has any weaknesses. They are also intended to give you information on which to base feedback to pupils and their parents or carers.

ASSESSMENT ADVICE

This is placed just before the assessment activity photocopiable sheets. Here you will find information on the aspects of mathematics that are to be assessed, some Oral and mental starter activities which can be used with the whole class, others which can be used with groups, pairs and individuals, and advice on using the photocopiable assessment tasks provided.

GROUP ASSESSMENT ACTIVITIES

These activities have been designed so that you can observe pupils at work and ask questions. Explain the purpose of the activity to them before they begin, as this will help them to demonstrate to you the things that you want to observe, such as clear recording, discussion of which strategy they used, why they used it and so on. Target small groups for a specific activity and period of time and work with them, observing how individuals respond to the activity. You may find it useful to have a notebook handy to make informal notes on observations and discussions. If you have a classroom helper, he or she can also be involved in the assessment process.

ASSESSMENT PHOTOCOPIABLE SHEETS

There are two photocopiable sheets for each half-term assessment period. Each sheet has specific assessment criteria written at the bottom. Photocopy the pages for pupils to complete while you observe others undertaking the assessment activities.

Mark the completed sheets, then give pupils feedback on their strengths and set targets for improvement in their areas of weaknesses. Keep the sheets in a portfolio as part of the evidence of the children's achievement.

CLASS ASSESSMENT RECORDING SHEET

A 'Class assessment recording sheet' is given on page 12. This lists the key objectives for Year 6 from the National Numeracy Strategy *Framework for Teaching Mathematics*. Photocopy the sheet, enlarge it to A3, and record individuals' progress on it. By the end of the year, after six assessments, you will have complete assessment evidence to pass on.

Each half-term assessment offers opportunities to assess all the relevant key objectives that have been taught. Some key objectives re-occur in later assessments. It is not necessary to assess every child each time. Use your assessment records to decide whether to re-assess a child or whether it is appropriate to leave a specific assessment objective because that child has already shown evidence that he or she has learned it.

STANDARD ASSESSMENT TESTS

The National Curriculum mathematics tests, SATs, for Year 6 have been borne in mind throughout the book. Many of the **Oral and mental starter** activities mirror the style and content of the mental arithmetic test, including timed questions. The **Main teaching activities** have been written to give children both the background and confidence to tackle the test questions. The half-termly assessments, described below, will help teachers to formulate the teacher assessment required as part of the testing procedures.

When the time comes to prepare the children for the test, consider how best to incorporate this revision work into the overall planning. The flexibility of approach provided in this book, with its hole punched and perforated pages, will enable you to interweave revision tasks into your resource files which you may have compiled from pages from this book along with complementary materials.

Weekly planning chart

(Photo-enlarge to A3.)

Week beginning:

Learning objectives
for oral and mental
starter:

	Oral and mental starter	Main teaching activity	Differentiation	Plenary	Resources
Monday					
Tuesday					
Wednesday					
Thursday					
Friday					

Year 6: class assessment record sheet

Key objectives: Year 6	Name																		
Multiply and divide decimals mentally by 10 or 100, and integers by 1 000, and explain the effect.																			
Reduce a fraction to its simplest form by cancelling common factors.																			
Use a fraction as an 'operator' to find fractions of numbers or quantities.																			
Solve simple problems involving ratio and proportion.																			
Order a mixed set of numbers with up to three decimal places.																			
Understand percentage as the number of parts in every 100, and find simple percentages of small whole-number quantities.																			
Extend written methods to column addition and subtraction of numbers involving decimals.																			
Derive quickly division facts corresponding to tables up to 10×10.																			
Extend written methods to short multiplication of numbers involving decimals.																			
Extend written methods to short division of numbers involving decimals.																			
Extend written methods to long multiplication of a three-digit by a two-digit integer.																			
Identify and use appropriate operations (including combinations of operations) to solve word problems involving numbers and quantities and explain methods and reasoning.																			
Solve a problem by representing, extracting and interpreting data in charts, tables and graphs.																			
Calculate the perimeter and area of simple compound shapes that can be split into rectangles.																			
Read and plot co-ordinates in all four quadrants.																			
Use a protractor to measure and draw acute and obtuse angles to the nearest degree.																			

1–100 Square

1	2	3	4	5	6	7	8	9	10
11	12	13	14	15	16	17	18	19	20
21	22	23	24	25	26	27	28	29	30
31	32	33	34	35	36	37	38	39	40
41	42	43	44	45	46	47	48	49	50
51	52	53	54	55	56	57	58	59	60
61	62	63	64	65	66	67	68	69	70
71	72	73	74	75	76	77	78	79	80
81	82	83	84	85	86	87	88	89	90
91	92	93	94	95	96	97	98	99	100

Answers to multiplication facts

32	36	35	40
45	30	42	36
48	54	24	28
49	56	63	64
72	81	27	21

This term's work reinforces and extends the work of Year 5. The Oral and mental activities involve addition and subtraction (including decimals), and multiplication and division of whole numbers. Children continue to develop skills, counting on and back in steps of 0.1, 0.2, 0.25 and 0.5, doubling two-digit numbers (including decimals) and multiples of 10 to 1000 together with corresponding halving. They also look at multiplying and dividing multiples of 10 (including decimals) and deriving quickly the division facts corresponding to tables up to 10 × 10. Estimating, approximating, ordering and rounding numbers to 1 000 000 together with written methods using columns for addition and subtraction (including decimals), short multiplication (Th, H, T, U by U) and short division (HTU by U) are taught. Ordering common and decimal fractions, finding equivalences, ratio, proportion and percentages are extended. Line graphs and bar charts with grouped discrete data, simple probability, acute and obtuse angles, 2–D and 3–D shapes, perimeters (including formulae), measures and shape and number sequences are all developed. Calculator skills are extended.

ENLARGE THIS SHEET TO A3 AND USE IT AS YOUR MEDIUM-TERM PLANNING GRID.

Oral and mental skills: Use known number facts and place value to consolidate mental addition, subtraction, multiplication and division, including decimals for addition and subtraction. **Derive quickly**, doubles of two digit numbers, including decimals and doubles of multiples of 10 to 1000 and the corresponding halves. Consolidate knowing by heart multiplication facts to 10 x10 (Year 5). Understand and use the relationships between the four operations. Fractions, decimals, percentages, ratios: Change an improper fraction to its equivalent mixed number and vice versa (Year5); recognise the equivalence between fractions and between decimal and fraction form of common fractions; order fractions and mixed numbers; count on in steps of 0.1, 0.2. 0.25, 0.5..... and then back; **multiply and divide decimals by 10 or 100 and explain the effect**; express simple fractions as percentages and vice versa; **solve simple problems involving ratio**. Find factors of any number to 100 (Year 5).

Unit	Topic	Objectives: children will be taught to...
1	Place value, ordering and rounding Using a calculator	• Read and write whole numbers in figures and words and know what each digit represents (Year 5). • Order a set of integers to a million (Year 5) • Use the vocabulary of estimation and approximation. Consolidate rounding an integer to the nearest 10, 100 or 1000. • Use appropriate operations to solve simple word problems involving number and quantities based on 'real life' and money. • Develop calculator skills and use a calculator effectively.
2-3	Understanding × and ÷ Mental calculation strategies (× and ÷) Pencil and paper procedures (× and÷) Money and 'real life problems. Making decisions and checking results including using a calculator	• Understand and use the relationships between the four operations, and the principles (not the names) of the arithmetic laws. Use brackets. • Express a quotient as a fraction or as a decimal rounded to one decimal place. Divide £.p by a two-digit number to give £.p • Round up or down after division, depending on the context. • Partition. • Use known number facts and place value to consolidate mental multiplication and division. • Approximate first. Use informal pencil and paper methods to support, record or explain multiplications and divisions. • **Extend written methods to**: multiplication of ThHTUx U (short multiplication); short division of TU or HTU by U (mixed number answer). • **Identify and use appropriate operations (including combinations of operations) to solve word problems involving numbers and quantities** based on 'real life', money or measures (including time), using one or more steps. • Develop calculator skills and use a calculator effectively
4-5	Fractions, decimals and percentages Ratio and proportion	• Recognise relationships between fractions. • **Reduce a fraction to its simplest form by cancelling common factors** in the numerator and denominator. • Order fractions by converting them to fractions with a common denominator and position them on a number line. • Develop decimal notation for tenths, hundredths and thousandths. • **Order a mixed set of numbers with up to three decimal places.** • **Multiply and divide decimals mentally by 10 or 100** and explain the effect. • Recognise the equivalence between decimal and fraction forms of common fractions. • Begin to convert a fraction to a decimal using division, including comparing and ordering. • **Understand percentage as the number of parts in every 100**. Express simple fractions as percentages. **Find simple percentages of whole number quantities.** • Solve simple problems involving ratio and proportion. • **Solve a problem** by representing, **extracting and interpreting data in tables.** • Develop calculator skills and use a calculator effectively.
6	Handling data Using a calculator	• **Solve a problem** by representing, **extracting and interpreting data in tables, graphs, charts** and diagrams, including line graphs and bar charts with grouped discrete data. • **Use the language associated with probability to discuss events, including those with equally likely outcomes** (sampling and predicting outcomes). • Develop calculator skills and use a calculator effectively
7	Assess and review	• **Multiply and divide decimals by 10 and 100. Solve simple problems involving ratio and proportion. Reduce a fraction to its simplest form by cancelling common factors. Order a mixed set of numbers with up to three decimal places. Understand percentage as the number of parts in every 100. Find simple percentages of small whole number quantities. Solve a problem by extracting and interpreting data in tables. Identify and use appropriate operations (including combinations of operations) to solve word problems involving numbers and quantities.**

ORAL AND MENTAL SKILLS: Use factors. Use tests of divisibility. Use estimation and approximation. Use known number facts and place value to consolidate mental addition, subtraction, multiplication and division. Consolidate knowing by heart multiplication facts up to 10x10. **Derive quickly division facts corresponding to tables up to 10x10.** Multiply and divide multiples of 10. Calculate angles in a straight line (Year 5) and in a triangle. Convert smaller to larger units and vice-versa, mm to cm, cm to mm. Consolidate (and combine) mental calculation strategies including use the relationship between addition and subtraction. Round a number with two decimal places up to the next whole number. Recognise squares of numbers to 12x12.

Unit	Topic	Objectives: children will be taught to...
8-10	Shape and space Reasoning about shapes Measures including problems	• **Use a protractor to measure** and draw **angles**. Estimate angles. Calculate angles in a triangle (and in other polygons). Check that the sum of a triangle is 180º. • Classify triangles (Year5) and quadrilaterals using criteria such as parallel sides, equal angles, equal sides... • Make a shape with increasing accuracy. • Make and investigate a general statement about familiar shapes by finding examples which satisfy it. Develop from explaining a generalised relationship in words to expressing it in a formula using letters as symbols. • **Calculate the perimeter of simple and compound shapes** (and the total edge lengths of 3D shapes). • Use read and write standard metric units (km, cm, mm, kg, g, t, l, ml, cl) including their abbreviations and relationships between them. • Suggest suitable units and measuring equipment to estimate or measure length, mass and capacity. Record estimates and readings from scales to a suitable degree of accuracy. • Develop calculator skills and use a calculator effectively.
11	Mental calculation strategies (+ and −) Pencil and paper procedures (+ and −) Money and 'real life' calculations Making decisions and checking results including using a calculator	• Choose and use appropriate ways of calculating: mental, mental with jottings, to support, record or explain additions and subtractions. • Consolidate strategies from previous year, including: find a difference by counting up, add or subtract the nearest multiple of ten then adjust, partition. • Use known number facts and place value to consolidate mental addition. • **Extend written methods to column addition and subtraction of numbers involving decimals** (estimating before calculating). • **Solve word problems involving numbers and quantities** based on 'real life', money or measures. **Explain methods and reasoning.** • Develop calculator skills and use a calculator effectively. • Check with an equivalent calculation. • Check with the inverse operation when using a calculator.
12	Properties of numbers Reasoning about number	• Recognise and extend number sequences. • Make and investigate general statements about numbers and shapes. • Solve mathematical problems, explain patterns, generalise and predict. Suggest extensions asking 'What if...?' • Develop calculator skills and use a calculator effectively.
13	Assess and review	• **Derive quickly division facts corresponding to tables up to 10x10. Use a protractor to measure and draw acute and obtuse angles to the nearest degree. Calculate the perimeter of simple compound shapes. Extend written methods to column addition and subtraction of numbers involving decimals. Identify and use appropriate operations (including combinations of operations) to solve word problems involving numbers and quantities. Explain methods and reasoning.**

UNIT 1

ORGANISATION (3 LESSONS)

LEARNING OUTCOMES	ORAL AND MENTAL STARTER	MAIN TEACHING ACTIVITY	PLENARY
LESSON 1 • Read and write whole numbers in figures and words and know what each digit represents (Year 5). • Order a set of integers less than 1 million (Year 5). • Consolidate rounding an integer to the nearest 10, 100 or 1000.	ABOUT US: Practising operations to 'hit' a target number using 'personal' numbers.	WHERE DOES IT LIVE? Positioning numbers up to 1 000 000 on number lines.	Discuss where larger numbers are used in the world.
LESSON 2 • Read and write whole numbers in figures and words and know what each digit represents (Year 5). • Use the vocabulary of estimation and approximation. • Consollidate rounding an integer to the nearest 10, 100 or 1000. • **Use appropriate operations to solve word problems involving numbers and quantities** based on 'real life' and money. • Develop calculator skills and use a calculator effectively.	BAG NUMBERS: Adding and finding the difference between 2- or 3-digit numbers.	WHAT THE PAPERS SAY: Using, estimating and rounding large numbers. Investigating car and house prices.	Discuss answers.
LESSON 3 • Read and write whole numbers in figures and words and know what each digit represents (Year 5). • Use the vocabulary of estimation and approximation. • Consolidate rounding an integer to the nearest 10, 100 or 1000. • **Use appropriate operations to solve word problems involving numbers and quantities** based on 'real life' and money. • Develop calculator skills and use a calculator effectively.	BAG NUMBERS: Adding and finding the difference between 2- or 3-digit numbers and doubles of these numbers.	FOOTBALL CROWDS: Using, estimating and rounding large numbers. Investigating football match attendances.	Discussions centred on findings.

ORAL AND MENTAL SKILLS Use known number facts and place value to consolidate mental addition, subtraction and multiplication strategies from previous year(s). Consolidate mental addition and subtraction of any two numbers less than 100. **Derive quickly** doubles of all whole numbers 1 to 100 (Year 5).

In Unit 1 Lessons 1 and 2 are shown in full. Lesson 3 is an extension of what has already been taught and is given in outline.

RESOURCES

Sets of ten cards, each card marked with a number from 1 to 10 000 (one set for each table); five metres of string; Blu-Tack; a set of ten cards each marked with a number from 1 to 100 000; a set of cards marked with any number from 1 to 1 000 000; cards marked with 0, 10 000, 100 000 and 1 000 000; blank cards; pencils and paper.

PREPARATION

Provide the string and Blu-Tack. Make the cards.

LEARNING OUTCOMES

ORAL AND MENTAL STARTER
• Use known number facts and place value to consolidate mental addition, subtraction and multiplication strategies from previous year(s).

MAIN TEACHING ACTIVITY

● Read and write whole numbers in figures and words and know what each digit represents (Year 5).
● Order a set of integers less than 1 million (Year 5).
● Consolidate rounding an integer to the nearest 10, 100 or 1000.

VOCABULARY

Units, tens, hundreds, thousands, ten thousand, hundred thousand, million, ascending/ descending order, estimate, approximate, approximately, round to the nearest... .

ORAL AND MENTAL STARTER

ABOUT US: Explain that they are going to do calculations using numbers that are about themselves. Ask the children to write down their age, the day of the month they were born, their birthday month as a number (1 to 12), the first number of their postcode, the number of letters in their first name, the number in their surname and the total number of letters in their road name. Give them a target number and ask them to 'hit' it in some way by using their personal numbers together with any combination of the operations addition, subtraction or multiplication. Discuss which numbers and operations they used to 'hit' each target. Highlight any variations in strategy.

MAIN TEACHING ACTIVITY

WHERE DOES IT LIVE?: Tell the children that they are going to order and then position numbers. Give each table a set of cards (1 to 10 000). Ask some tables to place them in ascending order and others in descending order (explain the terms if necessary). Ask individuals to read their numbers to you, record them on the board and ask for numbers that lie between pairs of the numbers. Let the children who respond come out and record their numbers using digits and words.

Stretch the string across the room using the Blu-tack tack to hold it in place. Position the 0 and 10 000 cards at either end. Give out ten of the 1 to 10 000 cards to individual children and ask them in turn to position their card where they think it should be on the string. Here are three of the cards positioned on the string:

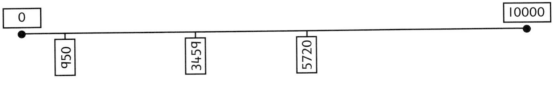

Discuss the placings and adjust any cards accordingly. Ask for their strategies. These should involve rounding and approximating. *I put the 5720 card down. 5000 is halfway and I rounded the number to 5700 and moved the card a little way further on.* Let the children choose their own numbers, write them on the blank cards and insert them on the line. Choose points on the line and ask: *Which number do you think 'lives' here?* Repeat the activity with numbers between 0 and 100 000 as the two end cards, this time giving out the ten prepared cards to a different set of children. Then repeat for 0 to 1 000 000.

DIFFERENTIATION

More able: Choose a point and discuss numbers that live there as the ranges alter, eg 2500, 25 000, 250 000 (one-quarter of a million). *What about 0 to 1000, 0 to 100, 0 to 10, 0 to 1?*
Less able: Concentrate on more than, greater than and between numbers.

PLENARY

Discuss units, tens, hundreds, thousands, ten thousands, hundred thousands and millions to check whether the children really understand the number system. Discuss where larger numbers are used in the world (as a precursor to Lesson 2). The children might suggest the National Lottery, house prices or crowd figures at sports events.

RESOURCES

1–100 number cards from photocopiable page 13 ('1–100 square'); bag or box; newspaper sections for car and house prices; question sheets for car prices; a book; calculators; pencils and paper.

PREPARATION

Collect newspaper sections of car and house prices. If your school has a CLA licence, you may photocopy enough for the class. Prepare and photocopy question sheets based on the car prices. The questions should be as wide ranging as possible and will be dependent on the data you provide. For example:

How many cars cost more than £12 500?

List the VWs that cost between £5000 and £6000.

Are there any cars for less than £1000? Write the type and the year they were made.

Can you find any cars with a mileage less than 50 000 that costs less than £4500? List them in ascending cost order.

Use a calculator to find the difference in price between the most expensive and cheapest BMW you can find.

Enlarge photocopiable page 13 ('1 to 100 square') and cut up the squares to make a set of 1–100 number cards.

LEARNING OUTCOMES

ORAL AND MENTAL STARTER

● Consolidate mental addition and subtraction of any two numbers less than 100.

MAIN TEACHING ACTIVITY

● Read and write whole numbers in figures and words and know what each digit represents (Year 5).

● Use the vocabulary of estimation and approximation.

● Consolidate rounding an integer to the nearest 10, 100 or 1000.

● **Use appropriate operations to solve word problems involving numbers and quantities** based on 'real life' and money.

● Develop calculator skills and use a calculator effectively.

VOCABULARY
Units, tens, hundreds, thousands, ten thousand, hundred thousand, million, estimate, approximate, approximately.

ORAL AND MENTAL STARTER

BAG NUMBERS: Place the number cards 1–100 in the bag. Children take turns to pick out two numbers for the whole class first to sum and then to find their difference. Write the numbers on the board. Discuss meaningful situations where some of the pairs of numbers would be added or subtracted. Include measures and try to develop as many different 'real life' situations as possible.

MAIN TEACHING ACTIVITY

WHAT THE PAPERS SAY: Tell the children that they are going to investigate how and where larger numbers are used. For example, ask: *About how many children are in school today? How did you arrive at your estimate? Now estimate how many words there are in this book.* Invite strategies and discuss how accurate they might be. Hold up a newspaper motoring section and say that you are going to search for the cheapest Renault. Explain how you did it. Distribute the car prices information and your prepared question sheets. Let the children work in pairs, going through your prepared sheet and recording their answers clearly. Invite children to write questions to be investigated by either their partners or other children.

DIFFERENTIATION

More able: Go on to ask questions based on house price information, taking them to prices up to and above £100 000.

Less able: Work with this group, helping them to create questions.

PLENARY

Choose various questions from your sheet and ask different pairs for their answer. Discuss why differences in price occur for similar type cars (for example the age of car, mileage and so on). Consider why stated mileages are usually rounded and to what degree (to the nearest thousand miles as more precise quotes mean little to the purchaser).

RESOURCES	Number cards 1 to 100; a bag or box, as prepared for Lesson 2; newspaper sport sections for football attendances; calculators; pencils and paper.
PREPARATION	Collect a football attendance section and, if you have a CLA licence which allows you to do so, photocopy this and any other football attendance data that you can find so that there is enough for the whole class.
LEARNING OUTCOMES	**ORAL AND MENTAL STARTER** ● Derive quickly doubles of all whole numbers 1 to 100 (Year 5). **MAIN TEACHING ACTIVITY** ● Read and write whole numbers in figures and words and know what each digit represents (Year 5). ● Use the vocabulary of estimation and approximation. ● Consolidate rounding an integer to the nearest 10, 100 or 1000. ● **Use appropriate operations to solve word problems involving numbers and quantities** based on 'real life' and money. ● Develop calculator skills and use a calculator effectively.
ORAL AND MENTAL STARTER	BAG NUMBERS: Repeat the activity from Lesson 2, extending to doubling the first number and adding the second, and then doubling the first and finding the difference between the result and the second number.
MAIN TEACHING ACTIVITY	FOOTBALL CROWDS: Talk about how many spectators might attend some Premiership and local football matches, cinemas, theatres, pop festivals etc. Distribute the football attendance pages and ask the children to round attendances to the nearest hundred at Third Division games and to the nearest thousand at Premiership games. *If it was stated that 23 000, to the nearest hundred, attended the game, what might the attendance have been?* Try others. Ask the children to find out and write down information about attendances at matches.
DIFFERENTIATION	More able: Write a report including comments, eg the difference between the highest and lowest attendances in Division 1 was about 11 000. Less able: Will need help in organising their work.
PLENARY	Ask individual children to report what they investigated and their findings.

UNITS 2-3

ORGANISATION (10 LESSONS)

	LEARNING OUTCOMES	ORAL AND MENTAL STARTER	MAIN TEACHING ACTIVITY	PLENARY
LESSON 1	• Understand and use the relationships between the four operations, and the principles (not the names) of the arithmetic laws. • Use brackets. • Partition. • Develop calculator skills and use a calculator effectively.	WHAT'S THE FACT?: Knowing multiplication facts: being told the answer and asked for the corresponding fact.	BRACKETS AND BUTTONS: Using brackets and partitioning numbers to multiply.	Discuss the use of brackets to aid calculation.
LESSON 2	• Understand and use the relationships between the four operations, and the principles (not the names) of the arithmetic laws. • Partition. • Use known number facts and place value to consolidate mental multiplication.	DOUBLING AND HALVING: Halving even numbers, doubling odd numbers.	MAKING IT MENTAL: Exploring strategies leading to mentally multiplying a 2-digit number by a single digit number.	Compare solutions. Discussing real world contexts.
LESSON 3	• Use known number facts and place value to consolidate mental multiplication.	MULTIPLYING 'TENS': Multiplying a 2-digit multiple of 10 by a number in the range 2–10.	TREASURE ISLAND: A game involving multiplying (mentally) 2-digit numbers by a single digit number.	Discuss strategies used.
LESSON 4	• Partition. • Approximate first. Use informal pencil and paper methods to support, record or explain multiplications. • **Extend written methods to** multiplication of ThHTU × U (short multiplication).	HIDDEN NUMBERS: Making numbers from four given digits and the four operations.	THINK IT OUT: Exploring written methods of multiplication.	Check results using a calculator.
LESSON 5	• **Extend written methods to** multiplication of ThHTU × U (short multiplication).	AS NEAR AS YOU CAN: Using digits and operations to reach a target number.	MAKE IT SNAPPY: Carrying out short multiplications to ThHTU × U.	Suggest number stories for given multiplication sums.
LESSON 6	• **Derive quickly division facts corresponding to tables up to 10x10.** • Use known number facts and place value to consolidate mental division. • Develop calculator skills and use a calculator effectively.	WHAT'S THE ANSWER?: Recalling divisions of 2-digit numbers by a single digit number.	NOUGHTS AND CROSSES DIVISION: Using a game to mentally divide a 2- or 3-digit number by a single digit number.	Discuss methods of mental calculation.
LESSON 7	• **Extend written methods to:** short division of TU or HTU by U (mixed-number answer).	THINK OF THE FUNCTION: Finding multiplication functions when given the input and output.	GETTING SHORTER: Introducing short division HTU ÷ U.	Discuss contexts and remainders.
LESSON 8	• **Extend written methods to:** multiplication of ThHTU × U (short multiplication); short division of TU or HTU by U (mixed-number answer).	THINK OF THE FUNCTION: Finding multiplication functions when given the input and output.	MAKE IT SNAPPY/ GETTING SHORTER: Practising short multiplication and division.	Discuss and compare methods.

LEARNING OUTCOMES		ORAL AND MENTAL STARTER	MAIN TEACHING ACTIVITY	PLENARY
LESSON 9	● **Identify and use appropriate operations (including combinations of operations) to solve word problems involving numbers and quantities** based on 'real life', money, measures (including time), using one or more steps.	TELL ME ABOUT IT: Finding properties of given numbers.	PROBLEMS 1: Solving multiplication and division problems.	Discuss and compare methods used in the main activity.
LESSON 10	● **Identify and use appropriate operations (including combinations of operations) to solve word problems involving numbers and quantities** based on 'real life', money or measures (including time), using one or more steps.	TELL ME ABOUT IT: Finding properties of given numbers.	PROBLEMS 2: Solving problems and writing number stories about multiplication and division sums.	Tell each other number stories from the main activity and discuss the suitability of the contexts.

ORAL AND MENTAL SKILLS Consolidate knowing by heart multiplication facts up to 10×10. **Derive quickly:** doubles of all whole numbers 1 to 100 and the corresponding halves (Year 5). Understand and use the relationships between the four operations. Use known number facts and place value to consolidate mental addition/subtraction. Use known number facts and place value to consolidate mental multiplication and division. Choose and use appropriate number operations to solve problems. Recognise squares of numbers to at least 12×12. Recognise prime numbers to at least 20. Recognise multiples up to 10×10. Know and apply simple tests of divisibility.

In Units 2–3 Lessons 1, 2, 4, 5, 7 and 9 are shown in full. Lessons 3, 6, 8 and 10 are an extension of what has been taught and are given in outline.

RESOURCES

Resource page 14 ('Answers to multiplication facts'); pencils and paper; calculators.

PREPARATION

Enlarge and cut out the cards from 'Answers to multiplication facts' (photocopiable resource page 14). Write these two sums on the board: $4 + (3 \times 6)$; $(4 + 3) \times 6$.

LEARNING OUTCOMES

ORAL AND MENTAL STARTER
● Consolidate knowing by heart multiplication facts to 10×10.

MAIN TEACHING ACTIVITY
● Understand and use the relationships between the four operations, and the principles (not the names) of the arithmetic laws.
● Use brackets.
● Partition.
● Develop calculator skills and use a calculator effectively.

VOCABULARY

Multiply, multiplied by, product, subtract, add.

ORAL AND MENTAL STARTER

WHAT'S THE FACT?: Tell the children that you are going to hold up some answer cards to multiplication facts; ask them to put up their hands and give you the fact that fits your answer. Turn the photocopied cards up one at a time for the children to see.

MAIN TEACHING ACTIVITY

BRACKETS AND BUTTONS: Tell the children that they are going to use brackets in calculations. Ask: *What can you remember about brackets from last year?* Hopefully one reply will be similar to 'You always do the calculation in the brackets first.' Point to the two sums on the board and ask the class: *Do these calculations give the same answers? Work them out mentally and see.* (The answers are 22 and 42.)

Write each of these on the board asking the children to work out the answers mentally:

$$(12 - 2) - 5; \quad 36 + (27 - 9); \quad (8 \times 7) - 2; \quad 32 - (7 \times 5)$$

Write 57 × 40 on the board and ask them for a different way of writing the sum. Say that they might find brackets helpful. Answers may include 40 × 57 (using commutativity); 57 × (10 × 4); (57 × 10) × 4 (using associativity). Check the answers. Now write some more examples, eg 23 × 32, 68 × 18, 35 × 17 and ask the children to write each in as many different ways as they can, going on to use the calculator to find the answers. They may use paper and jot down intermediate answers. *Now let's imagine that our calculators are wearing out. We want to find the answer to 18 × 47 but the [1] and [8] buttons are broken; what could we do? Tell me the buttons to press and I will record them on the board.* Answers may include [2] [0] [–] [2] [×] [4] [7] or [2] [×] [9] [×] [4] [7]. Tell them to check the answer to 18 × 47 on the calculator (the buttons are now fully functional!) Ask them to repeat for other calculations, eg 36 × 15 (with the 6 button broken), 83 × 45 (with 4 and 5 broken), recording possible button presses each time and then checking each answer on the calculator. Discuss the approaches used.

DIFFERENTIATION

More able: Go on to make up their own 'broken button' problems for each other to try.
Less able: May need more practise of writing examples in bracket form.

PLENARY

Discuss how to rewrite sums like 45 × 32. Answers may include: (45 × 30) + (45 × 2); 90 × 16; (50 × 32) – (5 × 32) etc.

RESOURCES

Set of 11–99 number cards from photocopiable resource page 13 (1–100 square); calculators; pencils and paper.

PREPARATION

Enlarge one copy of 1–100 square (page 13) and cut out the number cards 11–99. Write on the board, 'If odd then double, if even then halve'.

LEARNING OUTCOMES

ORAL AND MENTAL STARTER
● **Derive quickly:** doubles and halves of all whole numbers 1–100 (Year 5 revision).

MAIN TEACHING ACTIVITY
● Understand and use the relationships between the four operations, and the principles (not the names) of the arithmetic laws.
● Partition.
● Use known number facts and place value to consolidate mental multiplication.

VOCABULARY

Multiply, multiplied by, multiple, 'x' sign, odd, even.

ORAL AND MENTAL STARTER

DOUBLING AND HALVING: Read out the instruction you have written on the board and say that when you turn over a card (from the 11–99 set), they must quickly tell you the result of either doubling or halving the number shown, depending on whether it is an odd or even number. Select one child to note the number of questions completed in 10 minutes. Notice children who do not appear to be participating.

MAIN TEACHING ACTIVITY

MAKING IT MENTAL: Write 18 × 4 on the board and ask for estimates of the answer, such as '20 × 5 is 100 so the answer is a bit less'. Ask the children how they would find the answer mentally. Replies may include: '10 multiplied by 4 is 40 and 8 multiplied by 4 is 32, so the answer is 40 add 32 which is 72' (when written down, this becomes (10 × 4) + (8 × 4) = 40 + 32); 'I know that 18 doubled is 36 and 36 doubled is 72' (when recorded becomes (18 × 2) × 2); '18 multiplied by 4 gives the same answer as 9 multiplied by 8, that's 72' (written as 9 × 8). Record different replies and discuss each one. If replies are not forthcoming, give one partitioning example to start them off.

Write these multiplications on the board for the children to try: 36 × 5; 47 × 6; 23 × 7; 96 × 8. If necessary, let them jot down the methods used for discussion during the plenary. They then generate similar questions for their partner to solve mentally.

DIFFERENTIATION

More able: Include 3-digit numbers multiplied by a single-digit number.
Less able: Practise more statements using examples with low numbers, eg 24 × 3.

PLENARY

Discuss ways in which individuals tackled the statements, praising unusual but efficient approaches. Ask the children to consider situations in the real world when, say, 36 × 5 might occur. For example: *When we went to Tenerife there were five seats in a row and thirty-six rows in the aircraft, that's 36 × 5, which is one hundred and eighty altogether.*

RESOURCES	A set of 2–10 number cards; a copy of photocopiable page 30 ('Treasure Island') per pair; pencils; a calculator.
PREPARATION	Make a set of large 2–10 number cards. Write the multiples of 10 from 10 to 90 randomly on the board. Photocopy page 30 ('Treasure Island') to give out one copy per pair.
LEARNING OUTCOMES	**ORAL AND MENTAL STARTER** ● Use known number facts and place value to consolidate mental multiplication. **MAIN TEACHING ACTIVITY** ● Use known number facts and place value to consolidate mental multiplication.
ORAL AND MENTAL STARTER	MULTIPLYING TENS: Place the digit cards face down on the table. Choose one of the numbers on the board, say 40. Turn over a number card, say 6. The children must quickly give the result of multiplying the two numbers together (40 × 6).
MAIN TEACHING ACTIVITY	TREASURE ISLAND: Tell the children that they are going to play a game of 'Treasure Island', which involves mentally multiplying a 2-digit number by a single-digit number. Give an example such as 27 × 4. Ask how they would do this mentally, remembering the strategies that they have used before. They may suggest: '25 × 4 is 100 and 2 × 4 is 8 so the answer is 108'; 'I said 20 × 4 is 80 and 7 × 4 is 28 making 108'. Give each pair of children six individual single digit numbers to write one on each of their islands, in any order. Each pair's six 'islands' may all have different numbers or some repeated. Children then play the game according to the rules on the sheet.
DIFFERENTIATION	More able: Give these pairs a variety of larger numbers to use. Less able: Give these pairs low numbers to use such as 2 and 3.
PLENARY	Discuss strategies used – multiplying the tens digit first, doubling and halving, etc.

RESOURCES

1–9 numeral cards; pencils; paper; calculators.

PREPARATION

Make one set of large 1–9 numeral cards.

LEARNING OUTCOMES

ORAL AND MENTAL STARTER
● Understand and use the relationships between the four operations.

MAIN TEACHING ACTIVITY
● Partition.
● Approximate first. Use informal pencil and paper methods to support, record or explain multiplications.
● **Extend written methods to** multiplication of ThHTU × U (short multiplication).

VOCABULARY

Multiply, multiplied by, calculation.

ORAL AND MENTAL STARTER

HIDDEN NUMBERS: Place the numeral cards face down on the table and ask one child to select four cards. Write the chosen numbers, say, 4, 7, 3, 5, and the operations +, −, ×, ÷, on the board. Tell the children they can use two, three or all of the digits together with one, two or three operations to make the number but they may only use a digit or an operation once for each sum. Give them a number, say 41, to make, then record on the board the different ways they have come up with it, eg (3 × 7) + (5 × 4). Repeat for other numbers.

MAIN TEACHING ACTIVITY

THINK IT OUT: Write 436 × 7 on the board. Ask the children to estimate the result and to justify their estimates. They may suggest: 'It's about 3000 because 400 × 7 is 2800 and 436 is a bit more.' *Could you use brackets to write the multiplication in a different way? (400 × 7) + (30 × 7) + (6 × 7)?* Ask the children to tell you the answers to each of the calculations in the brackets. Record these on the board: 2800 + 210 + 42. Now ask for the answer: 3052. Refer back to last year and recording informally using the grid method. *How would you record the calculation 216 × 8 using the grid method?*

Ask one child to record their grid on the board (see example, left). Give the class other calculations to work on involving a 3-digit number multiplied by a single digit number, eg 398 × 6, 835 × 4, 129 × 7. Then move on to 4-digit numbers multiplied by a single-digit number, eg 2367 × 3, 4156 × 6. Remind the children to always estimate first.

×	2	1	6
8	1600	80	48

DIFFERENTIATION

More able: Go on to use larger digits, such as 7689 × 9.
Less able: Give them examples of 3-digit numbers multiplied by low single-digit numbers, for example 123 × 4.

PLENARY

Ask the children to check their results using calculators. Look at individuals' work and assess it informally, rectifying any errors.

RESOURCES

A set of 1–9 numeral cards (as prepared for Lesson 4); stop clock; scrap paper; prepared column board or whiteboard; '×' operator card; wiper; marker pen; pencils; paper; one set of prepared multiplication sums per child.

PREPARATION

Th	H	T	U

Make and label the column board as shown and cover it with self-adhesive plastic. Make an operator card with '×' marked on it. Photocopy suitable textbook pages or prepare multiplication sums of your own, enough for one copy per child.

LEARNING OUTCOMES

ORAL AND MENTAL STARTER
● Use known number facts and place value to consolidate mental addition/subtraction.
● Use known number facts and place value to consolidate mental multiplication/division.

MAIN TEACHING ACTIVITY
● **Extend written methods to** multiplication of ThHTU × U (short multiplication).

ORAL AND MENTAL STARTER

AS NEAR AS YOU CAN: Place the numeral cards face down on the table and invite a child to select four. Record these and the four operation symbols +, −, ×, ÷ on the board. Now ask another child to give you a number, say between 50 and 150, that will be the target number. *You will be given 20 seconds to get as near as you can to this target number using as many of the digits and operations as you wish.* If necessary, they can jot down any interim numbers or operations. Repeat for other examples.

VOCABULARY

Multiply, divide, add, subtract, estimate, operation, sign, units, tens, hundreds, thousands, column.

MAIN TEACHING ACTIVITY

MAKE IT SNAPPY: Ask the children to estimate the answer to 1472 × 6. Ask them where the digits 1, 4, 7 and 2 of the number should be placed on the column board and why. Place the '×' operator card and the '6' by the side of the board as shown.

Starting with the units, multiply each digit by 6 and record on the board, saying *2 multiplied by 6 is 12; we leave the 2 in the units column and carry the ten to the tens column, recording this '1' under the answer. Moving to the tens column, 7 multiplied by 6 is 42 tens (420) and adding the one ten makes 43 tens altogether. Leave the 3 in the tens column and carry the 4 to the bottom of the hundreds column. 4 hundreds multiplied by 6 is 24 hundreds but we also have 4 hundreds to add to this making 28 hundreds or 2 thousand, 8 hundred altogether. Move the 2 thousand to the thousands column. 1 multiplied by 6 is 6 but we also have 2 thousands to add on making 8 in all, so the total is 8832.*

	Th	H	T	U
☒ ⑥	1	4	7	2
	8	8	3	2
	2	4	1	

Wipe the board clean and ask the children to help you with another example, say 2546 × 3, remembering to estimate first. Now put the column board to one side and ask the children for help in calculating 2453 × 5 without the columns to help. Remind them that units should line up under units and so on. Give them your prepared examples to work on individually.

DIFFERENTIATION

More able: Go on to work with ThHTU × U, where the answer is above 10 000.
Less able: May still need practice using the column guides to help.

PLENARY

Ask the children to find suitable contexts and make up number stories about multiplication examples, starting with 2-digit numbers multiplied by a single digit number. For example, for 47 × 6 they might suggest something like: 'Yesterday mum bought six cans of cat food costing 47 pence a can, which was £2.82.' Ask for contexts for larger numbers, such as 1460 × 8 or 57 899 × 4. Perhaps if 1460 is expressed as £14.60 then the contexts will be easier to find, while 57 899 × 6 may result in a situation such as: *Those six houses are for sale at £57 899 each. How much is that altogether?*

LESSON 6

RESOURCES	List of division questions; copies of photocopiable page 31 ('Noughts and crosses division'); eight same-coloured counters (or Multilink cubes) per child; calculators; pencils; paper.
PREPARATION	Write a list of divisions with inputs in the range 50–120 and divisors 2, 3, 4 or 5, for example 64 ÷ 4. Copy page 31 ('Noughts and crosses division'), one per pair. Ensure that each child's set of counters is a different colour to their partner's.
LEARNING OUTCOMES	**ORAL AND MENTAL STARTER** ● Use known number facts and place value to consolidate mental division. **MAIN TEACHING ACTIVITY** ● **Derive quickly division facts corresponding to tables up to 10 × 10.** ● Use known number facts and place value to consolidate mental division. ● Develop calculator skills and use a calculator effectively.
ORAL AND MENTAL STARTER	WHAT'S THE ANSWER?: Choose a division statement from your list, say, 64 ÷ 4 and ask the children to give the answer. Ask how they did the mental calculation. Replies may include: '10 fours are 40, that leaves 24 and 6 fours are 24, making 16 altogether' or '10 fours are 40, so 11 is 44, 12 is 48... (counting on in fours to) 16 is 64'. Repeat for other division statements.
MAIN TEACHING ACTIVITY	NOUGHTS AND CROSSES DIVISION: Give out 'Noughts and crosses division' (page 31) and the counters. Explain that, working in pairs, they must choose one number in the box and divide it by a number in the triangle to make a quotient on the grid, for example 54 ÷ 3 = 18. If there is dispute then they should use the calculator to check the answer. The winner is the first child to get four counters in a line.
DIFFERENTIATION	More able: Go on to make up their own noughts and crosses division game using facts from other tables, eg ×7, ×8, ×9. Less able: May need help to play the game. Playing co-operatively at first will help.
PLENARY	Discuss and compare the efficiency of pupils' different methods of mental calculation.

RESOURCES

Column board (as for Lesson 5); marker pen; wiper; calculator; pencils and paper.

PREPARATION

Label the column board HTU. Locate, and copy if necessary, suitable short division practise calculations. Include examples which have remainders such as 213 ÷ 5, 178 ÷ 3, 219 ÷ 6.

LEARNING OUTCOMES

ORAL AND MENTAL STARTER

- Consolidate knowing by heart multiplication facts up to 10 × 10.
- Choose and use appropriate number operations to solve problems.

MAIN TEACHING ACTIVITY

- **Extend written methods to:** short division of TU or HTU by U (mixed-number answer).

VOCABULARY

Divide, divided by, divided into, divisible by, quotient, remainder, inverse.

ORAL AND MENTAL STARTER

THINK OF THE FUNCTION: Tell the children that you want them to give you input numbers, which you will then do something to and give them the output. They may try several different inputs, with you giving the corresponding output each time. When they are sure they know what you are doing to their number each time, they should challenge and give you the function, eg for 3 to 7, 12 to 25, the function is 'multiply by 2 then add 1'.

Concentrate on using multiplication facts up to 10 × 10 in your functions. Let individual children think of a function for others to guess.

MAIN TEACHING ACTIVITY

GETTING SHORTER: Ask the children to remember the work they did last year on division. Write a 3-digit by single-digit division on the board, eg 252 ÷ 6. Ask for estimates. Now ask how they might begin to tackle the division. Some children may say, '6 multiplied by 10 is 60, 60 doubled is 120, and 120 doubled is 240', while others will respond '20 × 6 doubled' or go straight to '40 × 6 is 240, leaving 12'. Ask the children to jot down their informal recording (see example, left).

$$6 \times 10 = 60$$
$$60 \times 2 = 120$$
$$120 \times 2 = 240 \qquad \text{or} \quad 40 \times 6 = 240$$
$$6 \times 2 = 12 \qquad\qquad\qquad 2 \times 6 = 12$$
Answer 42   Answer 42

Now remind the children of the written method begun last year. Stress the need to keep hundreds lined up under hundreds and tens under tens etc, as nought is not used as a place holder (see example, right).

The children then work on their own on different division examples. After a time, bring the class back together and ask for the answer to one of the sums, say 213 ÷ 5 (42r3). Discuss the idea of remainder and ask if it is possible to record it in any other way. *What does the calculator say? 42.6. So the calculator records the result as a decimal. What if we record the remainder as a common fraction? It will be 3 divide by 5, so that is three fifths.* Ask the children to go back to the examples and express all their division answers as mixed numbers consisting of whole numbers and common fractions.

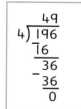

DIFFERENTIATION

More able: Use an even shorter method of division. 255 ÷ 6 may be written as:

$$42\tfrac{3}{6}$$
$$6\overline{)255}$$

They may also answer questions involving factors such as 'Find all the factors of 192'. Less able: Work with this group, making sure that they understand and can use the short division method. Let them set their division examples out on the column board used in Lesson 6.

PLENARY

Discuss contexts for 213 ÷ 5, and the ways in which the remainder is expressed. For example: *If we share £213 between five people they will each get £42.60; There are 5 cans of cola in a pack, how many complete packs will there be? 42. In neither example will the answer be 42r3!* Try other divisions and other contexts.

RESOURCES	Short multiplication and short division questions; column board (from Lesson 5); marker pen; wiper; pencils and paper.
PREPARATION	Find and copy textbook questions or produce your own.
LEARNING OUTCOMES	**ORAL AND MENTAL STARTER** ● Consolidate knowing by heart multiplication facts up to 10 × 10 **MAIN TEACHING ACTIVITY** ● **Extend written methods to:** multiplication of ThHTU × U (short multiplication); short division of TU or HTU by U (mixed-number answer).
ORAL AND MENTAL STARTER	THINK OF THE FUNCTION: Repeat the **Oral and mental starter** from Lesson 7.
MAIN TEACHING ACTIVITY	MAKE IT SNAPPY/ GETTING SHORTER: Revise the activities from Lesson 5 (short multiplication) and from Lesson 7 (short division). Work together on examples of each, then give the children your prepared practise questions for them to work through on their own.
DIFFERENTIATION	More able: Work on more difficult examples, extending to ThHTU × U and HTU ÷ U. Less able: Work with them and if necessary let them continue to use a column board for assistance.
PLENARY	Discuss the strategies used in 'Think of the function'. Begin to mark the sums done individually for the **Main teaching activity**. Question children about their work and rectify any errors they may have made.

RESOURCES

Large sheet of card; copies of photocopiable page 32 ('Multiplication and division problems'); an electricity bill; pencils and paper.

PREPARATION

Write words associated with numbers and operations, eg odd, even, sum, product, divided by, multiplied by, factor, multiple, prime, square, add to, subtract from, quotient, remainder and so on placed randomly on the large sheet of card. Photocopy page 32 ('Multiplication and division problems'), enough for one for each pair. Bring in an electricity bill and photocopy this, one per pair.

LEARNING OUTCOMES

ORAL AND MENTAL STARTER
● Recognise squares of numbers to at least 12 × 12.
● Recognise prime numbers to at least 20.
● Recognise multiples up to 10 × 10. Know and apply simple tests of divisibility.

MAIN TEACHING ACTIVITY
● **Identify and use appropriate operations (including combinations of operations) to solve word problems involving numbers and quantities** based on 'real life', money or measures (including time), using one or more steps.

ORAL AND MENTAL STARTER

TELL ME ALL ABOUT IT: Hold up the large card and give the children a number, say 108. Invite them to tell you as much as they can about this number using the words on the card, and any others they may choose. For example, 'It's even. It's divisible by three. 4 is a factor. It's 10 squared add 8' etc. Let the children take turns in choosing a number and checking the answers that are given.

MAIN TEACHING ACTIVITY

PROBLEMS 1: Give out the 'Multiplication and division problems' sheets (photocopiable page 32) and briefly discuss question 1 concerning electricity bills. Ensure that the children understand the meaning of 'quarter' and 'quarterly charge'. Give out copies of the electricity bill that you have brought in and interpret it together.

Let the children read the other questions on the page, then ask them if there is any aspect they do not understand. Tell them to take particular notice of the instructions at the top because they will be comparing their methods with others later. They may use paper for their jottings while working out, then write their answers next to the questions. Set the children to work with their partner.

ANSWERS

1) £44; 2) 58 @ 9p each = £5.22, 6 boxes cost £5.10, 5 boxes and 8 individual rosettes cost £4.25 + 72p = £4.97, so £4.97 is the cheapest way; 3) 765 raffle tickets are sold; 4) No, only enough for 5;

5)
$$\begin{array}{r} 1\,5\,7 \\ \times \quad 6 \\ \hline 9\,4\,2 \end{array}$$

6) 39.

DIFFERENTIATION

More able: Go on to make up their own 'missing number' problems.
Less able: Work with them to ensure that they understand the problems.

PLENARY

Discuss and compare the methods used to solve the problems.

RESOURCES	Examples of multiplication and division problems.
PREPARATION	Find textbook examples of multiplication and division problems involving up to 3-digit numbers multiplied by a single digit number or produce your own. List multiplication or division statements such as 127 × 18, 453 ÷ 23 for children to invent number stories about.
LEARNING OUTCOMES	**ORAL AND MENTAL STARTER** ● Recognise squares of numbers to at least 12 × 12. ● Recognise prime numbers to at least 20. ● Recognise multiples up to 10 x10. Know and apply simple tests of divisibility. **MAIN TEACHING ACTIVITY** ● **Identify and use appropriate operations (including combinations of operations) to solve word problems involving numbers and quantities** based on 'real life', money or measures (including time), using one or more steps.
ORAL AND MENTAL STARTER	TELL ME ALL ABOUT IT: Repeat the **Oral and mental starter** from Lesson 9.
MAIN TEACHING ACTIVITY	PROBLEMS 2: The children work on their own through the prepared multiplication and division questions. For the number story examples, let them use a calculator to check their results, taking care to express any remainders in a suitable way. For example, *Our class is going on a two-day trip. The total cost of the trip is £453 and there are 23 children in the class. How much must we each pay?* Answer: £19.70 (calculator answer 19.69565217); or *453 tickets have been sold for the concert, each row contains 23 seats, how many complete rows must be put out to seat everyone?* (20)
DIFFERENTIATION	More able: Let the children compare number stories Less able: Work with the group and discuss possible number stories
PLENARY	Discuss the number stories and the suitability of their contexts.

LESSON 10

Name

Treasure Island

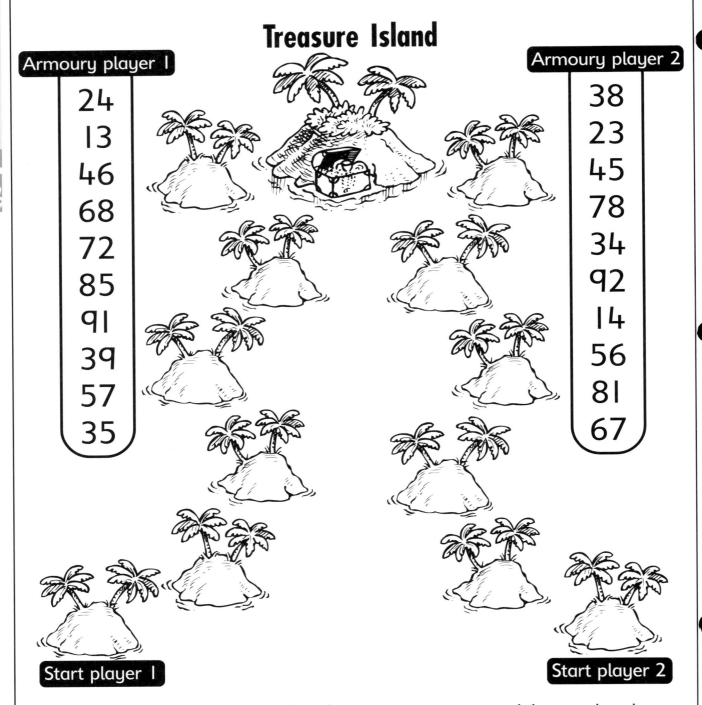

Armoury player 1

24
13
46
68
72
85
91
39
57
35

Armoury player 2

38
23
45
78
34
92
14
56
81
67

Start player 1

Start player 2

Take turns to choose a number from your armoury and, in your head,
multiply it by the number on your first island.

Your partner should check the result using a calculator.

If you are correct you capture the island.

Cross off the armoury number and also the island. Move to the next
island and wait for your next turn.

If you are not correct, stay on the island and do not cross off your
armoury number or the island. Try again next turn using a different
number from your armoury.

Now it is your partner's turn.

The winner is the first player to reach Treasure Island.

Noughts and crosses division

15	24	12	30
48	13	26	28
14	20	16	40
32	19	17	18

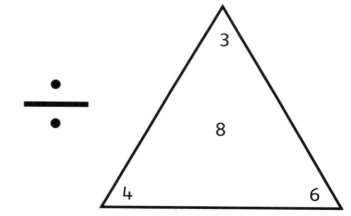

Choose a number from the bottom square and divide it by a number in the triangle to give a quotient on the grid.

Tell your partner the result.

If your partner does not agree with you then check using the calculator.

If you are correct place a counter on this quotient.

If you are not correct, you lose your turn. Now it is your partner's turn.

The winner is the first player to get four counters in a line vertically, horizontally or diagonally.

UNITS 2–3

Multiplication and division problems

Solve these problems. Do not use a calculator. Use numbers signs and symbols to show your working.

1. Mum's electricity bill says that for this quarter we have used 500 units @ 7p per unit. There is also a quarterly charge of £9.00. What is the total amount due?

2. On Sports Day, I want to give each of the 58 contestants a cardboard rosette. I find that they cost 9p each or a box of ten costs 85p. What is the cheapest way to buy the rosettes and how much will they cost?

3. Raffle tickets are sold at 50p for a strip of 5 tickets. The total money taken is £76.50, how many raffle tickets were sold?

4. I am making cushions. Each is square and has edges 45cm long. I want to put piping all around the edges of the cushions and have 10m of piping. Do I have enough for six cushions?

5. Fill in the missing digits. All the digits are different.

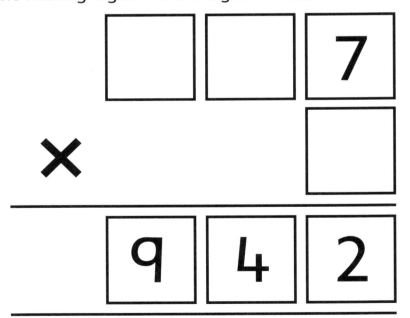

6. I think of a number then add 3 to it. If I divide this new number by 7 the answer is 6, what was the original number?

   Make up some similar number puzzles for your partner to try. Write them on the back of this sheet.

UNITS 4-5

ORGANISATION (10 LESSONS)

	LEARNING OUTCOMES	ORAL AND MENTAL STARTER	MAIN TEACHING ACTIVITY	PLENARY
LESSON 1	● Recognise relationships between fractions (including equivalence). ● **Reduce a fraction to its simplest form by cancelling common factors** in the numerator and denominator.	PROPER OR IMPROPER: Changing improper fractions to mixed numbers.	WHAT CAN YOU SAY?: Giving facts about particular fractions. Developing equivalent fractions patterns.	Discuss the work leading to finding the simplest form by cancelling.
LESSON 2	● Order fractions by converting them to fractions with a common denominator and position them on a number line.	FRACTION MATCH: Recognising equivalent fractions.	ON THE LINE: Marking fractions on a number line. Ordering fractions by using a common denominator.	Discuss calculation strategies and rectifying any misconceptions.
LESSON 3	● **Reduce a fraction to its simplest form by cancelling common factors** in the numerator and denominator. ● **Solve a problem by representing, extracting and interpreting data in tables.**	HOW MANY IN...?: Finding how many fractional parts in a mixed number.	FRACTIONS FROM DATA: Describing survey and experimental data using common fractions.	Discuss the use of statistical information presented in fractional form.
LESSON 4	● **Solve simple problems involving ratio and proportion.**	GREATER OR LESS: Recognising fractions that are greater than, less than or in between whole numbers.	HOW TO MAKE: Using ratio ideas when making mortar, lemonade and ginger cookies.	Patterning equal ratios eg 3 to 1, 6 to 2, 9 to 3..... Introducing proportion ideas.
LESSON 5	● **Solve simple problems involving ratio and proportion.**	QUICK-FIRE RATIOS: Giving equivalent ratios.	IS IT FAIR?: Exploring ratio and proportion by using unequal sharing and developing applications of the concepts.	Emphasise the differences between ratio and proportion.
LESSON 6	● Use decimal notation for tenths, hundredths and thousandths. ● **Order a mixed set of numbers with up to three decimal places.** ● Give a decimal fraction lying between two others.	DECIMAL 'POINTS': Counting on and back in steps of 0.1, 0.2, 0.25, 0.5 etc from various starting numbers.	WHERE DOES IT LIVE?: Ordering tenths, hundredths and thousandths both on and off number lines. Exploring decimal fractions lying between two others.	Discuss digit values of whole numbers and numbers with decimal parts.
LESSON 7	● **Multiply and divide decimals mentally by 10 or 100 and explain the effect.** ● Use decimal notation for tenths, hundredths and thousandths. ● Develop calculator skills and use a calculator effectively.	MAKE IT BIGGER, MAKE IT SMALLER: × 10 then ÷ 10, including decimals.	FURTHER AND FURTHER, NEARER AND NEARER: Repeatedly × 10 then ÷ 10 using distance and number line ideas. Attempting to reach 0 and then move into negative numbers.	Discuss the decimal point and nought. First ideas of a mathematical limit.

	LEARNING OUTCOMES	ORAL AND MENTAL STARTER	MAIN TEACHING ACTIVITY	PLENARY
LESSON 8	● Recognise the equivalence between the decimal and fraction forms of common fractions. ● Begin to convert a fraction to a decimal using division. ● Develop calculator skills and use a calculator effectively. ● Order fractions.	DECIMAL TARGETS: Adding and subtracting 2-digit decimal numbers less than 10 to reach a target number less than 20.	LET'S CHANGE: Expressing common fractions as decimal fractions using Base 10 equipment and then by dividing. Predicting answer and using a calculator for the division.	Compare and order common fractions by converting them to decimal fractions using a calculator.
LESSON 9	●**Understand percentage as the number of parts in every 100.** Express simple fractions as percentages. ●**Solve simple problems involving proportion.** ● Solve a problem by **representing, extracting and interpreting data in tables.**	FRACTIONS TO DECIMALS: Converting fractions to decimals and vice-versa.	ALL OUT OF 100: Finding proportions and percentages from survey data.	Marking and discussing the work covered.
LESSON 10	● Express fractions as percentages and vice-versa. ●**Understand percentage as the number of parts in every 100.** ● Solve problems involving proportion.	FRACTIONS TO PERCENTAGES: Converting fractions to percentages and vice-versa	WHAT'S THE OFFER?: Solving problems involving discounts expressed with and without percentages.	Marking and discussing the work covered.

ORAL AND MENTAL SKILLS Change an improper fraction to its equivalent mixed number and vice-versa (Year 5 revision). Recognise the equivalence between fractions. **Order** fractions and **a mixed set of numbers. Solve simple problems involving ratio.** Count on in steps of 0.1, 0.2, 0.25, 0.5…, and then back. **Multiply and divide decimals by 10 or 100 and explain the effect.** Use known number facts to consolidate mental addition/subtraction (of decimal numbers). Recognise the equivalence between the decimal and fraction forms of common fractions. Express simple fractions as percentages and vice-versa.

In Units 4–5, Lessons 1, 3, 4, 5, 6, 8 and 9 are shown in full. Lessons 2 and 7 extend what has already been taught and are shown in outline.

RESOURCES
Two 10- or 12-sided dice of different colours; pencils and paper.

LEARNING OUTCOMES

ORAL AND MENTAL STARTER
● Change an improper fraction to its equivalent mixed number and vice versa (Year 5 revision).

MAIN TEACHING ACTIVITY
● Recognise relationships between fractions (including equivalence).
● **Reduce a fraction to its simplest form by cancelling common factors** in the numerator and denominator.

VOCABULARY
Fraction, proper/ improper fraction, mixed number, numerator, denominator, equivalent, reduced to, cancel.

ORAL AND MENTAL STARTER

PROPER OR IMPROPER: Introduce the vocabulary 'proper fraction', 'improper fraction' and 'mixed number'. Children should take turns to throw both dice, one colour for the numerator and the other for the denominator. Write the results on the board and ask whether the fractions are proper or improper. If they are improper, ask for the mixed number. Go on to ask quick-fire questions such as *How many eighths in $1^7/_8$?*

MAIN TEACHING ACTIVITY

WHAT CAN YOU SAY: On the board write a large $^1/_2$. *What can you say about this fraction?* Write their responses around the fraction; 'Twice as much as a quarter'; 'Can be written as $^2/_4$'; 'Three times as much as a sixth $^3/_6$'; 'A third of $1^1/_2$'. Then ask them to jot down all they can say about $^1/_4$, $^1/_{10}$, making sure that they include some equivalent fractions. After a couple of minutes, bring the class together to share their ideas. Highlight the equivalent fractions. Discuss that a half is both $^2/_4$ and $^3/_6$. *How many eighths is it?* Record $^1/_2 = ^2/_4 = ^3/_6 = ...$ and then build up to $^8/_{16}$ with the numerator increased by 1 each time and the denominator by 2 accordingly. Discuss the fact that $^6/_{12}$ is clumsy when you could use $^1/_2$ instead. How *do you get from $^6/_{12}$ to $^1/_2$?* (Divide both the numerator and denominator by 6). Ask them to try other equivalence patterns, eg for $^1/_4$, $^1/_3$, $^2/_3$.

DIFFERENTIATION

More able: *What can you say about $^1/_{10}$? $^1/_{10}$ of a kilometre is 100 metres, $^1/_{10}$ of an hour is 6 minutes.* Try $^5/_8$, $^3/_{16}$ for the equivalence patterns.
Less able: Constantly multiply by 2 giving $^1/_4 = ^2/_8 = ^4/_{16}$. Reassure them and help them work towards the full pattern.

PLENARY

Summarise what has been learned. Emphasise that all the fractions in any one pattern or 'family' are equal to each other and that the first one written can represent all the others and is in the simplest form possible. Ask children to express given fractions in their simplest form by dividing both the numerator and denominator by the same number. Taking, say $^{16}/_{24}$ and dividing by 8 gives $^{16}/_{24}$ $^2/_3$. Introduce the word 'cancel'.

LESSON 2

RESOURCES	A set of equivalent fraction cards, from photocopiable page 44 ('Equivalent fractions'); unmarked floor fraction line; water based pen; wiper; examples of ordering fractions; pencils and paper.
PREPARATION	Enlarge photocopiable page 44 ('Equivalent fractions') and cut out to make a set of fraction cards. Make the fraction line by drawing a line 5m long on to pieces of card joined together. Mark 0 at one end, ten equal spaces and 1 at the other end and cover with transparent self-adhesive plastic. Find textbook examples or produce your own sets of fractions that can be ordered, including sets with more than two different denominators and some mixed numbers.
LEARNING OUTCOMES	**ORAL AND MENTAL STARTER** ● Recognise the equivalence between fractions. **MAIN TEACHING ACTIVITY** ● Order fractions by converting them to fractions with a common denominator and position them on a number line.
ORAL AND MENTAL STARTER	FRACTION MATCH: Give each child a fraction card. Ask one child to hold up his or her card. Children with an equivalent fraction should show their card. Check that four cards are displayed each time. Children change cards every turn.
MAIN TEACHING ACTIVITY	ON THE LINE: Place the fraction line on the floor and invite children to mark, say, $^3/_{10}$, $^2/_5$, $^1/_2$, $^7/_{10}$, $^4/_5$ on the line with the marker. Each marked fraction should be agreed by the class. Discuss other equivalent fractions which could be shown eg $^4/_{10}$, $^5/_{10}$. Try $^1/_4$, $^3/_4$, $^1/_3$, $^2/_3$. Talk about fractions being ordered. *What if we have a set of fractions to order and no line?* Show a set that will need some fractions changing to an equivalent fraction by using a common denominator, for example the set $^1/_3$, $^2/_3$, $^2/_9$, $^4/_9$, $^8/_9$ would all need to be changed to ninths (multiplying the numerator and denominator of those not already in ninths by 3). Give the children sets of fractions to write in order for themselves.
DIFFERENTIATION	More able: Write their own examples, trying themselves before inviting others to try. Less able: Use sets with only two different denominators and simple mixed numbers.
PLENARY	Mark the written work and ask the children to explain how they tackled the mixed numbers. Rectify any misconceptions.

RESOURCES

A 1–6 dice per pair; pencils and paper.

LEARNING OUTCOMES

ORAL AND MENTAL STARTER

● Change an improper fraction to its equivalent mixed number and vice versa (Y5 revision).

MAIN TEACHING ACTIVITY

● **Reduce a fraction to its simplest form by cancelling common factors** in the numerator and denominator.
● **Solve a problem by** representing, **extracting and interpreting data in tables.**

VOCABULARY

Fraction, proper/ improper fraction, mixed number, numerator, denominator, equivalent, reduced to, cancel.

ORAL AND MENTAL STARTER

HOW MANY IN...?: Write on the board 'How many halves in $2\frac{1}{2}$?' When the children give you the answer discuss how they found out. Ask other questions involving say halves, quarters, thirds, fifths, eighths, tenths. *How many fifths in 2?; How many tenths in $4\frac{1}{10}$?*

MAIN TEACHING ACTIVITY

FRACTIONS FROM DATA: Tell the children that they are going to produce some data and write what they find out in fractional form. Gather some data from the children (see example, below) and write it on the board, taking care with the layout.

Ask the children for more questions that can be used to gather data about the class: 'How many regularly stay for lunch?'; 'How many are 10 years old?' Record the results. Ask them individually to write this information using fractions in their simplest form. Compare answers. Make the point that if, for example, 9 wear glasses, 18 don't, so $\frac{1}{3}$ wear glasses and $\frac{2}{3}$ don't.

Now ask the children to gather some data from an experiment rolling dice. In pairs, they should roll their dice 24 times and record the outcomes using a tally and totalling. They then record how many times each number was thrown as a fraction of the total number of throws and draw up a table of their results. For example:

There are 27 children in our class

20 can swim more than 25 metres	$\frac{20}{27}$	
9 wear glasses	$\frac{9}{27}$ =	$\frac{1}{3}$
15 walk to school	$\frac{15}{27}$ =	$\frac{5}{9}$

Numbers which can be thrown	How many tally	Total	Fraction of the total number of throws (24)	
1	|||	3	$\frac{3}{24}$	$\frac{1}{8}$
2	||||	5	$\frac{5}{24}$	
3	||	2	$\frac{2}{24}$	$\frac{1}{12}$

DIFFERENTIATION

More able: Discuss whether the results are as they expected considering what chances they thought there were of throwing each number (ie an even chance with an even dice, so in theory all numbers should occur 6 times, but in practice this is not the case).
Less able: Give help with recording by tallying.

PLENARY

Ask one of the more able children to report on 'What are the chances of throwing each number?' Use one pair's results to make the point that the sum of the fractions, when all represented in 24ths, is 1. Discuss the types of information that is sometimes given in fractional form, eg *About three-quarters of the children attended the school fete, about three-tenths of adults smoke, which means that seven-tenths don't.*

RESOURCES

Large sheet of paper with a set of both fractions and mixed numbers written on it; Instructions for making mortar, lemonade or ginger cookies written on board or acetates; OHP; pencils and paper.

PREPARATION

On a large sheet of paper write the following fractions inside a circle:

$\frac{15}{8}$ $1\frac{5}{8}$ $\frac{23}{6}$ $\frac{1}{5}$ $\frac{5}{12}$ $\frac{25}{4}$ $\frac{6}{10}$ $\frac{4}{3}$ $2\frac{1}{2}$ $\frac{21}{16}$

Write the following making instructions on the board or on to acetate:

How to make: **Mortar:**   Mix 3 buckets of builder's sand to every bucket of cement. Mix quite dry.

Lemonade: Use 4 tablespoons of lemonade powder for each litre of water.

Ginger Cookies:

Ingredients: (Makes about 12.)
50g margarine
40g castor sugar
$1\frac{1}{2}$ level tablespoons golden syrup
100g plain flour
1 level teaspoon ground ginger
50g rolled oats
$\frac{1}{2}$ teaspoon bicarbonate of soda
$\frac{1}{2}$ tablespoon milk

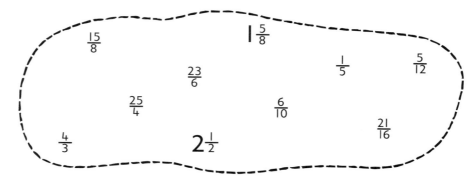

LEARNING OUTCOMES

ORAL AND MENTAL STARTER
● Order fractions and mixed numbers.

MAIN TEACHING ACTIVITY
● **Solve problems involving ratio and proportion.**

VOCABULARY

Fraction, proper/improper fraction, mixed number, numerator, denominator, equivalent, reduced to, cancel, ratio, to every, proportion, in every.

ORAL AND MENTAL STARTER

GREATER OR LESS: Ask questions about the fractions written on the large sheet of paper such as *Tell me a fraction less than 1. Are there any more? Can you find a fraction that is greater than 1 but less than 2? Are there any greater than 4?*

MAIN TEACHING ACTIVITY

HOW TO MAKE: Point to the mortar making instructions and explain to the children what they mean. Emphasise that the instructions compare part to part, and that with this ratio, 3 to 1, we can work out how many buckets of sand are needed if we use two, three or four buckets of cement. Ask for suggestions. Now turn to the lemonade making instructions and ask for the ratio of the number of tablespoons of lemonade powder to the number of litres of water (4 to 1). Ask questions such as, *How many tablespoons of powder are needed for 3 litres?* (12). *If I use 20 tablespoons of powder how much lemonade will it make?* (5 litres). Ask children how they calculated their answers. Next work with the children to create the ingredients list for making 60 cookies for a party (five times the number of people than in the recipe, so the ratio for each ingredient must be 5 to 1. Each amount must be multiplied by 5). The children should work individually to create the ingredients list for other amounts of cookies.

DIFFERENTIATION

More able: Calculate the ingredients list for making, say 6 cookies (1 to 2) and 18 (3 to 2).
Less able: Make the list for 24 cookies (2 to 1).

PLENARY

Return to the mortar making, comparing buckets of sand to buckets of cement. Develop the idea of 3 to 1, 6 to 2, 9 to 3 etc, and conversely buckets of cement to buckets of sand 1 to 3, 2 to 6, 3 to 9 etc. Then consider how much mortar you are making in total each time, eg 3 buckets of sand and 1 bucket of cement makes 4 buckets of mortar, 6 buckets of sand and 2 buckets of cement makes 8 buckets of mortar and so on.

RESOURCES

20 marbles; Multilink cubes; examples of simple ratio and proportion; pencils; paper.

PREPARATION

Gather the marbles. Find textbook examples involving simple ratio and proportion or produce your own (page 27 of the 'Supplement of examples: Years 4, 5 and 6' in the *Framework for Teaching Mathematics* may be a helpful guide).

LEARNING OUTCOMES

ORAL AND MENTAL STARTER
● **Solve problems involving ratio.**

MAIN TEACHING ACTIVITY
● **Solve simple problems involving ratio and proportion.**

VOCABULARY

Fraction; proper/improper fraction; mixed number; numerator; denominator; equivalent; reduced to; cancel; ratio; to every; proportion; in every.

ORAL AND MENTAL STARTER

QUICK-FIRE RATIOS: Tell the children that they must respond to your ratio with two numbers that have the same ratio. So, 1 to 3 might produce 2 and 6, 5 and 15 etc. Go on to say 5 to 6, then ask for equivalent ratios where one of the numbers is above, say 20.

MAIN TEACHING ACTIVITY

IS IT FAIR?: Talk with the children about unequal sharing. For example, *Louise shares out marbles with Chloe. For every marble she gives to Chloe she takes three for herself.* Ask two children to come to the front and share marbles out like this. Record their sharing, making the point that marbles are being shared in the ratio 3 to 1.
Introduce the fact that Chloe gets 1 in every four or $^1/_4$. *This compares what she gets to the number given out after every 'share out'. The proportion (fraction) that Chloe gets is $^1/_4$ while Louise's proportion is $^3/_4$.* Let them try other ratios eg 4 to 1, 3 to 2 (without using the marbles) creating tables as shown. They then move on to solve your prepared ratio and proportion problems.

Chloe	1	2	3	4	5
Louise	3	6	9	12	15
Given out	4	8	12	16	20

DIFFERENTIATION

More able: Think up real life contexts for the ratios involving, perhaps, money (eg 'We are sending £3 to the RNLI for every £2 to the Guide Dogs for the Blind. We have written the proportion as $^3/_5$ RNLI, $^2/_5$ Guide Dogs').
Less able: Use Multilink equipment to help with the ratio and proportion problems.

PLENARY

Emphasise the difference between ratio (for example, Chloe received 1 marble to every 3 Louise took) and proportion (Chloe received 1 marble in every four). Share any interesting contexts generated by the more able children with the rest of the class.

RESOURCES

5m of string; Blu-Tack; a set of five decimal fraction number cards less than 1 using a single decimal place; a set of five number cards giving numbers to two decimal places; a 0 and a 1 card; a set of blank cards; small pieces of paper; pencils and paper.

PREPARATION

Prepare the number cards. Set up a number line using the string, Blu-Tack and the 0 and 1 number cards at either end.

LEARNING OUTCOMES

ORAL AND MENTAL STARTER
● Count on in steps of 0.1, 0.2, 0.25, 0.5..., and then back.

MAIN TEACHING ACTIVITY
● Use decimal notation for tenths, hundredths and thousandths.
● **Order a mixed set of numbers with up to three decimal places.**
● Give a decimal fraction lying between two others.

VOCABULARY
Decimal fraction, decimal, decimal point, decimal place, thousandth.

ORAL AND MENTAL STARTER

DECIMAL 'POINTS': Organise the children into mixed ability groups. As a group they write down any numbers from 3 to 5 inclusive that they think will be included when counting up in 0.25s from 0. Then together do the count. They score points for each recorded number that occurs in the count. *Which group got the most points?* Repeat for other decimal steps, 0.1, 0.2, 0.3, 0.25, 0.5 etc from various starting points.

MAIN TEACHING ACTIVITY

WHERE DOES IT LIVE?: Tell the children that they are to position decimal cards on the number line. First use the one-place decimal cards, then put the two-place cards in between. Give out the cards and invite children up in turn. Each time the positions should be agreed or adjusted by the class. Ask the children for other numbers that could go along the line. Write these on the blank cards and invite them to be placed on the line. You could ask, for example, for numbers between 0.5 and 0.6 and then less than 0.3. Away from the line, ask for numbers between 3.2 and 3.9, extending to two decimal places. Record their answers, then ask the children to order them. Discuss strategies used. Question digit values. *What is the smallest number you can think of?*

DIFFERENTIATION

More able: Move on to the third decimal place of numbers that lie between, for example, 0.12 and 0.13. Point out that if we continue this idea to create more places of decimals, we can always find a number in between two others (ie that numbers are infinite).
Less able: Practise the main activity using the number line.

PLENARY

Consider digit values from whole numbers to decimal fractions. Discuss the fact that there was always a number lying between two others.

UNITS 4–5

RESOURCES	A large '0' card; a large '1' card; columns board prepared for Lesson 5, Units 2–3; calculators; pencils and paper.
PREPARATION	Make the 0 and 1 cards. Prepare some examples for the end of the **Main teaching activity**. Write the 'Make it bigger, make it smaller' pattern on the board: **× 10** 3 30 300 3000 **÷ 10** 300 30 3 0.3 0.03
LEARNING OUTCOMES	**ORAL AND MENTAL STARTER** ● **Multiply and divide decimals by 10 or 100 and explain the effect.** **MAIN TEACHING ACTIVITY** ● **Multiply and divide decimals by 10 or 100 and explain the effect.** ● Use decimal notation for tenths, hundredths and thousandths. ● Develop calculator skills and use a calculator effectively.
ORAL AND MENTAL STARTER	MAKE IT BIGGER, MAKE IT SMALLER: Discuss the × 10, ÷ 10 pattern and extend to 0.003 at the bottom. Go on to build similarly at the top, like this: 0.003 0.03 0.3 to complete the symmetry of the number pattern. Discuss the movement of the digits, relative to the decimal point, for × 10, ÷ 10, × 100, ÷ 100. Ask the children questions such as 6 ÷ 10, 0.8 × 10, 2.4 ÷ 10, 4.25 ÷ 100, 0.004 × 10.
MAIN TEACHING ACTIVITY	FURTHER AND FURTHER, NEARER AND NEARER: Explain that you are going to develop ideas of × 10 and ÷ 10. One child stands holding the large '0' card and another, a step away, represents '1'. *Where will 10 be?* The children consider 10 steps and respond accordingly. Now ask them to use their local knowledge of the area to approximate where 100 will be, and then 1000 and 10 000. Ensure that they understand that each selected number is the previous number multiplied by 10. Say that they should imagine that they are standing at 10 000 (mentioning the location) and ask where they will be if they divide 10 000 by 10. Follow this by asking what will happen if 1000, then 100, then 10 is divided by 10, with a final destination of 1. *Try dividing by 10 again, where will you land?* 'One tenth of the distance from 0 to 1; very close to 0.' Discuss other answers, eg 'At 1 on the other side of 0'. From 0.1, keep dividing by 10 to get nearer and nearer to 0. *When will we reach 0?* (Never). *How can we get to the other side of 0?* 'Stand at 1 and move back 2, landing at –1, or 1 – 2 = –1' Provide written examples where the children have to find the function which changes 0.3 to 3, 2.8 to 280, 252 to 2.52 etc. Let them use a calculator to check answers once all the calculations are complete.
DIFFERENTIATION	More able: Discuss with you a mathematical limit, like getting nearer and nearer to a number you will never reach, as in reaching 0, above. Mention numbers which lie between, say 5 and 6. Say 5.9 becomes 5.99 etc. getting nearer and nearer to 6 but never reaching it. Try others. Less able: Keep written examples to × 10, ÷ 10.
PLENARY	Discuss and show on the column board what happens when you constantly divide by 10, starting from 1. Emphasise that the decimal point and nought are clearly different. Many children need help over this. ones tenths hundredths thousandths I 0 . I 0 . 0 I 0 . 0 0 I smaller and smaller towards 0.0

RESOURCES

A small blank card per child; pencils; timer; Base 10 equipment; a blank column board per group; a calculator per pair; paper.

PREPARATION

Provide every child with a blank card and a pencil. Each table will need Base 10 equipment and a column board. Prepare similar columns, units to thousandths on the board or on acetate if you have an OHP available.

LEARNING OUTCOMES

ORAL AND MENTAL STARTER

● Use known number facts to consolidate mental addition/subtraction (of decimal numbers).

MAIN TEACHING ACTIVITY

● Recognise the equivalence between the decimal and fraction forms of common fractions.
● Begin to convert a fraction to a decimal using division.
● Develop calculator skills and use a calculator effectively.
● Order fractions.

VOCABULARY

Decimal fraction, decimal, decimal point, decimal place, tenth, hundredth, thousandth, recurring decimal.

ORAL AND MENTAL STARTER

DECIMAL TARGETS: Organise the children into mixed ability groups. Give each child a blank card and ask them to write a 2-digit decimal number less than 10 on it, eg 5.6. The group's cards are then placed in the centre of the table. You choose a target decimal number from 0 to 20, eg 12.6. The groups use their numbers with the addition or subtraction operations to try to hit the target in 30 seconds. The nearest group to the target when the time is up scores a point. Repeat for other target numbers.

MAIN TEACHING ACTIVITY

LET'S CHANGE: Tell the children that they are going to use Base 10 equipment and calculators to help them to change common fractions to decimal fractions.

For today let the block (1000) represent 1. What does a flat, a long and a unit represent? ($^1/_{10}$, $^1/_{100}$, $^1/_{1000}$). Record these at the top of the columns on the board. Discuss how to show $^1/_2$ with the equipment (5 flats; $^5/_{10}$), then $^1/_4$ (2 flats, 5 longs; $^2/_{10}$ and $^5/_{100}$), then $^1/_8$ (1 flat, 2 longs, 5 units; $^1/_{10}$, $^2/_{100}$ and $^5/_{1000}$). Discuss strategies – probably halving the equipment used each time. Ask them to place the equipment on their column board and then record in numbers on the board as shown. *What about $^1/_3$? 3 flats, 3 longs, 3 units. Oh dear, I need a saw!; $^3/_{10}$ and $^3/_{100}$ and $^3/_{1000}$ and the threes go on!* Let the children try $1 ÷ 3$ on their calculators (0.3333333). Tell the children that decimal fractions that go on forever are called recurring decimals. Ask them first to predict and then to divide, using the calculator to check $^3/_4$ (0.75). Let them also try $^4/_5$, $^{40}/_{1000}$, $^3/_8$ and so on, predicting all the answers before using the calculator to check.

	Ones		tenths	hundredths	thousandths
	I		$^1/_{10}$	$^1/_{100}$	$^1/_{1\,000}$
$^1/_{10}$	0	.	I		
$^1/_{100}$	0	.	0	I	
$^1/_{1\,000}$	0	.	0	0	I
$^1/_2$	0	.	5		
$^1/_4$	0	.	2	5	
$^1/_8$	0	.	I	2	5
$^1/_3$	0	.	3	3	then 4 more threes with the calculator

DIFFERENTIATION

More able: Investigate recurring decimals using a calculator eg $2/3$ (0.6666666, twice $1/3$). Try $1/9$, $2/9$, $1/6$ and discuss that $1/9$ (0.1111111) is $1/3$ (0.3333333) divided by 3.
Less able: Try other fractions with Base 10 and the column board eg $1/5$, $3/4$.

PLENARY

Compare common fractions by dividing to produce decimal fractions eg *Which is less, $3/5$ or $5/8$?* The children use calculators while you record. Order a set of decimal fractions. Then order a set of common fractions; point out that it is helpful to change them to decimal fractions first. Explain that decimal fractions continue the whole number system and are very powerful, allowing you to express numbers that are very small and be very accurate.

RESOURCES

Copies of photocopiable page 45 ('All out of 100'); pencils and paper.

PREPARATION

Photocopy page 45 ('All out of 100'), enough for one per child.

LEARNING OUTCOMES

ORAL AND MENTAL STARTER
● Recognise the equivalence between the decimal and fraction forms of common fractions.

MAIN TEACHING ACTIVITY
● **Understand percentage as the number of parts in every 100.** Express simple fractions as percentages.
● **Solve simple problems involving proportion.**
● **Solve a problem by** representing, **extracting and interpreting data in tables.**

VOCABULARY

Percentage, per cent, %, proportion.

ORAL AND MENTAL STARTER

FRACTIONS TO DECIMALS: Tell the children that they must respond to your common fraction with its equivalent decimal fraction and vice versa. Keep the questions to those fractions explored in Lesson 8.

MAIN TEACHING ACTIVITY

ALL OUT OF 100: Give out page 45 ('All out of 100'). Read the 'Taste test' information together and ask the children what they think and why. Point out that if each result was shown as a 'similar' fraction they could then be compared.

Number of children who passed the test	Girls $\frac{19}{25}$	Boys $\frac{16}{20}$
Number of children tested		

What fraction could they be changed to? (This could be hundredths, giving Girls $76/100$ and Boys $80/100$.) Tell the children that fractions written in hundredths are sometimes called percentages. *'per' means 'out of', and 'cent' means '100'.* Introduce the % symbol with its suggestion of a fraction and/or a 1 and two 0s. Use the symbol for Girls: 76% passed, and Boys: 80% passed. *What percentages of girls and boys failed?* (24%, 20%). Ask the children to complete the 'Tummy bug' table, making sure that they have understood Miss Bayes' statistics.

ANSWERS:
Mr. Williams $2/5$, 40%; Mrs Hawkins $1/3$, $33\frac{1}{3}$%; Mrs Evans $1/2$, 50%; Mr Stubbs $1/4$, 25%.
Proportion of children absent from school: 50 in 150 = 1 in 3 = $33\frac{1}{3}$%.

DIFFERENTIATION

More able: Go on to survey 25 words in a book recording the number of words with:

	1 letter	2 letters	3 letters	4 letters	5 letters	6 letters	more than 6 letters
Number of words							
Percentage							

Ensure they check their results.

Less able: Talk through the 'Tummy Bug' question from page 45 with them, explaining what they have to do. Give your support when they are working on it.

PLENARY

Mark and discuss the work covered.

LESSON 10

RESOURCES	Copies of photocopiable page 46 ('What's the offer?'); pencils.
PREPARATION	Photocopy page 46 ('What's the offer?'), enough for one per child.
LEARNING OUTCOMES	**ORAL AND MENTAL STARTER** ● Express fractions as percentages and vice-versa. **MAIN TEACHING ACTIVITY** ● **Understand percentage as the number of parts in every 100.** ● **Solve problems involving proportion.**
ORAL AND MENTAL STARTER	FRACTIONS TO PERCENTAGES: Children respond to your common fraction with its equivalent percentage and vice-versa. Keep questions simple.
MAIN TEACHING ACTIVITY	WHAT'S THE OFFER?: Give out the page 46 ('What's the offer?'). Discuss each of the 'What's the offer?' statements shown at the top of the sheet. Give examples for the children to work out, for example *Buy one get second half price for a chocolate bar costing 60p. 20% off is how much in the pound?* The children then work individually to complete the rest of the sheet. **Answers:** 1a) Jeans £8.64, Tee shirt £5.67, Trousers £13.50, Shirt £11.25, Socks £2.16, Jumpers £12.33; b) Jeans £9.12, Tee shirts £5.98, Trousers £14.25, Shirts £11.88, Socks £2.28, Jumpers £13.02; 2a) £210; b) £3; c) £50; d) £300.
DIFFERENTIATION	More able: Organise, say, a 'Number of children in family' survey for 20 children and consider proportions and percentages of the total number of families. Less able: Tell them to leave out question 1b.
PLENARY	Mark and discuss the work covered drawing together any points that you or the children wish to make.

Equivalent fractions

$\frac{1}{2}$	$\frac{2}{4}$	$\frac{3}{6}$	$\frac{4}{8}$
$\frac{1}{4}$	$\frac{2}{8}$	$\frac{3}{12}$	$\frac{4}{16}$
$\frac{1}{3}$	$\frac{2}{6}$	$\frac{3}{9}$	$\frac{4}{12}$
$\frac{1}{10}$	$\frac{2}{20}$	$\frac{3}{30}$	$\frac{4}{40}$
$\frac{1}{7}$	$\frac{2}{14}$	$\frac{3}{21}$	$\frac{4}{28}$
$\frac{2}{5}$	$\frac{4}{10}$	$\frac{6}{15}$	$\frac{8}{20}$
$\frac{3}{8}$	$\frac{6}{16}$	$\frac{9}{24}$	$\frac{12}{32}$

UNITS 4–5

All out of 100

Taste test

Two classes of children at Broadham Primary School have been given a coffee grains taste test. Here are the results:

	Number of children who were tested	Number of children who passed
Girls	25	19
Boys	20	16

Were the girls or the boys better in this test?

Can you be sure?

Tummy bug!

Last week a survey was made at the school of the number of children absent with a tummy bug on Friday. The table below shows the results:

Class	Number of children absent on Friday	Number of children in the class	Proportion (fraction) absent	Percentage
Miss Bayes	6	30	$\frac{1}{5}$	20
Mr Williams	10	25		
Mrs Hawkins	9	27		
Mrs Evans	16	32		
Mr Stubbs	9	36		

Complete the table. Make sure that your fractions are in their simplest form.

What proportion of the children were absent from the school in total?

How is this written as a percentage?

What's the offer?

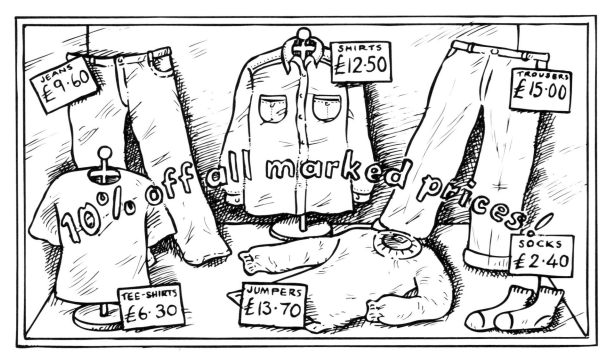

1. a. How much is each item with 10% off?

    b. What are the costs with a discount of 5%?

2. Find:

    a. 50% of £420

    b. 5% of £60

    c. 10% of £500

    d. 60% of £500

UNIT 6

ORGANISATION (8 LESSONS)

	LEARNING OUTCOMES	ORAL AND MENTAL STARTER	MAIN TEACHING ACTIVITY	PLENARY
LESSON 1	• **Solve a problem by** representing, **extracting and interpreting data in tables, graphs, charts.**	FIND THE FACTORS: Finding quickly the factors of a given number.	HOLIDAY IN PORTUGAL: Interpreting tables and charts of holiday information.	Share questions about the information.
LESSON 2	• **Solve a problem by** representing, **extracting and interpreting data in tables, graphs, charts** and diagrams including line graphs.	BEAT THE CLOCK: Finding the difference between two 2-digit numbers.	HOLIDAY SUNSHINE: Comparing temperatures and representing the data on graphs.	Display and discuss graphs.
LESSON 3	• **Solve a problem by** representing, **extracting and interpreting data in tables, graphs, charts** and diagrams including line graphs.	BEAT THE CLOCK: Finding the difference between two 2-digit numbers.	INTERPRETING DATA: Representing given data in diagrammatic form.	Discuss, display and make general statements about the data.
LESSON 4 + 5	• **Solve a problem by** representing, **extracting and interpreting data in tables, graphs, charts** and diagrams including line graphs and bar charts with grouped discrete data.	PRODUCTS: Making as many products as possible from four digits.	WORKING WITH DATA: Drawing bar charts with grouped discrete data. Interpreting data from textbooks, databases and other sources.	Discuss graphs and findings.
LESSON 6	• Use the language associated with probability to discuss events, including those with equally likely outcomes.	OVER THE TOP: Doubling decimal numbers to exceed a target number.	EVENS: Exploring the idea of evens chance using coins.	Discuss results including predictions of repeat experiments.
LESSON 7	• Use the language associated with probability to discuss events, including those with equally likely outcomes.	OVER THE TOP: Doubling decimal numbers and then adding or subtracting 1 or 2 after each turn to exceed a target number.	THROWING DICE: Exploring probabilities.	Discuss theory and results. Using a probability scale.
LESSON 8	• Use the language associated with probability to discuss events.	DOUBLE TROUBLE: Quick-fire doubling questions.	BASKET BEAN BAG: Introducing sampling to enable probability predictions where no evidence is to hand. Quoting predictions as percentage chances.	Emphasise salient points.

ORAL AND MENTAL SKILLS Find factors of any number to 100 (Year 5 revision). Use known number facts and place value to consolidate mental subtraction. Use known number facts and place value to consolidate mental multiplication. **Derive quickly:** doubles of two-digit numbers, including decimal fractions. **Derive quickly:** doubles of multiples of 10 to 1,000 and the corresponding halves.

In Unit 6 Lessons 1, 2, 4, 6 and 8 are shown in full. Lesson 5 extends the work of Lesson 4 and is shown after it. Lessons 3 and 7 are extensions of what has already been taught and are given in outline.

RESOURCES

Copies of photocopiable pages 54 ('Holiday in Portugal 1') and 55 ('Holiday in Portugal 2'); calculators; pencils; paper.

LESSON 1

PREPARATION

Photocopy pages 54 and 55 ('Holiday in Portugal' 1 and 2), one copy of each per pair. Make a list of numbers up to 100 which have several factors, eg 48, 54, 72, 84 etc.

LEARNING OUTCOMES

ORAL AND MENTAL STARTER
● Find factors of any number to 100 (Year 5 revision).

MAIN TEACHING ACTIVITY
● **Solve a problem by** representing, **extracting and interpreting data in tables, graphs, charts.**

VOCABULARY

Factor, statistics, range, maximum and minimum value.

ORAL AND MENTAL STARTER

FIND THE FACTORS: Give the children a number, for example 72, and ask individuals to tell you a factor of that number as quickly as they can.

MAIN TEACHING ACTIVITY

HOLIDAY IN PORTUGAL: Tell the children to imagine that they are arranging a holiday and ask them to tell you the sort of decisions that need to be made. These may include where to go, how to get there, the accommodation they require, the currency used. Discuss the points that arise. Give out the photocopiable sheets, one copy of each for each pair. *What information are you given about accommodation?* 'The information caters for up to 10 people'; 'The charges range from £249 to £1195'. *What about the cost of car hire and flights?* Ask each pair to imagine that they are going to Portugal. They should decide how many there will be in their party, no more than five, and use the information discussed to make up questions about the holiday, eg *Four of us want to stay at Villa Kimbo for one week at the end of March, how much will it cost?; We want to fly from Exeter; our holiday starts 28 March. Can we?* They then find solutions for each one, using calculators to help them if necessary.

DIFFERENTIATION

More able: Go on to give their questions to another group to solve.
Less able: Be prepared to give them guidance on the type of question to write and help in finding the solution.

PLENARY

Ask each group to give at least one of their questions to the class for discussion.

RESOURCES

11–99 number cards; copies of photocopiable page 55 ('Holiday in Portugal 2'); prepared graph axes; water-based pen; cm graph paper; felt-tipped pens; pencils; stop clock.

PREPARATION

Provide a set of 11–99 number cards and a copy of page 55 ('Holiday in Portugal 2') per pair. Mount a piece of 2cm² squared paper on to card and cover it with transparent self-adhesive plastic. With a water-based pen draw two axes, but do not label them. Have enough graph paper for the children to have a sheet each. Make sure that each child has a sharp pencil.

LEARNING OUTCOMES

ORAL AND MENTAL STARTER
● Use known number facts and place value to consolidate mental subtraction.

MAIN TEACHING ACTIVITY
● **Solve a problem by** representing, **extracting and interpreting data in tables, graphs, charts** and diagrams including line graphs.

ORAL AND MENTAL STARTER

BEAT THE CLOCK: Give out the number cards face down, one per child. Set the stop clock to 8 minutes. Choose two children to hold up their cards for the class to see. Ask the class to quickly find the difference between the two-digit numbers and tell you the result. Then choose another pair and repeat the activity. Record the number of correct answers given in the time allowed.

MAIN TEACHING ACTIVITY

HOLIDAY SUNSHINE: Ask the children to look at the weather statistics represented on the table on 'Holiday in Portugal 2' (page 55). *What does it tell you?* Look for the reply: 'In Portugal it's hottest in August and there are 12 hours of sunshine. In London both July and August are the same'. Discuss what is meant by 'average daily temperature and hours of sunshine'. *Could the information be more clearly represented by drawing some type of graph?* They may suggest 'We can draw two bar charts, one for Portugal and one for London showing the same information, such as hours of sunshine'; 'We can put two different axes on one graph then we can show temperature and sunshine'; 'I think we can just draw lines instead of bars.' In pairs, the children then choose the information they would like to represent and draw a suitable graph of this data. If possible, their graph should show a comparison between the Algarve and London. Remind them to give the graph a title and to label the axes.

DIFFERENTIATION

More able: Show all the data on one graph using different colours and superimposing one scale on to another. Consider the information given on the exchange rate and produce a diagram which gives the exchange of small amounts, say up to £5.
Less able: Gather these children together and discuss further the information they may choose to represent and the scales involved.

PLENARY

Display and discuss all graphs.

RESOURCES	Number cards 11–99; prepared data sheets; graph paper; felt-tipped pens; pencils.
PREPARATION	Collate sufficient data for all groups. This may include statistics about the children themselves such as month of birth, date of birth, day of birth, number in family etc. Alternatively, you may choose to discuss and set up experiments to gather information about the children's skill, such as the number of hops, skips or catches they can do in a set time. Photocopy the statistics once they have been gathered, enough copies for one between two.
LEARNING OUTCOMES	**ORAL AND MENTAL STARTER** ● Use known number facts and place value to consolidate mental subtraction. **MAIN TEACHING ACTIVITY** ● Solve a problem by representing, **extracting and interpreting data in tables, graphs, charts** and diagrams including line graphs.
ORAL AND MENTAL STARTER	BEAT THE CLOCK: Repeat the **Oral and mental starter** from Lesson 2 and try to better the previous score.
MAIN TEACHING ACTIVITY	INTERPRETING DATA: In pairs, the children choose data from your prepared sheet and represent it in a graph of their choice. They may use some or all of the data.
DIFFERENTIATION	More able: Encourage combining different statistics, and draw conclusions from them such as 'In our class, the boys seem to be better at hopping but the girls are better at skipping.' Less able: Discuss the data they choose to represent, and the way in which they are going to do this before they begin.
PLENARY	Discuss and display findings and make general statements about the data.

RESOURCES

Pencils; scrap paper; copies of photocopiable 56 ('Cotleigh Swimathlon'); graph paper; calculators; graph board as made for Lesson 3; 2–9 numeral cards; collected data charts and tables.

PREPARATION

Photocopy page 56 ('Cotleigh Swimathlon'), and cut each sheet in half. Save Part B, the graph, for group assessment. For Lesson 5 select textbook pages, a computer database or other resource such as holiday brochures, car magazines or shopping catalogues, which will give children practise in interpreting data, grouping and drawing bar charts using discrete data. Try to find material that will be suitable for the different ability ranges within the class.

LEARNING OUTCOMES

ORAL AND MENTAL STARTER

● Use known number facts and place value to consolidate mental multiplication.

MAIN TEACHING ACTIVITY

● **Solve a problem by** representing, **extracting and interpreting data in tables, graphs, charts** and diagrams including line graphs and bar charts with grouped discrete data.

VOCABULARY

Group, data bar chart, axes, statistics, frequency.

ORAL AND MENTAL STARTER

PRODUCTS: The children each write down four different digits, at least two of which are greater than 5. They then make as many products as they can with their numbers by multiplying one or two of the digits by one of the remaining digits. For example 3, 6, 8, 2 can make 8×2, 3×8, 28×6, 63×8, 86×3 etc. They record each multiplication followed by the answer found mentally.

MAIN TEACHING ACTIVITY

WORKING WITH DATA: Give out part A of page 56 ('Cotleigh Swimathlon'). *All the children in Mr Ray's class were encouraged to take part, even if they couldn't swim very far. The class had predicted that they would raise more than £500.* Ask the children, in pairs, to use their calculator to see if the class was successful. (Answer: Yes – they raised £520.) *Each child has been asked to display the results of their swim. Two of the children in Mr Ray's class have decided that the information could be shown as a bar chart. How can they do this when the range of lengths swum is so wide? They would need to represent from 1 to 56. Any ideas?* Encourage the children to consider grouping the data. *What would be a suitable grouping?* Some may suggest grouping in tens while others may feel that fives will give a clearer picture. Remind them that if they are grouping 1 to 5, then the next group goes from 6 to 10, not 5 to 10 and so on. Working in pairs, the children produce the graph. Some children may choose to compare boys and girls while others may want to make a graph of the class as a whole. Remind them to label both axes and give the graph a title. If time allows then each pair should write a question about their data, eg 'How many of the class managed to swim more than 20 lengths?' 'Did anyone manage to swim a kilometre?'

DIFFERENTIATION

More able: Go on to group the data in different ways, such as grouping in 20s and seeing how this affects the picture. *If we group in 20s the graph makes it look as if the class is not very good at swimming because 13 children are in the 1–20 group and we can't tell if they have swum 1 or 20 lengths!*
Less able: May need your help with labelling the axes, especially the horizontal grouping. You may wish to demonstrate on the graph board made for Lesson 3.

PLENARY

Ask the children to exchange papers from the **Oral and mental starter** part of the lesson and quickly check the answers using calculators. Score one point for each correct answer. Who scored the most?

Discuss the graphs and grouping data. Expect replies such as: 'We grouped in fives because we thought that it would give the most accurate picture: 3 children swam less than 5 lengths and if we had grouped in tens this would not have shown'; 'If we had grouped in less than fives then we could not have got the axis on the page and the picture would not have been as clear.' Select pairs to ask their questions for others to answer.

LESSON 5

Repeat the **Oral and mental starter** from Lesson 4. For the **Main teaching activity,** tell the children that they are going to work on their own, interpreting data and drawing graphs. For differentiation, give the more able children more sophisticated data to interpret with irrelevant information included. Less able children may need your help to interpret and illustrate the data. For the **Plenary,** ask the children to exchange papers from the **Oral and mental starter** part of the lesson and quickly check the answers using calculators. Go on to discuss and display the data presentations.

RESOURCES

2p and 1p coins; scrap paper; graph paper; felt-tipped pens.

PREPARATION

Provide coins, one of each per pair.

LEARNING OUTCOMES

ORAL AND MENTAL STARTER
● **Derive quickly** doubles of two-digit numbers, including decimal fractions.

MAIN TEACHING ACTIVITY
● Use the language associated with probability to discuss events, including those with equally likely outcomes.

VOCABULARY
Equally likely, chance, equal chance, even chance, fifty-fifty chance, predict.

ORAL AND MENTAL STARTER

OVER THE TOP: Tell the children that they are going to keep doubling decimal numbers and the first group to reach a number higher than the whole number selected as the target will win the point for that round. Divide the class into five or six groups. One child in the first group selects a 'starter' decimal (to one decimal place) which is less than 2. Another child picks the 'target' whole number between, say 10 and 30. Write the two numbers on the board. The next group doubles the 'starter', the next doubles again and so on until a table says a number above the 'target' number and scores the point. Repeat.

MAIN TEACHING ACTIVITY

EVENS: Show the children a coin and say that if you toss it, it can come down either heads or tails. Ask for a prediction, head or tail, then toss the coin. Try a few more times. *What is the chance of tossing a head? There are two possibilities with heads being one of them, so there is a 1 in 2 chance. What about tossing a tail? The same.* Say that there is an equal or even chance of it being a head or a tail. Discuss other evens situations such as the gender of the next puppy born (male or female); dropping toast, which side up? Return to the coin and ask children to come to the front and toss it while you record the results on the board. After 10 tosses, total the heads and tails and discuss the results. For example, *There are more heads than tails. Shouldn't it be 5 and 5?* Say that it may be necessary to try some more because although there is an even chance for each throw, we may not toss an equal number of heads as tails. In pairs, the children toss a coin 10 times and record the number of heads and tails to investigate the even chance of a head or tail.

DIFFERENTIATION

More able: Prepare a neat recording sheet using graph paper and felt-tipped pens to show all the class results. As each pair finishes they give their results to the recorders, who record and finally total them.

Less able: Work with them to check their recordings. Ask them to predict what is going to happen.

PLENARY

Show the final results to the class and write on the board how many tosses were made and the total number of heads and tails. Discuss, emphasising the point that although results do not necessarily show the same number of heads as tails, there is still an equal (even) chance each time we toss a coin of getting heads and an equal chance of getting tails. *When we 'toss up', it's fair.* Ask the children to predict what would happen if you repeated the experiment tomorrow.

LESSON 7

RESOURCES	Four 1–6 dice; large graph paper (half sheets); felt-tipped pens; paper.
PREPARATION	Prepare four tables, each with one dice and a set of the other resources on.
LEARNING OUTCOMES	**ORAL AND MENTAL STARTER** ● **Derive quickly:** doubles of two-digit numbers, including decimal fractions. **MAIN TEACHING ACTIVITY** ● Use the language associated with probability to discuss events, including those with equally likely outcomes.
ORAL AND MENTAL STARTER	OVER THE TOP: Repeat the activity from Lesson 6 and extend to starting with a number between 2 and 4, and adding or subtracting 1 or 2 after doubling the result in each turn.
MAIN TEACHING ACTIVITY	THROWING DICE: Arrange the children around four tables. Remind them about the coin tossing probability activity in Lesson 6. Show them a dice and explain that all the numbers appear once, so each number has an equal chance of being rolled. Ask, *What is the chance of rolling a 6?* (1 in 6) *What about either a 1 or a 2?* (1 in 3) *An odd number?* (1 in 3) *A number less than 5?* (2 in 3). Give each group one of the above tests to try as an experiment, recording the results of 12 rolls. They should draw up a table for results not only for their group but also for the results of the three groups that will follow. Emphasise clear recording. Change around so that every table tries everything and make sure that every child participates. When each group reaches the last experiment, ask them to total the results for the 48 rolls.
DIFFERENTIATION	More able: Consider other possibilities, eg rolling zero, a number greater than 6, either a 1 or a number greater than 2. Less able: Discuss the experiments with them as you move around the groups.
PLENARY	Discuss the difference between the 'what is the chance' theory and the actual results for each experiment. Place the probabilities on a scale on the board like this: $0 \qquad \frac{1}{6} \qquad\qquad \frac{1}{2} \qquad\qquad\qquad 1$ Impossible 1 in 6 evens certain rolling a six

LESSON 8

RESOURCES

Empty wastepaper basket; masking tape; bean bag; large recording sheet; felt-tipped pens; paper; resources for other tests.

PREPARATION

Mark a position on the floor 5m from the wastepaper basket with masking tape and prepare a score sheet with YES and NO columns. Have available measuring equipment and so on for the other tests.

LEARNING OUTCOMES

ORAL AND MENTAL STARTER
● **Derive quickly:** doubles of multiples of 10 to 1000 and the corresponding halves.

MAIN TEACHING ACTIVITY
● Use the language associated with probability to discuss events.

VOCABULARY

Chance, even chance, likelihood, predict.

ORAL AND MENTAL STARTER

DOUBLE TROUBLE: Ask quick-fire questions involving doubling multiples of 10 to 1000, eg 230 × 2, 960 × 2, and halving results, eg 460 ÷ 2. Discuss halving multiples of 10, such as 130, 850, then try others.

MAIN TEACHING ACTIVITY

BASKET BEAN BAG: Tell the children that they are going to be trying their skills at throwing a bean bag into a wastepaper basket. *How many of us will get a bean bag in with only one turn?* Point out that you have no evidence on how difficult it is. *Let's try ten of us as a sample.* Record YESs and NOs and consider results, such as 6 YES 4 NO. *From our results, we can predict that there is a 6 in 10 (3 in 5 or 60%) chance of getting a bean bag in and a 4 in 10 (2 in 5 or 40%) chance of not getting it in. If we test for the rest of the class, about how many YESs and NOs do we predict?* Complete the experiment and discuss results. *How sure can we be that our prediction will be correct?* Skill is playing its part here and this is different to the coins or dice situations of previous lessons. *What if a basketball team tried? What about children from the Reception Class?* Invite children and teachers from other classes to try at break-time. Later count the YES and NO results. *How did they match up with the 60% YES, 40% NO result?*

Ask the children to think up some other possible tests. Try one or two of them that can be quickly arranged, sampling and predicting first, eg bunny jumping more than a metre, reading a paragraph of a book backwards in a stated time. In each case have several testings going on at the same time. Encourage clear and neat recordings.

DIFFERENTIATION

More able: Let them arrange the tests.
Less able: Encourage their ideas and use them wherever possible.

PLENARY

Pull together the salient points emphasising again how sample tests were needed before you could predict the chance. Don't forget to discuss the break-time survey results later in the day.

Holiday in Portugal (1)

ACCOMMODATION: LAGOS & WESTERN ALGARVE

Flight, car hire & accommodation £ per person / Based on Departure Date	Page number	Number of persons	Low Season 28 Mar–15 May 26 Sept–31 Oct		Mid Season 16 May–29 May 6–19 June 12 Sept–25 Sept		High Season 30 May–5 June 20 June–17 July 22 Aug–11 Sept		Peak Season 18 July–21 Aug	
			1 week	2 weeks	1 week	2 weeks	1 week	2 weeks	1 week	2 weeks
Quinta do Sapo	23	4	410	545	460	682	509	775	609	915
		5	358	521	407	611	463	661	563	791
		6	351	502	401	597	451	647	541	757
		7	292	445	342	540	402	590	482	690
		8	275	410	302	500	352	540	442	640
		9	262	390	290	485	332	525	422	595
		10	249	370	275	430	310	485	405	555
Residencia Buganvilla	24	2	565	795	595	925	695	1125	745	1195
		3	425	595	465	655	525	825	575	875
		4	395	545	425	585	505	795	565	835
Villa Kimbo	24	2	580	890	675	993	-	-	-	-
		3	470	685	530	777	608	828	720	932
		4	410	540	460	630	510	685	597	788
Horta da Avozinha	25	2	605	930	695	1035	-	-	-	-
		3	480	710	545	805	620	845	725	955
		4	420	565	468	655	520	695	615	805
		5	375	516	425	605	477	660	575	755
Mazuli's Cottages Studio	26	2	351	500	382	548	409	603	440	650
Mazuli's Cottages 1 bedroom cottage	26	2	395	578	442	659	487	748	517	795
		3	334	456	370	514	399	574	424	611
		4	295	386	325	434	347	478	369	509
Mazuli's Cottages 2 bedroom cottage	26	2	513	825	565	900	605	990	654	1076
		3	415	645	448	675	477	736	515	795
		4	365	525	382	563	415	608	446	657
Quinta da Alfarrobeira 1 bedroom cottage 2 bedroom cottage	27	2	435	645	455	685	515	750	535	775
		2	575	895	665	995	-	-	-	-
		3	457	680	517	770	592	820	702	920
		4	395	535	445	625	495	675	580	775

CAR HIRE

Group	Type of car (or similar)	Number of persons	Low Season April–June October	High Season July–September
A	Opel Corsa 3 door	4	£115	£135
B	Opel Corsa 5 door	5	£125	£150
C	Renault Clio 5 door	5	£135	£160
D	Ford Escort 5 door	5	£160	£190
E	Opel Astra 5 door	5	£235	£295
F	Ford Transit	9	£340	£420
G	Nissan Serena	7	£410	£495
H	Ford Fiesta 5 door auto	5	£185	£235

UNIT 6

Holiday in Portugal (2)

FLIGHTS TO THE ALGARVE (FARO) – SATURDAYS

Flight Code	From	Dates of operation First outbound/last inbound	Depart UK	Return UK landing	Flight Supplement per Person						Pre-bookable seats
					20 Mar–30 Apr	1 May-18 Jun	19 Jun-16 Jul	17 Jul-27 Aug	28 Aug	29 Aug-31 Oct	
6FLA	Gatwick	20 March–13 Nov	1430	2105	NIL	NIL	NIL	NIL	NIL	NIL	YES
6FLB	Gatwick	27 March–06 Nov	0700	1325	NIL	£3	£3	£3	£3	£3	YES
6FLC	Gatwick	01 May–06 Nov	0600	1255	-	NIL	NIL	NIL	NIL	NIL	YES
6FSA	Stansted	01 May–30 Oct	1455	1355	-	£8	£8	£8	£8	£8	YES
6FRA	Bristol	03 April–24 April	1620	2010	£20	-	-	-	-	-	YES
6FRA	Bristol	01 May–13 Nov	1735	2340	-	£20	£16	£20	£15	£20	YES
6FTA	Exeter	03 April–24 April	1355	1230	£20	-	-	-	-	-	YES
6FTA	Exeter	01 May–13 Nov	1045	1000	-	£20	£20	-	-	£20	NO
6FBA	Birmingham	03 April–06 Nov	0745	2230	£20	£21	£21	£21	£18	£21	YES
6FEA	East Midlands	03 April–24 April	1345	2020	£20	-	-	-	-	-	YES
6FEA	East Midlands	01 May–13 Nov	1550	2225	-	£23	£23	£23	£18	£23	YES
6FMA	Manchester	20 March–13 Nov	0615	1315	-	£22	£22	£24	£18	£24	YES
6FMB	Manchester	01 May–06 Nov	1445	2055	£18	£18	£18	£20	£15	£20	YES
6FMC	Manchester	29 May–30 Oct	1100	1750	-	£32	£32	£34	£28	£34	NO
6FNA	Newcastle	01 May–30 Oct	1815	1725	-	£30	£34	£34	£22	£30	NO
6FHA	Humberside	24 July–11 Sept	1115	1030	-	-	-	£32	£20	-	NO

TEMPERATURE AND SUNSHINE

	April		May		June		July		August		September		October	
	T	S	T	S	T	S	T	S	T	S	T	S	T	S
Algarve	65	9	70	10	78	12	84	12	85	12	78	9	72	8
London	55	5	61	6	69	7	70	6	70	6	65	5	58	3

T = Average daily maximum temperature (°F)
S = Average daily hours of sunshine

Exchange rate: 280 escudos to the pound

Cotleigh swimathlon – Part A

Raise money for new changing rooms!
Cotleigh School Swimathlon

Tom Fox of Fox & Sons Builders has kindly offered to donate £1 for every length swum!
Come along and try – every length counts!
Pool available Thursday and Friday 2nd & 3rd June.
Pool length 20 metres.

MR RAY'S CLASS			
Sylvie	6	Alex	24
Anne	4	Tom	18
Amanda	25	Paul A	7
Mark C	15	Steven	42
Joe	45	Paul B	36
Harry	16	Mark B	27
Ann B	1	Lyndsey	30
Susan	2	Paula	56
Jo	28	Kim	18
Cary	12	Charlotte	14
Max	16	Emilia	31
Cherie	34	Marcus	13

Cotleigh swimathlon – Part B

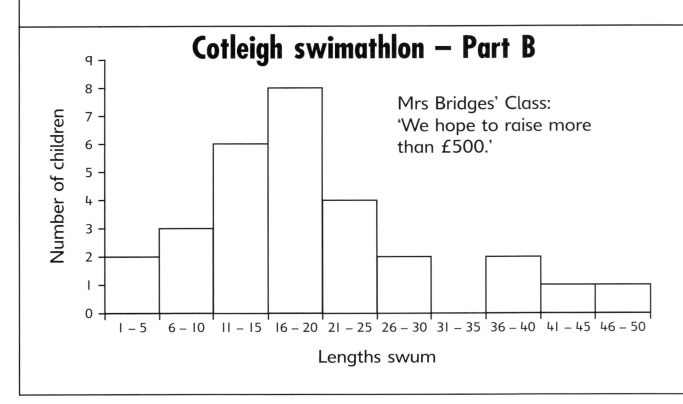

Mrs Bridges' Class:
'We hope to raise more than £500.'

Number of children (y-axis)
Lengths swum (x-axis): 1 – 5, 6 – 10, 11 – 15, 16 – 20, 21 – 25, 26 – 30, 31 – 35, 36 – 40, 41 – 45, 46 – 50

UNIT 7: Assess & Review

ASSESS AND REVIEW

Choose from these activities. During the group activities, some children can be completing assessment worksheets 1a and 1b which assess various skills covered during the previous half-term. The specific assessment criteria for the assessment sheets are to be found at the bottom of each sheet.

RESOURCES

Graph paper; felt pens; copies of Part B of photocopiable page 56 ('Cotleigh Swimathlon' – see Lesson 4, Unit 6) and of Assessment sheets 1a and 1b; calculators; pencils and paper.

PREPARATION

Write the results of a 'Favourite TV programme' survey on the board: '8 Coronation Street, 5 Eastenders, 4 Top of the Pops, 3 A Question of Sport'. Copy Assessment sheets 1a and 1b, enough for one per child.

ORAL AND MENTAL STARTER

ASSESSMENT

Can the children: Multiply and divide decimals by 10 and 100? Solve simple problems involving ratio?
BIGGER AND SMALLER, BY 10 OR 100: Start by asking questions involving × 10 and ÷ 10, then × 100, ÷ 100 using both whole number questions and answers, eg 32 × 10, 80 ÷ 10, 14 × 100, 3600 ÷ 100. Move on to decimals, eg 1.2 × 10, 27 ÷ 10, 0.04 × 100, 729 ÷ 100.
SAME RATIO: The children give equivalent ratios to 1 to 4 (2 to 8, 3 to 12, 5 to 20), 8 to 12 (2 to 3, 16 to 24, 7 to 21) and so on. After each answer ask: *Are there any more ratios?* Encourage answers that are not simply derived from doubling or halving, as suggested above, and note the children who find this difficult.

GROUP ACTIVITIES

ASSESSMENT

Can the children: Solve simple problems involving proportion? Reduce a fraction to its simplest form by cancelling common factors? Understand percentage as the number of parts in every 100? Solve a problem by extracting and interpreting data in graphs?
PERCENTAGE AND PROPORTION: Give each child graph paper, a felt-tipped pen and a pencil and paper. Ask them to draw a rectangle 20 squares long and to colour squares in to show how 20 children voted in a 'Favourite TV programme' survey, based on the information on the board. Ask them to give the proportion of children who voted for each programme as a fraction in its simplest form and as a percentage (ensuring the percentages sum to 100%).
INTERPRETING GROUPED DISCRETE DATA: Give each child 'Cotleigh Swimathlon' (page 56). Ask questions such as: *How many children swam more than 20 lengths? How many more children swam from 1 to 20 than from 31 to 50 lengths?* Go on to ask, *Do you think Mrs Bridges' class raised more than £500? What is your evidence?* (Remind them that for each length Fox and Sons Builders has kindly offered to donate £1.)

ANSWERS

Assessment 1a 1a) $\frac{1}{2}$; b) $\frac{4}{5}$; c) $\frac{1}{3}$; d) $\frac{3}{7}$; e) $1\frac{1}{3}$; f) $7\frac{1}{4}$; g) $6\frac{4}{5}$; h) $18\frac{1}{3}$. 2a) 8.89, 8.9, 9.03, 9.26, 9.4; b) 0.139, 0.14, 0.143, 0.2, 0.3; 3a) various answers; b) various answers; 4a) £130; b) £16; c) £30; d) £48; e) 25%.
Assessment 1b 1) 11 jars and 96p change; 2) 192cm (1m 92cm); 3) 452 people; 4) 3 Serenade 1.8l, £21 957; 2 Serenade 2.0l, £16 650; 4 Carmen 1.16l, £33 560; 8 Trekker 1.8l, £79 840.

Assessment sheet 1a

1. Write these fractions in their simplest form:

a) $\frac{2}{4}$

b) $\frac{8}{10}$

c) $\frac{6}{18}$

d) $\frac{9}{21}$

e) $1\frac{3}{9}$

f) $7\frac{8}{32}$

g) $6\frac{12}{15}$

h) $18\frac{14}{42}$

2. Put these numbers in order from the lowest to highest:

a)   9.03   9.4   8.9   9.26   8.89

_____   _____   _____   _____   _____

Now try these:

b)   0.2   0.14   0.139   0.143   0.3

_____   _____   _____   _____   _____

3. Write three decimal numbers that are between:

a) 7.32 and 7.36   _____   _____   _____

b) 0.4 and 0.43   _____   _____   _____

4. Find:

a) 50% of £260   _____

b) 20% of 80   _____

c) $33\frac{1}{3}$ of £90   _____

d) 15% of £320   _____

e) the discount when a pair of trousers usually costing

£20 is on offer at £15.   _____

- Reduce a fraction to its simplest form by cancelling common factors.
- Order a mixed set of numbers with up to three decimal places.
- Find simple percentages of small whole-number quantities.

UNIT 7

Name

Assessment sheet 1b

Find the answers to these problems. Do not use a calculator.

1. What is the maximum number of jars of coffee that can
   be bought for £30, if each jar costs £2.64?   _____

   How much change will there be?   _____

2. Lauren is making some doll's house furniture from balsa wood.
   She has 2 metre lengths of wood and needs 8 lengths of
   5cm, 6 lengths of 16cm and 4 lengths of 14cm. Work
   out the total length required.   _____

3. At one of the turnstiles of York City Football Club, £3616 was the
   total amount of money taken. It costs £8 to attend a match, so
   how many people went through this turnstile?

   _____

	Serenade	Carmen	Trekker
1.6l	£6427	£8390	£9240
1.8l	£7319	£9106	£9980
2.0l	£8325	£9943	£10 575

The sales for Week 6 are shown below. Complete the table.

Cars sold	Model	Money taken
3	Serenade 1.8l	£
2	Serenade 2.0l	£
4	Carmen 1.6l	£
8	Trekker 1.8l	£

- Identify and use appropriate operations (including combinations of operations) to solve word
  problems involving numbers and quantities.
- Solve a problem by extracting and interpreting data in tables.

UNITS 8–10

ORGANISATION (15 LESSONS)

LEARNING OUTCOMES	ORAL AND MENTAL STARTER	MAIN TEACHING ACTIVITY	PLENARY
LESSON 1 • **Use a protractor to measure** and draw **angles to the nearest degree.** • Estimate angles.	FACTOR LOOPS: Finding factors from given numbers.	ANGLES: Estimating, drawing and calculating angles.	Discuss strategies for finding factors. Check results for angles.
LESSON 2 • **Use a protractor to measure** and draw **angles**. • Calculate angles in a triangle.	TELL ME THE OTHER: Giving the other angle when told one of the angles in a straight line.	TRIANGLES: Constructing and measuring angles in a triangle.	Name triangles drawn. Make statements about the sum of the angles.
LESSON 3 • Check that the sum of the angles of a triangle is 180°. • Make a general statement about familiar shapes by finding examples which satisfy it.	AS NEAR AS YOU CAN: Using digits and operations to reach a target number.	TRIANGLES AGAIN: Investigating the angle sum of a triangle.	Discuss findings and make a general statement about the angle sum.
LESSON 4+5 • Draw angles. • Classify triangles. (Year 5 revision)	GIVE ME THE OTHER ONE: Given two angles of a triangle, find the other one.	CAN YOU FIND ONE?: Constructing triangles to satisfy given criteria.	Name the triangles.
LESSON 6 • Classify quadrilaterals, using criteria such as parallel sides, equal angles, equal sides....	TELL ME ABOUT IT: Finding properties of given numbers.	SORTING QUADRILATERALS: Sorting quadrilaterals using a Venn diagram.	Discuss the Venn diagram produced.
LESSON 7 • Classify quadrilaterals, using criteria such as parallel sides, equal angles, equal sides....	TELL ME ABOUT IT: Finding properties of given numbers.	MAKING QUADRILATERALS: Feeding quadrilaterals through a Yes/No decision tree.	Discuss attributes.
LESSON 8 • Calculate angles in a triangle (and in polygons). • Make and investigate a general statement about shapes.	BEAT THE CLOCK: Adding and finding the difference between two 2-digit numbers.	MAKING POLYGONS: Making polygons from triangles and recording results.	Discuss results.
LESSON 9 • Make shapes with increasing accuracy. • Identify different nets for a closed cube.	QUICK BONDS: Making multiplication and division bonds from a given number.	CUBES: Drawing nets and making cubes.	Discuss strategies.
LESSON 10 • Make shapes with increasing accuracy. • Visualise 3–D shapes from 2–D drawings.	QUICK BONDS: Making multiplication and division bonds from a given number.	NETS: Drawing nets of polyhedron.	Discuss sketches and completed polyhedron.
LESSON 11 • Use, read and write standard metric units (cm, mm) including their abbreviations, and relationships between them. • **Calculate the perimeter of simple shapes.** • Make and investigate a general statement about familiar shapes by finding examples that satisfy it. Develop from explaining a generalised relationship in words to expressing it in a formula using letters as symbols.	ALL CHANGE BINGO: Changing centimetres to millimetres.	AROUND THE SIDES: Finding perimeters of simple 2–D shapes, generalising in words and using formulae.	Pulling together the children's findings.

	LEARNING OUTCOMES	ORAL AND MENTAL STARTER	MAIN TEACHING ACTIVITY	PLENARY
LESSON 12	● Use, read and write standard metric units (cm, mm) including their abbreviations, and relationships between them. ● Describe properties of solid shapes such as edges (and calculate total edge lengths). ● Make and investigate a general statement about familiar shapes by finding examples that satisfy it. Develop from explaining a generalised relationship in words to expressing it in a formula using letters as symbols.	VICE VERSA: Naming regular polygons. Calculating perimeters from edge lengths and vice versa.	3–D AROUND THE EDGES: Finding total edge lengths of 3–D shapes and generalising in words and using formulae.	Ask individual children to describe their findings.
LESSON 13	● Use, read and write standard metric units (cm, mm) including their abbreviations, and relationships between them. ● **Calculate the perimeter of simple compound shapes.** ● Develop calculator skills and use a calculator effectively.	MILLIMETRE BAG NUMBERS: Changing millimetres to centimetres.	WHAT'S THE PERIMETER: Calculating the perimeters of simple shapes.	Compare strategies.
LESSON 14 +15	● Use, read and write standard metric units (km, cm, mm, kg, g, l, ml, cl) including their abbreviations, and relationship between them. ● Suggest suitable units and measuring equipment to estimate or measure length, mass or capacity. ● Record estimates and readings from scales to a suitable degree of accuracy.	MULTIPLES OF TEN: Multiplying and dividing of multiples of 10.	ESTIMATING: Estimating and measuring length, mass and capacity. Finding equivalence of metric measures.	Discuss problems. Extend work to include tonnes (t) and centilitres (cl). Explore the use of measures, eg in a supermarket, a garage, and a chemist's shop.

ORAL AND MENTAL SKILLS Use factors. Apply simple test of divisibility. Calculate angles (in a straight line). Use estimation and approximation. Calculate angles in a triangle. Use known number facts and place value to consolidate addition, subtraction, multiplication and division. Consolidate knowing by heart multiplication facts up to 10 × 10. Use the relationship between multiplication and division. **Derive quickly: division facts corresponding to tables up to 10 × 10.** Convert smaller to larger units and vice versa (eg, mm to cm, cm to mm). Multiply and divide decimals mentally.

Lessons 1, 3–6, 9, 11, 14 and 15 are shown in full. Lessons 2, 7, 8, 10, 12 and 13 are extensions of what has already been taught and are only outlined.

RESOURCES

One copy of photocopiable page 72 ('Measuring angles') per child; protractors (circular if possible); rulers; sharpened pencils.

PREPARATION

Make sure that all pencils are hard (H or 2H) and well sharpened.

LEARNING OUTCOMES

ORAL AND MENTAL STARTER
● Use factors.
● Apply simple tests of divisibility.

MAIN TEACHING ACTIVITY
● **Use a protractor to measure** and draw **angles to the nearest degree.**
● Estimate angles.

ORAL AND MENTAL STARTER

FACTOR LOOPS: Draw some circles on the board and in each one write a number that has several factors, for example 84, 120, 105 etc. Tell the children that they are going to find as many factors as they can in, say, eight minutes. They may choose any of the numbers and give you a factor of that number as quickly as they can. When they have found a factor

VOCABULARY

Factor, divisible by, angle, ...is a greater/ smaller angle than, degree, angle measurer, protractor, right angle, acute, obtuse, reflex.

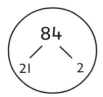

they should put up their hand, tell you the factor, and to which number it belongs. Record the given factor in the relevant circle (see left). After the eight minutes are up, discuss the different strategies used, emphasising the value of each. For example, did they use tests of divisibility? Were they methodical, starting from divisibility by two or three and working up to higher numbers?

MAIN TEACHING ACTIVITY

ANGLES: Explain to the children that they are going to measure and draw angles. Before they begin, it is important to see how much they remember from last year. Ask: *What is an angle?* Replies may include: 'It's a corner', 'It's a point' etc. If these are not forthcoming, then give the children the more mathematical definition: *When two straight lines meet at a point then an angle is formed.* Then ask: *How are angles measured?* (in degrees using a protractor). *What types of angle can you name?* (acute – less than 90°, right angle – 90°, obtuse – between 90° and 180°). *What does an angle of 180° give?* (a straight line). Introduce angles between 180° and 360°. Tell the children that these are called 'reflex' angles. Ask: *What happens if the angle is 360°?* Expect answers similar to: 'The arms of the angle will lie on top of each other because it's a complete turn.'

Give out 'Measuring angles' (photocopiable page 72). Ask the children first to name the type of each angle, and to estimate its size justifying their estimates: 'Well it's about half a right angle, so that's half of 90, so it's about 45°'. Give out protractors and ask them to remind you how to use them. *What does each small division represent?* Set the children to work measuring each of the angles to the nearest degree. They can then refer back to their estimate for guidance. *Is your answer accurate? If so, record it on your sheet.* They then go on to draw the angles specified on the sheet.

DIFFERENTIATION

More able: Draw angles for their partner to measure.
Less able: Spend more time on the first part of the exercise. It may be helpful if they work as a group initially and you work with them, making sure that they use the protractor correctly. They may need to be given additional angles to estimate and measure.

PLENARY

Check and discuss results. Discuss angles in the real world and why right angles are most common in structures. *Are all angles fixed and formed by straight lines?*

RESOURCES	One copy of photocopiable page 73 ('Measuring angles of triangles') per child; protractors; rulers; pencils.
PREPARATION	Photocopy 'Measuring angles of triangles' (page 73), one for each child.
LEARNING OUTCOMES	**ORAL AND MENTAL STARTER** ● Calculate angles (in a straight line). **MAIN TEACHING ACTIVITY** ● **Use a protractor to measure** and draw **angles.** ● Calculate angles in a triangle.
ORAL AND MENTAL STARTER	TELL ME THE OTHER: Give the children one of the angles from a straight line and ask the children to work out what the other should be.
MAIN TEACHING ACTIVITY	TRIANGLES: Give out 'Measuring angles of triangles' (page 73), telling the children that in this lesson they are going to work with triangles. *What can you say about the triangles? Number one looks equilateral because its sides look the same length.* Refresh their memories about other triangles such as isosceles, scalene. Ask them to name the triangles on the sheet – they may need to measure the sides first. They should then measure the angles and record these in each vertex. They add together the number of degrees in the three angles and record the total inside the triangle.
DIFFERENTIATION	More able: Go on to draw and measure angles for other triangles. Less able: They may only manage to measure two or three triangles in the time allowed.
PLENARY	Discuss the names of the triangles and the children's findings concerning the sum of the angles of each triangle. *Is the total for each nearly the same?*

RESOURCES

Two sheets of thin card and one pair of scissors per child; two large sheets of paper; felt-tipped pens; rulers; glue; pencils; sheets of paper.

PREPARATION

Cut out a large triangle from one of the large pieces of paper; draw a straight line across another.

LEARNING OUTCOMES

ORAL AND MENTAL STARTER
- Use known number facts and place value to consolidate mental addition/subtraction.
- Use known number facts and place value to consolidate mental multiplication/division.
- Use the four operations +, −, ×, ÷.

MAIN TEACHING ACTIVITY
- Check that the sum of the angles of a triangle is 180°.
- Make a general statement about familiar shapes by finding examples which satisfy it.

VOCABULARY

Triangle, angle, degree, straight line.

ORAL AND MENTAL STARTER

AS NEAR AS YOU CAN: Play the game from Lesson 5 of Unit 2.

MAIN TEACHING ACTIVITY

TRIANGLES AGAIN: Tell the children that you are going to look again at triangles, but first you want them to say what they can remember about angles in a straight line. Answers should include: 'A straight line is two right angles', or 'it's 180°'. *What can you say about the sums of the angles of all the triangles that you measured last time?* They were almost the same. Tell the children that you have made a triangle and you are going to find the sum of the angles in a different way. Using a felt-tipped pen mark the corner of each angle on your large triangle then cut it off – if you cut in a curve or wavy line it will be less confusing.

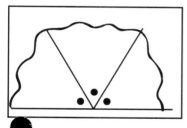

Mark a point along the line on the large sheet of paper which you have previously drawn, and place each of the three angles of the triangle on that point. *What do you notice?* Replies may include: 'They all fit, they must be 180°'.

Say: *Perhaps this is a special triangle, you give it a try.* Set the children to work, telling them to draw a straight line on one of their sheets of paper and to mark a point somewhere along the line. On the sheet of thin card, draw any triangle and cut it out. Tell the children: *Mark each vertex of the triangle with a line as I did then cut them out and stick each vertex on the point you have marked on your line.*

DIFFERENTIATION

More able: Go on to draw other triangles to test the angle sum of a triangle.
Less able: May need your help to draw triangles.

PLENARY

Discuss findings and the accuracy of measuring. *What can you say about the angle sum of all triangles? It is always 180°.*

RESOURCES

A3 sized copies of photocopiable page 74 ('Triangles'); protractors; set squares; glue; rulers; sharp pencils.

PREPARATION

Photocopy and enlarge to A3 size 'Triangles' (page 74), one per pair.

LEARNING OUTCOMES
ORAL AND MENTAL STARTER
- Calculate angles in a triangle.
- Use known number facts and place value to consolidate mental addition/subtraction.

MAIN TEACHING ACTIVITY
- Draw angles.
- Classify triangles. (Year 5 revision)

VOCABULARY

Angle, ...is a greater/smaller angle than, degree, angle measurer, protracto, right angle, acute, obtuse, reflex, equilateral triangle, isosceles triangle, scalene triangle.

ORAL AND MENTAL STARTER

GIVE ME THE OTHER ONE: Ask each child in turn to think of the sum of two angles in a triangle, say 123°. Another child, selected by you, replies giving the third angle (57°), by subtracting from 180° mentally. Discuss different strategies and how the child visualised the problem to come up with the answer.

MAIN TEACHING ACTIVITY

CAN YOU FIND ONE?: Give out copies of 'Triangles' (page 74), one per pair. Tell the children that during the next two lessons they are going to find all the types of triangles possible. Begin by looking at the grid and asking the children about the headings of the columns and rows. For example: *Which type of triangle will live in box number 1? Tell me about it.* 'It will have all its sides the same and all its angles acute.' *What about box number 5?* 'It must have a right angle and two sides the same length'. Working in pairs or groups, the children try to draw triangles to fit in as many boxes as possible. They cut these out and stick them in the box where they belong, one triangle for each box. Continue this work next lesson.

DIFFERENTIATION

More able: Should be able to pursue this activity without further help.
Less able: May need to work in groups. Give each pair in the group a specific triangle to try to draw. Let them discuss within the group and with you if they have been able to succeed.

PLENARY

Discuss progress so far and any problems encountered.

LESSON 5

Repeat the **Oral and mental starter** from Lesson 4. In the **Main teaching activity**, the children should continue to make triangles to fit the boxes of the grid. When they have made all that they can (seven are possible) discuss the triangles that fit the empty boxes. Ask the children, for example: *What would the triangle need to have to fit in box number 2?* 'To fit box number 2 the triangle must have all sides equal and a right angle.' *Is this possible?* Ask the children to justify their decisions, for example: 'If all the sides are equal then all the angles are equal too and it's impossible to have three right angles in a triangle.' Let the more able create another grid with the label on one side relating to the attributes of angle (as before) and the other side with attributes of line symmetry (eg having no line symmetry, having only one line of symmetry, having more than one line of symmetry). They then find shapes that fit each box. In the **Plenary**, name each triangle according to its individual attributes as shown on the left. Help the children towards the idea that these seven triangles are representative of all possible triangles. This lesson may be used with Lesson 7, one half of the class working on each activity on each of the two days.

	All acute angles	Having a right angle	Having an obtuse angle
All sides the same length	Equilateral 		
Two sides the same length	Acute angled isosceles 	Right angled isosceles 	Obtuse angled isosceles 
All sides different lengths	Acute angled scalene 	Right angled scalene 	Obtuse angled scalene 

RESOURCES

Set of word cards as prepared for Lesson 9, Unit 3; a set of quadrilaterals per group of four as listed below; paper; felt-tipped pens; flip chart.

PREPARATION

Reproduce the Venn diagram on the right on the flip chart or board (and copies for the class, if desired). Provide a set of the following quadrilaterals per group: square, oblong, rhombus, parallelogram, trapeziums (one right angled, one symmetric, one asymmetric), arrowhead, scalene quadrilaterals (one with a re-entrant angle). These could be selected from a commercially produced set and supplemented with others you have made.

SORTING QUADRILATERALS

One pair of parallel lines
Two pairs of parallel lines
All sides equal
All angles right angles

LEARNING OUTCOMES

ORAL AND MENTAL STARTER

- Recognise squares of numbers to at least 12 × 12.
- Recognise prime numbers to at least 20.
- Recognise multiples up to 10 × 10, and apply simple tests of divisibility.
- Use known number facts and place value to consolidate mental addition/subtraction.
- Understand and use the relationships between the four operations.

MAIN TEACHING ACTIVITY

- Classify quadrilaterals, using criteria such as parallel sides, equal angles, equal sides.

ORAL AND MENTAL STARTER

TELL ME ALL ABOUT IT: Repeat the activity from Lesson 9, Unit 3.

MAIN TEACHING ACTIVITY

SORTING QUADRILATERALS: Split the children into groups of about four (you may wish to group according to ability) and give each group a set of quadrilaterals. Explain to the children that they are going to find out about the attributes of different quadrilaterals and then go on to name them specifically. First ask what they can tell you about any of the shapes in the set in front of them. Replies may include: 'This is a square. It has all its sides the same and all its angles are right angles', 'This one has parallel sides, so has this one, but I think its sides are the same length too', 'This one's symmetric'. Ask what they mean by, for example, parallel or symmetric and whether any of the other shapes in the set have these attributes. You may need to introduce the names 'trapezium', 'rhombus' and 'parallelogram' if the children are not familiar with them. Provide each group with copies of the diagram above and then discuss the Venn diagram and its labelling.

DIFFERENTIATION

More able: Go on to consider the diagonals or the lines symmetry of the quadrilaterals in the set and construct their own Venn diagrams to show these attributes.
Less able: May need to place extra quadrilaterals, eg other parallelograms and trapeziums, on their diagrams before being able to make general statements about them.

PLENARY

Discuss the Venn diagram. Name the shapes by attribute, for example *all shapes with one pair of parallel sides are trapeziums, shapes with two pairs of parallel sides are parallelograms* (point out that they are also trapeziums), *the rhombus has all of its sides equal and is also a special parallelogram; the oblong is a member of the family of rectangles* and so on. Then consider the intersection of two circles on the diagram. *What about the square? The square is a rectangle; it is also a rhombus and a parallelogram because all rectangles and rhombi are parallelograms, and likewise a trapezium.*

VOCABULARY

Kite, parallelogram, trapezium, rhombus, rectangle, oblong, square, quadrilateral, equal sides, right angle, symmetrical.

LESSON 7

RESOURCES	Set of word cards as prepared for Lesson 9, Unit 3 per group of 4; one set of attribute cards made from photocopiable page 75 ('Attributes of quadrilaterals'); a decision tree (see below) drawn on card; a set of quadrilaterals as for Lesson 6.
PREPARATION	Using the large sheets of card, draw a decision tree on each (see figure, right). Copy and enlarge 'Attributes of quadrilaterals' (page 75) and cut out the cards, one set per group. At least one right angle At least one line of symmetry If yes go left
LEARNING OUTCOMES	**ORAL AND MENTAL STARTER** ● Recognise squares of numbers to at least 12 × 12. ● Recognise prime numbers to at least 20. ● Recognise multiples up to 10 × 10. Apply simple tests of divisibility. **MAIN TEACHING ACTIVITY** ● Classify quadrilaterals with criteria such as parallel/equal sides, equal angles etc.
ORAL AND MENTAL STARTER	TELL ME ALL ABOUT IT: Repeat the activity from Lesson 9 of Unit 3.
MAIN TEACHING ACTIVITY	MAKING QUADRILATERALS: Split the children into groups. As a class, look at each attribute card in turn and discuss its meaning. Select two of the attribute cards, for example, 'at least one pair of parallel sides' and 'at least one right angle'. Tell the class to place these cards on their tree, with the 'at least one pair of parallel sides' statement at the first decision. (The 'at least one right angle' attribute applies to both junctions at the next level.) Now ask the groups to carefully feed their quadrilaterals through the tree, remembering 'if yes, go left'. Discuss the results: *We have found two shapes that have both attributes, a square and a rectangle* etc.
DIFFERENTIATION	More able: Go on to make up their own attribute cards or play a 'Think the attribute' game where they place the quadrilaterals and another group has to decide what the attributes were and in which order on the tree they were placed. Less able: Spend time discussing the attributes necessary to get to the various branch ends. You may find it helpful to write in 'yes'/'no' as appropriate.
PLENARY	Discuss findings, for example: 'The square seems to have all the attributes that we have on our card', or 'If a quadrilateral has opposite sides equal then these sides must be parallel'.

LESSON 8

RESOURCES	1 set of 11–99 number cards from photocopiable page 13 ('1–100 square'); two large sheets of paper; felt-tipped pens; plain paper; rulers; calculators; pencils.
PREPARATION	Provide the number cards prepared from '1–100 square' (page 13). Using a large sheet of paper and the felt-tipped pen, draw a triangle with another triangle so that it shares an edge with the first (a quadrilateral). On the other sheet begin the following table:
LEARNING OUTCOMES	**ORAL AND MENTAL STARTER** ● Use known number facts and place value to consolidate mental addition/subtraction. **MAIN TEACHING ACTIVITY** ● Calculate angles in a triangle (and in polygons). ● Make and investigate a general statement about shapes.
ORAL AND MENTAL STARTER	BEAT THE CLOCK: Give out the number cards, two per child, and set the stop clock to, say, five minutes. Choose two children to hold up their cards. The rest of the class should give the result of adding them and then finding the difference.
MAIN TEACHING ACTIVITY	MAKING POLYGONS: Explain to the children that they are going to investigate 'triangles growing'. Show the children the quadrilateral you have drawn out of two triangles. Ask them to tell you about it: 'It's two triangles joined together.' *What about the sum of the angles?* 'Two triangles, that's 180° doubled.' Enter this on to your table then add another triangle to make a pentagon. Place this triangle carefully so the resultant shape has five and not six sides. Tell the children to work in pairs, copy the table, draw a triangle then add another to it, each time recording the number of triangles and the angle sum of the resulting shape, using calculators to help. You may wish to make a recording chart for the whole class to fill in.
DIFFERENTIATION	More able: Can go on to make general statements about the relationships between the number of edges, number of triangles and the sum of the angles. Less able: Help them to appreciate the relationship between the number of edges and the number of triangles and perhaps make a general statement about these.
PLENARY	Discuss results and general statements such as: *There are always two less triangles than the number of sides of the shape.* Go on to ask the children if they can use these results to find the size of each internal angle of a regular polygon.

No. of sides	No. of triangles	Sum of the angles
3	1	180°
4	2	360°
5		

RESOURCES

Resource page 14 ('Answers to multiplication facts'); one set of a variety of different-sized cubes per pair; six large squares; a sheet of cm square graph paper per child; plain paper; Sellotape; protractors; rulers; pencils.

PREPARATION

Enlarge and cut out the cards from 'Answers to multiplication facts' (photocopiable page 14). Place them face down on the table.

LEARNING OUTCOMES

ORAL AND MENTAL STARTER
● Use the relationship between multiplication and division.
● **Derive quickly: division facts corresponding to tables up to 10 × 10.**

MAIN TEACHING ACTIVITY
● Make shapes with increasing accuracy.
● Visualise 3–D shapes from 2–D drawings and identify different nets for a closed cube.
● Recognise and estimate angles.

VOCABULARY
Three dimensional, cube, sketch, draw, construct, net.

ORAL AND MENTAL STARTER

QUICK BONDS: Turn over one card and ask the children to give you four facts – multiplication or division – associated with this number. For example, 28 gives 7 x 4 = 28, 4 x 7 = 28, 28 ÷ 4 = 7, 28 ÷ 7 = 4. Repeat for other cards.

MAIN TEACHING ACTIVITY

CUBES: Tell the children that they are going to be working with three-dimensional shapes. Ask: *What does three-dimensional mean?* Answers may include: 'It's got thickness', 'It's not flat'. Say that you want to begin by finding everything the children know about a cube. Ask questions about the shape and number of faces (square, 6); the number of edges and vertices (12 edges, 8 vertices); the number of edges that meet at one vertex (3); the sum of the angles at each vertex (270°: 3 right angles) etc. *If you were going to make a hollow cube out of a sheet of graph paper, what would the 'plan' or 'net' look like?* Replies may include: 'It will have 6 squares joined together', or 'You will have to join the squares in special ways'. Invite two children to arrange six squares to form the net of a cube. Place small strips of Sellotape at the edges of the squares so that they may be lifted into shape to verify their position. Now ask the children to use their sheet of graph paper and draw as many different nets of the cube as possible. Let each square represent one face. Emphasise that each net must be different and not just in a different orientation. They should then choose one of the nets they have drawn and use this plan, together with rulers and protractors, to construct the net of a cube having an edge length of 5cm.

DIFFERENTIATION

More able: Go on to construct the net of a cuboid.
Less able: Children may need to use an actual cube as a template to make the net of a same-sized cube instead of using measuring instruments to construct it.

PLENARY

Did your net make a cube? Discuss the strategies used in planning the nets and the ways in which the children constructed them.

RESOURCES	Answers to multiplication facts cards prepared for Lesson 9; a variety of polyhedrons including cuboids, pyramids (square and hexagonal based), prisms (pentagonal and octagonal based), tetrahedrons (various); a set of polygons containing the same shapes as the faces of the polyhedrons; adhesive tape; compasses; rulers; pencils.
PREPARATION	Provide one polyhedron per child. Make sure that each child has a set of drawing instruments as listed above.
LEARNING OUTCOMES	**ORAL AND MENTAL STARTER** ● **Derive quickly: division facts corresponding to tables up to 10 × 10.** **MAIN TEACHING ACTIVITY** ● Make shapes with increasing accuracy. ● Visualise 3–D shapes from 2–D drawings.
ORAL AND MENTAL STARTER	QUICK BONDS: Repeat the activity from Lesson 9.
MAIN TEACHING ACTIVITY	NETS: Give out the 3–D shapes explaining that these are a set of polyhedrons (all flat faces) made entirely from regular polygons. Ask the children to talk about their shape and name it if possible. Let them select the polygons that match the faces of their shape. Tell the children that they are going to draw sketches, then construct a net of their shape and decide where to draw tabs for gluing so that the shape may be built. They should then move on to build the shape. You may wish to do away with the need for tabs by giving them adhesive tape to use instead.
DIFFERENTIATION	More able: Give more complicated shapes to construct. Less able: Let them use the faces of the shapes or the set of polygons as templates and draw round these to create their net.
PLENARY	Display sketches and completed polyhedrons and discuss.

RESOURCES
Rulers with cm and mm markings; a variety of polygons; a large square and regular hexagon; sharp pencils; paper.

PREPARATION
Make a large square and regular hexagon from card. Provide various regular polygons for each table, eg a regular pentagon a regular octagon etc.

LEARNING OUTCOMES
ORAL AND MENTAL STARTER
● Convert smaller to larger units (eg mm to cm) and vice versa.

MAIN TEACHING ACTIVITY
● Use, read and write standard metric units (cm, mm) including their abbreviations, and relationships between them.
● **Calculate the perimeter of simple shapes.**
● Make and investigate a general statement about familiar shapes by finding examples that satisfy it. Develop from explaining a generalised relationship in words to expressing it in a formula using letters as symbols.

VOCABULARY
Centimetre (cm), millimetre (mm), regular polygons, perimeter, formula.

ORAL AND MENTAL STARTER
ALL CHANGE BINGO: Write 1cm = 10mm on the board and ask conversion questions such as *Change 3 centimetres to millimetres. How many millimetres in 0.7 centimetres? Try 8 centimetres, 4 millimetres* etc. Ask each child to write three lengths of their choosing, in millimetres, between 1mm and 30mm. Now ask them to change the lengths you are going to give them to millimetres and if the answer is one of the lengths written on their sheet they can cross that one out. Give lengths between 0.1cm and 3cm. The winner is the first child to cross out all three of their lengths.

MAIN TEACHING ACTIVITY
AROUND THE SIDES: This activity develops from finding perimeters of polygons in Year 5, to expressing relationships between lengths of sides and perimeters using formulae with

letters as symbols. Tell the children that they are going to find perimeters of polygons. Show them the large square and ask how to find the distance around it: 'Measure it'; 'Measure one side and multiply the answer by 4.' Say: *The perimeter of a square is found by multiplying the length of one side by 4. So if the value of one side, length l, is multiplied by 4, the perimeter will be known.* Using letters, write on the board P = l × 4 (P = 4l). Ask: *Will this be true for any square?* Now develop this idea to the perimeter of a regular hexagon (P = 6l). Get the children to find the perimeters of some regular shapes found on their table and express these in formulae first in words and then using letters to create an equation. For example: *The perimeter of a rectangle is twice the value of the length add twice the value of the breadth = 2l +2b,* or 'The value of the length, add the value of the breadth multiplied by two, or P = (l + b) × 2, or perhaps 2 (l + b). Will the formula work for all rectangles?

DIFFERENTIATION

More able: Investigate for a symmetric trapezium. *The perimeter is the sum of a and d added to the value of c multiplied by two, or a + d + (c × 2) or perhaps a + d + 2c.* They may also make connections between shapes by saying, 'The formula for a rhombus is like that for a square'.

Less able: Will need to keep to simple shapes and if possible shapes where the lengths of sides are whole numbers of centimetres. They will also need help with formulae such as that for a regular pentagon, p = l x 5; *To find the perimeter measure the length of one side "l" and multiply the value by 5.*

PLENARY

Pull together the findings of different children. For example: *The parallelogram formula is like the one for the rectangle. Let's look at this together. Sadie thinks that to work out the perimeter of any regular shape you simply measure one side and multiply this value by the number of sides. What do you think?*

LESSON 12

RESOURCES	Rulers with cm and mm markings; a variety of 3–D shapes including cartons of interesting shapes; sharp pencils and paper.
PREPARATION	Collect cartons and provide a variety of 3–D shapes for each table.
LEARNING OUTCOMES	**ORAL AND MENTAL STARTER** ● Consolidate knowing by heart multiplication facts up to 10 × 10. ● **Derive quickly: division facts corresponding to tables up to 10 × 10.** **MAIN TEACHING ACTIVITY** ● Use, read and write standard metric units (cm, mm) including their abbreviations, and relationships between them. ● Describe properties of solid shapes such as edges (and calculate total edge lengths). ● Make and investigate a general statement about familiar shapes by finding examples that satisfy it. Develop from explaining a generalised. relationship in words to expressing it in a formula using letters as symbols.
ORAL AND MENTAL STARTER	VICE VERSA: Make sure that the children know the names of the regular polygons from three sides to ten (equilateral triangle, square, regular pentagon, hexagon, heptagon, octagon, nonagon, decagon). Use quick-fire questioning giving lengths of side for the children to then give you the perimeter. For example, *What's the perimeter of a nonagon whose sides are of length 3cm?* (27cm) Go on to give perimeters for the children to tell you the length of each side: eg *What's the length of the sides of a hexagon whose perimeter is 36cm?* (6cm)
MAIN TEACHING ACTIVITY	3–D AROUND THE EDGES: Show and talk about the total edge length of a cube, leading to *Measure one edge, e, and multiply its value by 12, giving t, the total edge length.* (t = e × 12 or t = 12e). The children then measure and develop total edge lengths and formulae for the 3-D shapes on their tables, for example a hexagonal prism with base and top edge lengths, b (say, 2cm), and joining edges, j (say, 10 cm) gives a total edge length, t of (2 × 12) + (6 × 10) = 84cm, leading to the formula t = (b × 12) + (j × 6) or 12b + 6j. Let children check each other's conclusions.
DIFFERENTIATION	More able: Use more complex shapes. Less able: Work with these children using simpler shapes and help them to develop their formulae.
PLENARY	Let the children describe their findings to the class.

LESSON 13

RESOURCES	Number cards 1–100, prepared from photocopiable page 13 ('1–100 square'); bag or box; photocopiable page 76 ('What's the perimeter?'); rulers with cm and mm markings; calculators; pencils and paper.
PREPARATION	Collect a set of 1–100 number cards made for the 'Bag numbers' activity, Lesson 2, Unit 1, and put them in the bag. Photocopy 'What's the perimeter?' (page 76), one per child.
LEARNING OUTCOMES	**ORAL AND MENTAL STARTER** ● Convert smaller to larger units (eg mm to cm, cm to mm) and vice versa. **MAIN TEACHING ACTIVITY** ● Use, read and write standard metric units (cm, mm) including their abbreviations, and relationships between them. ● **Calculate the perimeter of simple compound shapes.** ● Develop calculator skills and use a calculator effectively.
ORAL AND MENTAL STARTER	MILLIMETRE BAG NUMBERS: Place the numbers 1–100 in the bag. Say that the numbers drawn are millimetres and that they must respond with the equivalent in centimetres. Repeat this for about 20 numbers, injecting pace into the activity. Now draw two numbers, write them on the board and ask the children to add them together as millimetres, and to give their response in centimetres.
MAIN TEACHING ACTIVITY	WHAT'S THE PERIMETER?: Tell the children that they are going to find perimeters of shapes and that there may be short ways of finding them. They may use calculators to help. The children work in pairs but have a sheet each. Some children may work using millimetres while others use centimetres involving decimals. They can choose which they prefer.
DIFFERENTIATION	More able: Encourage them to add numbers mentally and to record their answers in both centimetres and millimetres. Less able: Will rely on using the calculator.
PLENARY	Single out some of the shapes. Ask about and compare strategies used. For example, *In number 1, I found that the two long sides were 4cm while the four short sides were 2cm each. So I multiplied 2 by 8 and got 16cm*, against *I said the short sides make 8cm, 2 × 4, and the long sides make 8cm, 4 × 2, so I got 16cm as well.*

LESSON 14 +15

RESOURCES

Copies of prepared question sheet; metric measuring equipment for length (rulers, metre rulers, tape measures etc); mass (scales – both bathroom and kitchen etc); and capacity (measuring jugs and cylinders, litre cubes etc); other less common measuring equipment (map measure, 75cl wine bottle etc); appropriate objects for measuring; metric equivalences displayed on board or flip chart; pencils and paper.

PREPARATION

Provide the equipment listed under **Resources** and set up one table for length, one for mass and one for capacity, with appropriate objects for measuring on each table.

Prepare and photocopy a question sheet titled 'Finding equivalences'. Possible questions might include:

Write down the equivalent of one hundredth of a) 1 l in ml; b) 1 km in m; c) 1 kg in g.
Convert a) 7.75 km to m; b) 12.5 l to ml.
Where might a) 5000m; b) 454g; c) 440ml be used in the world?

Other examples of questions can be found on page 91 of the 'Supplement of examples: Years 4, 5 and 6' in the *Framework for Teaching Mathematics*. Photocopy the completed sheet enough for 1 per child.
Write the following metric equivalences on the board:

1 metre (m)	= 100 centimetres (cm) or 1000 millimetres (mm)
1 centimetre (cm)	= 10 millimetres (mm)
1 kilogram (kg)	= 1000 grams (g)
1 litre (l)	= 1000 millilitres (ml)

LEARNING OUTCOMES

ORAL AND MENTAL STARTER

- Multiply and divide decimals mentally.

MAIN TEACHING ACTIVITY

- Use, read and write standard metric units (km, cm, mm, kg, g, t, l, ml, cl) including their abbreviations, and relationship between them.
- Suggest suitable units and measuring equipment to estimate or measure length, mass or capacity.
- Record estimates and readings from scales to a suitable degree of accuracy.

VOCABULARY

Kilometre (km), metre (m), centimetre (cm), millimetre (mm), kilogram (kg), gram (g), tonne (t), litre (l), millilitre (ml), centilitre (cl), metric.

ORAL AND MENTAL STARTER

MULTIPLES OF TEN: Split the children into five groups. Tell them that each group will be given a multiplication to do, say 3×9, and that they must work as a group giving other related multiplications with answers such as $30 \times 9 = 270$, $0.3 \times 9 = 2.7$, $300 \times 9 = 2700$ etc. Say that you will allow time for the responses to be made into a list and that one child, as spokesperson, will present it to the class. Order their responses and write them on the board. Discuss the digit patterns, eg $500 \times 6 = 3000$, $50 \times 6 = 300$, $5 \times 6 = 30$, to $0.005 \times 6 = 0.03$.

MAIN TEACHING ACTIVITY

ESTIMATING: Explain that in this lesson half of the class is going to be estimating and measuring involving length, mass and capacity, while the other half works from the question sheet you have prepared, and that they will swap activities in the next lesson. Point out that you have written metric equivalences on the board as a reminder. Discuss these before you begin.

Give out your prepared question sheet to half of the class and leave the children to work through these on their own. Split the remaining half of the class into three groups and start each group at a table. Explain that they must first decide as a group the unit of measurement for each object or container to be measured and then in pairs estimate. Only when all estimates have been made and recorded should the children measure, using suitable equipment, and record. Once complete, they move to another table and repeat. Spend your time with these groups ensuring that all children participate, that all recordings are clear and that the children's estimates and readings from scales are given to a suitable degree of accuracy.

DIFFERENTIATION

More able: Those working on the 'finding equivalences' activity could go on to give examples of metric measurements used in the real world.
Less able: Help those working on the practical activity with estimating, measuring and rounding their answers.

PLENARY

Discuss any problems that may have arisen but do not give any answers in this lesson. Extend the equivalences table written on the board to include tonnes (t) (as in potato yields, lorry weights, for example), and centilitres (cl) (quantity of drink in a container, eg 33cl in a can of cola):

1 tonne (t)	= 1000 kilograms
1 litre (l)	= 100 centilitres (cl)
1 centilitre (cl)	= 10 millilitres (ml)

LESSON 15

Repeat Lesson 14, but in the **Oral and mental starter** introduce divisions, eg $8 \div 2$, $80 \div 2$, $800 \div 2$, $0.8 \div 2$, $0.08 \div 2$. In the **Main teaching activity** swap the class around so that they cover the other activity from Lesson 14. In the **Plenary**, pull together the work of the two lessons highlighting and rectifying any measuring problems that you noted, eg not reading scales correctly. Ask the children to look out for units of measurement which are used in, for example a supermarket, garage or chemist's shop and keep a class list.

Measuring angles

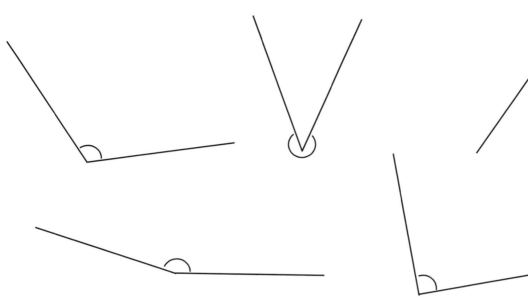

Draw these angles: 36°   108°   76°   200°

Name

Measuring angles of triangles

Triangles

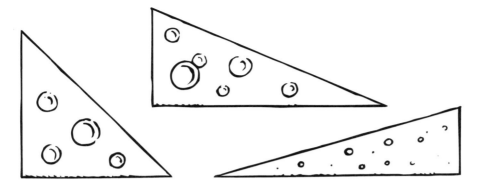  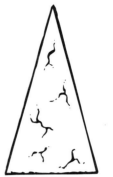

	Having all acute angles	Having a right angle	Having an obtuse angle
All sides the same length	1	2	3
Two sides the same length	4	5	6
All sides different lengths	7	8	9

For each box, make a triangle that fits. Can you fill all of the boxes?

Attributes of quadrilaterals

the diagonals intersect at right angles

at least one line of symmetry

at least one pair of parallel sides

at least one pair of opposite sides equal

at least one right angle

at least one pair of adjacent sides equal

Name

What's the perimeter?

1.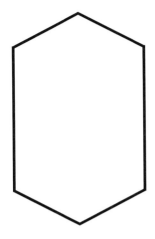

2.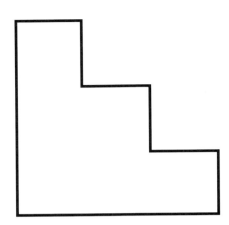

3.  4. 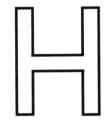 5.

6.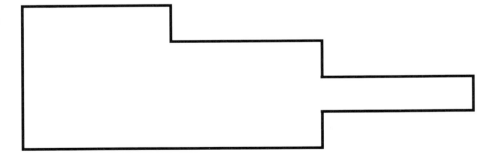

Estimate the length of each perimeter and record your estimate alongside the shape.

Change sheets with your partner and find and record the perimeters. Make sure that you measure accurately and look for short ways of finding the answers.

On another piece of paper write down any short ways you found.

Compare your strategies with your partner's.

ORGANISATION (5 LESSONS)

	LEARNING OUTCOMES	ORAL AND MENTAL STARTER	MAIN TEACHING ACTIVITY	PLENARY
LESSON 1	• Choose and use appropriate ways of calculating: mental, mental with jottings. • Consolidate strategies from previous year, including: find a difference by counting up; add or subtract the nearest multiple of ten then adjust. • Partition. • Check with an equivalent calculation.	WHAT'S THE NUMBER?: Using the relationship between addition and subtraction in 'box' notation and in words, involving addition sentences.	GOING MENTAL!: Exploring strategies used for adding and subtracting numbers, including decimals.	Discuss strategies used.
LESSON 2	• Use known number facts and place value to consolidate mental addition.	WHAT'S THE NUMBER?: Repeat from Lesson 1.	ROBIN HOOD: Adding two 2-digit numbers mentally, including decimals, using a game.	Discuss any difficulties that arose.
LESSON 3	• **Extend written methods to column addition of numbers involving decimals.**	PARTNERS: Adding two 2-digit numbers together and adding their multiples of ten.	LINE THEM UP ADDITION: Adding numbers using column addition for decimals.	Highlight key points to be remembered.
LESSON 4	• **Extend written methods to column subtraction of numbers involving decimals.** • **Solve word problems involving numbers and quantities** based on 'real life', money or measures. • Develop calculator skills and use a calculator effectively. • Check with the inverse operation when using a calculator.	PARTNERS: Subtracting two 2-digit numbers, together with their multiples of ten.	LINE THEM UP SUBTRACTION: Discussing 'real life' applications of additions and subtractions involving decimals. Using column subtraction for decimals.	Consider more 'real life' examples of additions and subtractions involving decimals, extending to mass or weight, capacity and temperature.
LESSON 5	• **Extend written methods to column addition and subtraction of numbers involving decimals.** • **Identify and use appropriate operations (including combinations of operations) to solve word problems involving numbers and quantities. Explain methods and reasoning.**	DECIMAL ROUND UP: Rounding up decimals to the next whole number, saying what must be added to reach that whole number.	WHAT'S THE PROBLEM?: Using both mental and column additions and subtractions to solve 'real life' problems involving decimals.	Discuss how different children tackled the problems. Use calculators to check answers.

ORAL AND MENTAL SKILLS Use the relationship between addition and subtraction. Use number facts and place value to consolidate mental addition and subtraction. Round a number with two decimal places to the nearest whole number.

In Unit 11, Lessons 1–4 are shown in full. Lesson 5 is an extension of what has been taught and is given in outline.

LESSON 1

RESOURCES

Prepared sheet of addition and subtraction sums; pencils and paper.

PREPARATION

Provide suitable questions for three ability levels, including decimals; for example:

Less able: 39 + 43; 259 + 71; 125 – 97.
Average: 159 + 162; 914 – 782; 1.8 + 16.9.
More able: 7450 + 2900; 15.7 + 16.8; 117.5 – 89.3.

LEARNING OUTCOMES

ORAL AND MENTAL STARTER
● Use the relationship between addition and subtraction.

MAIN TEACHING ACTIVITY
● Choose and use appropriate ways of calculating: mental, mental with jottings.
● Consolidate strategies from previous year, including: find a difference by counting up; add or subtract the nearest multiple of ten then adjust.
● Partition.
● Check with an equivalent calculation.

VOCABULARY

Add, sum, total, double, near double, subtract, difference between, strategy, method.

ORAL AND MENTAL STARTER

WHAT'S THE NUMBER?: Tell the children that they are going to express number sentences in words and then calculate the answers. For example, write ? + 26 = 35 on the board. Say: *To express this in words we would say 'Think of a number, add 26 and the answer is 35'. What is the number?* Use quick-fire questioning.

MAIN TEACHING ACTIVITY

GOING MENTAL!: Explain to the children that they are going to explore how to calculate mentally using larger numbers and decimals. Write on the board and discuss the sum 2500 – 1829. *The difference could be found by adding up from 829 to 900 (71), then to 2000 (100) then to 2500 (500), giving an answer of 671.* This strategy is often named 'Goes up to'. Write on the board:

2500 – 1829   is   71 + 100 + 500   or   71 + 600   or   171 + 500
                       = 671   = 671   = 671

Try some more sums on the board. Write, say, 393 + 415 and discuss using doubling. *Double 400, add 15, subtract 7.*

393 + 415   is $(400 \times 2) + 15 - 7$ or $(400 \times 2) + (15 - 7)$
            = $(800 + 15) - 7 = 800 + 8$
            =   815 – 7
            =   808

When is this a useful strategy? When you can round each number to the same nearest 100 and double.

Write 5.9 + 3.7 on the board and discuss: *5.9 is nearly 6, and 6 add 3.7 is 9.7 but then I must subtract 0.1 giving 9.6:*

5.9 + 3.7   is $(6 + 3.7) - 0.1$ or $8 + 1.6$
          =   9.7 – 0.1
          =   9.6

Split the children into three groups by ability and give your examples for them to work on. Tell the children that for each question they should be able to explain their approach.

DIFFERENTIATION

More able: Encourage the children to try various strategies.
Less able: Talk to them about their approaches.

PLENARY

Discuss the various strategies used by children, clarifying their methods.

RESOURCES

Prepared version of photocopiable page 83 ('Robin Hood') plus some blank copies; pencils; calculators.

PREPARATION

Prepare 'Robin Hood' game master sheets for three levels of ability by writing the following numbers in the arrows and target boards:

Less able: On the arrow write 17, 21, 38, 25, 32, 44, 50, 41
On one target write the following numbers (one number per circular space starting from the middle): 42, 55, 66, 82, 94
On the other write 46, 65, 73, 79, 88
Average: On the arrow write 38, 17, 51, 65, 43, 28, 86, 92
On one target write 71, 81, 89, 130, 143
On the other write 66, 82, 93, 103, 151
More able: On the arrow write 1.4, 0.8, 0.2, 0.6, 1.2, 0.3, 3.5, 3.7, 2.4, 2.5
On one target write 0.9, 1.4, 3.6, 4.9, 6.2
On the other write 1.8, 3.8, 3.9, 4.7, 7.2.

Make sufficient photocopies of each sheet allowing for the fact that some children may work 'through' more than one ability level. Photocopy spare copies of the sheet without writing in any numbers, and provide one calculator per pair.

LEARNING OUTCOMES

ORAL AND MENTAL STARTER

● Use the relationship between addition and subtraction.

MAIN TEACHING ACTIVITY

● Use known number facts and place value to consolidate mental addition.

VOCABULARY

Add, sum, total, double, near double, subtract, difference between, strategy.

ORAL AND MENTAL STARTER

WHAT'S THE NUMBER?: Repeat the activity from Lesson 1 but this time use subtraction sentences. For example, write: – 14 = 46 on the board. *Think of a number so that when 14 is subtracted from it the answer is 46. What's the number?*

MAIN TEACHING ACTIVITY

ROBIN HOOD: Talk through strategies that may be used to add two 2-digit numbers, including decimals. For example 42 + 41, 86 + 55, 0.9 + 33.8, rounding, doubling and particularly partitioning. Write on the board and discuss the following partitioning example:

$$16.4 + 27.8 = 16 + 27 = 43$$
$$\text{and } 0.4 + 0.8 = 1.2$$
$$\text{giving } 43 + 1.2 = 44.2$$

Tell the children that they are going to play a game in pairs. Give out the various sheets according to the ability level of each pair. Read through the rules and let the children play. They may play several games, changing targets with their partner or trying the next level.

DIFFERENTIATION

More able: Let them go on to create their own 'Robin Hood' games for others to play using blank copies of photocopiable page 83.
Less able: Can play co-operatively before playing against each other.

PLENARY

Discuss and help with any difficulties that either you have noticed or the children have expressed while playing the games.

RESOURCES

Prepared column board or whiteboard; water-based pen; wiper; examples of additions involving decimals; pencils and paper.

PREPARATION

Prepare a 4 column board, as shown below, and cover it with self-adhesive plastic or use a whiteboard. Provide textbook examples of additions involving decimals or make up your own. Make sure that the examples are presented horizontally, eg 26.9 + 2.34 + 0.07.

LEARNING OUTCOMES

ORAL AND MENTAL STARTER

● Use known number facts and place value to consolidate mental addition.

MAIN TEACHING ACTIVITY

● Extend written methods to column addition of numbers involving decimals.

VOCABULARY

Estimate, approximately, add, total.

ORAL AND MENTAL STARTER

PARTNERS: Organise the children into mixed ability pairs. Tell them that you are going to give them two 2-digit numbers to add but they must not reply until they can give the result of this addition and the result of multiplying each number by 10 and adding the resulting two numbers together. Give them an example, such as 28 + 46. They should answer 74 (28 + 46) and 740 (280 + 460).

MAIN TEACHING ACTIVITY

LINE THEM UP ADDITION: Tell the children that they are going to add decimal numbers using a column board. Remind them that they have done column additions in Year 5. Using a water-based pen, write on the column board an addition involving Th, H, T, U and ask the children to estimate the answer and then work it out with you (see example, right):

	Th	H	T	U
	6	2	5	9
+	1	9	3	7

What if the question had been 62.59 add 19.37.
What is your estimate now? Some children may reply 81.96 having already appreciated the place value connections. *How should I label the board?* Clean the column headings and insert tens, units, tenths and hundredths, or 10, 1, $^1/_{10}$, $^1/_{100}$ and the relevant decimal points (see example, left).

	10	1	$\frac{1}{10}$	$\frac{1}{100}$
	6	2 •	5	9
+	1	9 •	3	7
	8	1 •	9	6

Wipe off the numbers leaving the column headings and the decimal points and try 0.31 + 14.8, emphasising the digit positions and the lining up of the decimal points under each other. Next give the children an example involving three decimal numbers to be added, for example 15.7 + 21.24 + 1.09. Ask for estimates and how children arrived at them. Invite them, individually, to calculate the answer without labelling the columns. When they finish, ask a child to lay out the addition on the column board and complete it.

Give out the prepared examples for them to work through individually. Tell the children not to bother to label the column headings.

DIFFERENTIATION

More able: Go on to work with additions involving higher numbers and three place decimals.
Less able: May need help with lining up the digits and the decimal points under each other.

PLENARY

Ask the children what they consider to be the key points to be remembered, for example the lining up of the decimal points, estimating as a rough check. Discuss the importance of lining up digits if no decimals are involved, eg:

$$\begin{array}{r} 254 \\ -123 \\ \hline 131 \end{array}$$

RESOURCES

Prepared column board (as for Lesson 3); water-based pen; wiper; examples of subtractions involving decimals; pencils and paper.

PREPARATION

Label the column board Th, H, T, U using the water-based pen. Provide textbook examples of subtractions involving decimals or make up your own. Make sure that the examples are presented horizontally as before, eg 26.4 – 13.09 = .

LEARNING OUTCOMES

ORAL AND MENTAL STARTER

● Use known number facts and place value to consolidate mental subtraction.

MAIN TEACHING ACTIVITY

● **Extend written methods to column subtraction of numbers involving decimals**.
● **Solve word problems involving numbers and quantities** based on 'real life', money or measures.
● Develop calculator skills and use a calculator effectively.
● Check with the inverse operation when using a calculator.

VOCABULARY
Estimate, subtract, difference between.

ORAL AND MENTAL STARTER

PARTNERS: Repeat the activity from Lesson 3 but this time involve subtractions.

MAIN TEACHING ACTIVITY

LINE THEM UP SUBTRACTION: Give out calculators. Remind the children about the work covered in Lesson 3 and follow this by creating relevant contexts for some additions using calculators, *eg 27.9 + 27.5 + 26.9 + 27.8 = 110.1 The numbers are close together so they could be a good swimmer's total time in seconds for four consecutive lengths, whereas 132.27 + 52.56 + 9.18 = 194.01 could be the total amount of money spent on clothes. What about 1789.3 – 1456.7 = 332.6?* (solved by using calculators). *It could be electricity meter readings giving the units of electricity used. What about 8.72 – 8.49 = 0.23? This could be the difference between the Gold and Silver Long Jump distances at the Olympics in metres.* For each example ask for, listen and comment on the children's suggestions.

10	1	$\frac{1}{10}$	$\frac{1}{100}$
$^2\cancel{3}$	$^{14}\cancel{5}$.	$^{15}\cancel{6}$	$^{10}0$
1	7 .	8	2
1	7 .	7	8

Use the approach used for 'Line them up addition' (Lesson 3) to introduce column subtractions. Remind the children that they have subtracted using column subtractions in Year 5. Always ask for estimates first. Include examples such as 35.6 – 17.82, which necessitates recording the 35.6 as 35.60 in order to complete the calculation (see example, left). Discuss this, including the idea that if the numbers were metres, 35.6m could be written as 35m 60cm. Also introduce varying numbers of digits, eg 1352.7 – 26.04. Give out the prepared examples for the children to work through individually. When they have finished, let them check their calculations using a calculator.

DIFFERENTIATION

More able: Ask them to check their results by addition, using a calculator. For example, in the column board subtraction shown above 17.82 + 17.78 = 35.6.
Less able: Will need help, particularly with the insertion of noughts. Try 86 – 35.48 using the board to help.

PLENARY

Ask the children for examples of additions and subtractions involving decimals in the 'real world' and money. *We have already met time, distance, electrical units and money.* Ask for examples relating to mass (*How much heavier am I than when I was nine?*); capacity (*How much will the containers hold altogether?*) and temperature (*comparing body temperatures through an illness*).

RESOURCES	Copies of photocopiable page 84 ('What's the problem?'); pencils and paper.
PREPARATION	Photocopy 'What's the problem?' (page 84), enough for one each. Prepare additional questions for more able children.
LEARNING OUTCOMES	**ORAL AND MENTAL STARTER** ● Round a number with two decimal places to the nearest whole number. **MAIN TEACHING ACTIVITY** ● Extend written methods to column addition and subtraction of numbers involving decimals. ● Identify and use appropriate operations (including combinations of operations) to solve word problems involving numbers and quantities. **Explain methods and reasoning.**
ORAL AND MENTAL STARTER	DECIMAL ROUND UP: Tell the children that you are going to give them a number involving either one or two decimal places. They must round up to the next whole number, and say what must be added to the decimal to reach that whole number. Illustrate with, say, 3.4 giving 'rounded to 4. Add 0.6 to reach 4' as the reply. Give them some single digit numbers to try. Now go on to two places of decimals, say, 6.79, rounded to 7, add 0.21 to reach 7 as the answer. Give numbers involving addition to just one decimal place for the less able.
MAIN TEACHING ACTIVITY	WHAT'S THE PROBLEM?: Mention that the work of the last two lessons has centred on decimal calculations for additions and subtractions. Give out photocopiable page 84 ('What's the problem?'), for the children to work through individually. Before they begin, read the instructions at the top of the page with them and tell them to show their working neatly.
DIFFERENTIATION	More able: Go on to additional questions such as: At the Olympics in Innsbruck in 1964, the four man bobsledding team from Canada won the Olympic Gold Medal with a time of 4 minutes 14.46 seconds. In 1994, Germany won with 3 minutes 27.78 seconds. How much faster has the time become during the 30 years? Less able: Discuss with individual children any questions which they do not understand or are not sure how to tackle.
PLENARY	Discuss how different children tackled the questions and work out each answer together using calculators.

Robin Hood

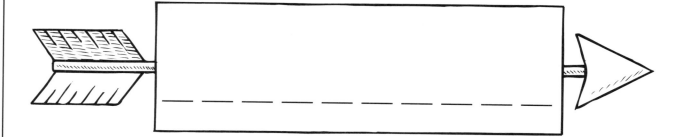

Name _____

Name _____

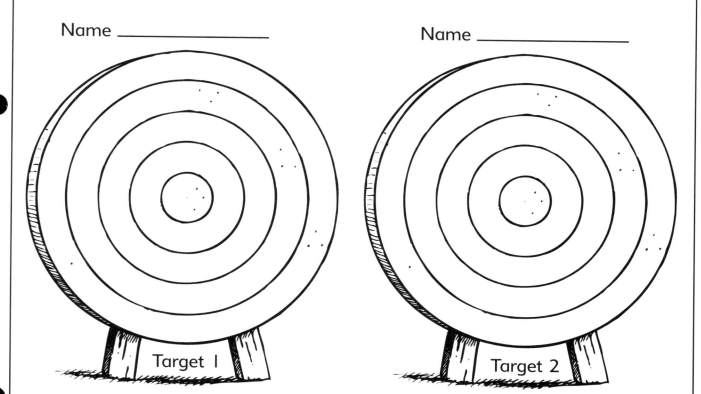

Target 1

Target 2

You will need a calculator and a pencil.

Decide which target board you will each use and write your name above it. Choose who will go first.

Take turns to select two numbers from the arrow which you think, when added together, will make one of your target numbers.

Your partner should add the two numbers on the calculator. If you are correct cross off the number on your target.

If you are not correct and the answer is on your partner's target he or she should cross it off their board.

Now it is your partner's turn.

The winner is the first player to cross out all the numbers on their target board.

What's the problem?

Try these problems. Some you may be able to do mentally but for most you will probably need to write things down.
Do not use a calculator.

1. How much change do I get from a £20 note if I buy:

> **Boxes of Chocolate**
>
> | | |
> |---|---|
> | Chocos | £3·24 |
> | Twisters | £3·50 |
> | Whirlies | £4·09 |
> | Nutty Crunchies | £2·81 |

a) 1 box of Chocos and
   1 box of Whirlies?   _____

b) 2 boxes of Twisters and
   1 box of Nutty Crunchers?   _____

c) 1 box of each?   _____

2. What is the difference between Mum and Dad's weight?
   Mum weighs 62.5kg and Dad 79kg.   _____

3. In the Athletics World Championships the longest discus throw was 70.03m, the shortest 58.95m. What was the difference in the length between the two throws?   _____

4. Mr James uses his car for work. How many litres of petrol did he buy in November?

October 29	43·2
November 2	17·0
November 5	47·8
November 10	29·5
November 17	47·1
November 26	38·4
December 3	32·7

_____

5. I think of a number, add 17.36 and the answer is 105.7. What was my number?

_____

Make up some similar questions for your friends to try. Write them on another piece of paper. Be sure that you know the answers.

UNIT 12

ORGANISATION (5 LESSONS)

LEARNING OUTCOMES	ORAL AND MENTAL STARTER	MAIN TEACHING ACTIVITY	PLENARY
LESSON 1 • Recognise and extend number sequences, such as the sequence of square numbers. • Make and investigate a general statement about familiar numbers or shapes. • Develop calculator skills and use a calculator effectively.	SQUARES: Using multiplication facts including square numbers.	IS IT A SQUARE?: Investigating square numbers through building shape sequences.	Discuss the number sequence for each shape.
LESSON 2 • Recognise and extend number sequences. • Make and investigate a general statement about familiar numbers or shapes. • Develop calculator skills and use a calculator effectively.	TARGET NUMBERS: Using square numbers to reach targets.	FIND THE DIFFERENCES: Develop the difference pattern in the square number sequence. Making squares by summing odd numbers. Using 'term' to denote numbers in a sequence.	Discuss findings.
LESSON 3 • Recognise and extend number sequences, such as the sequence of triangular numbers. • Make and investigate a general statement about familiar numbers or shapes. • Develop calculator skills and use a calculator effectively.	TARGET NUMBERS: Using square numbers to reach targets greater than 100.	TRY TRIANGLES: Generating triangular numbers from spatial growth and from summing the counting numbers. Finding values of terms.	Discuss the links between summing to produce square and triangular numbers.
LESSON 4 • Recognise and extend number sequences. • Make and investigate a general statement about familiar numbers or shapes. • Develop calculator skills and use a calculator effectively.	USE THE FUNCTION: Using an addition function on 2- and 3-digit numbers.	SEQUENCES: Linking square and triangular numbers. Investigating number sequences for hollow squares and hollow triangles patterns.	Display and describe their findings.
LESSON 5 • Recognise and extend number sequences. • Make and investigate a general statement about familiar numbers or shapes. • Solve mathematical problems, explain patterns, generalise and predict. Suggest extensions asking What if.....? • Develop calculator skills and use a calculator effectively.	USE THE FUNCTION: Using a subtraction function on 2- and 3-digit numbers.	12 DAYS OF CHRISTMAS: Developing number sequences from the Christmas song.	Discuss findings.

ORAL AND MENTAL SKILLS Derive quickly: division facts corresponding to table up to 10 × 10. Use known number facts and place value to consolidate mental multiplication and division. Recognise squares of numbers to 12 × 12. Use known number facts and place value to consolidate mental addition/subtraction.

In Unit 12, Lessons 1, 2 and 3 are given in full. Lessons 4 and 5 follow on from what has already been taught.

RESOURCES

14 square floor tiles or base 10 flats (use the non-serrated face uppermost); copies of paper with tesselating equilateral triangles; sets of 2–D shapes (oblongs, right-angled triangles and parallelograms); felt-tipped pens; calculators; pencils and paper.

PREPARATION

Prepare enough copies of the equilateral triangle sheets for one per pair. Provide enough shapes of each type for each pair to develop the pattern.

LEARNING OUTCOMES
ORAL AND MENTAL STARTER
- **Derive quickly: division facts corresponding to tables up to 10 × 10.**
- Use known number facts and place value to consolidate mental multiplication/division.
- Recognise squares of numbers to 12 × 12.

MAIN TEACHING ACTIVITY
- Recognise and extend number sequences, such as the sequence of square numbers.
- Make and investigate a general statement about familiar numbers or shapes.
- Develop calculator skills and use a calculator effectively.

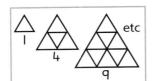

VOCABULARY

Next, sequence, predict, continue, rule, relationship, square number.

ORAL AND MENTAL STARTER

SQUARES: Give a target number and ask the children for two numbers which, when multiplied together give that number. For example, 63 invites an answer 7 and 9, 25 invites 5 and 5. Ask questions, within the known facts, which only give square number answers such as 3 × 3, 5 × 5, 8 × 8. Remind the children that these are the square numbers. Try 11 x 11 and 12 x 12 (calculated by, say 11 x 10 = 110, 110 + 11 = 121). Discuss how the children found the answers.

MAIN TEACHING ACTIVITY

IS IT SQUARE?: Explain that this lesson is about the sequence of square numbers and its relationship with 2–D shapes. Remind the children that when a number is multiplied by itself it makes a square number. *For example, 3 squared (3^2) is 9. What is 5 squared? Which number multiplied by itself gives 49?* Put one of the floor tiles down and say that it is the first square. Then build the next square (4 tiles). *How many are needed for the next square?* (9). Continue in this way, developing the square number sequence. Record 1, 4, 9 and ask: *How do you think the numbers for each new square will grow?* (4 × 4, 5 × 5 etc). In pairs, use the equilateral triangle sheets and the rule 'Make the next shape', to develop the number sequence. They should then choose other shapes as templates and build the pattern for the progression of similar shapes, recording the corresponding number sequence (1, 4, 9 etc). Some children may go on to record the square number sequence to 10 × 10 and use calculators or partitioning strategies to extend the sequence to, say, 15 × 15 or even beyond.

DIFFERENTIATION

More able: Go on to explore regular hexagons using equilateral triangles as the basic unit.
Less able: After working with the triangles, ask these children to explore oblongs.

PLENARY

Ask individuals to say the number sequence which resulted from the shapes they used, leading to the idea that perhaps all shapes grow in the same way!

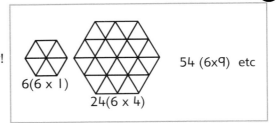

RESOURCES

9 square floor tiles or base 10 flats (use the non-serrated face uppermost); 1cm graph paper – half a large sheet each; felt-tipped pens; calculators; pencils and paper.

LEARNING OUTCOMES
ORAL AND MENTAL STARTER
- Recognise squares of numbers to 12 × 12.
- Use known number facts and place value to consolidate mental addition/subtraction.

MAIN TEACHING ACTIVITY
- Recognise and extend number sequences.
- Make and investigate a general statement about familiar numbers or shapes.
- Develop calculator skills and use a calculator effectively.

VOCABULARY

Next, sequence, pattern, continue, relationship, difference pattern, consecutive, term, square number.

ORAL AND MENTAL STARTER

TARGET NUMBERS: Tell the children that they must reach the target you give them by using one (or more) square numbers and either an addition or a subtraction, eg 47 is $6^2 + 11$ or $7^2 - 2$; 13 is $3^2 + 4$ or $3^2 + 2^2$. Keep the target numbers to less than 100.

MAIN TEACHING ACTIVITY

FIND THE DIFFERENCES: Explain that this lesson will involve exploring the square number sequence. Invite the children to help you build the sequence to 144 on the board. Ask the children how to get from 1 to 4 (+3) and from 4 to 9 (+5). Record these differences, using a different coloured chalk.

1   4   9   16   25   36   49   64   81   100   121   144

\3/ \5/ \7/ . . . .\21/ \23/

Continue in this way to 144, asking them what they notice about the difference sequence ('They are all odd numbers'; 'They go up in twos'; 'They are the odd numbers except 1.'). Generate the next square number (169) with the children by adding 25 to 144 and check by calculating 13×13, perhaps using a calculator. Continue to, say, 225. Introduce the word 'term' to denote individual numbers in the original sequence, eg 36 is the 6th term. Ask the children for the 4th term (16, which is 4^2) etc, ensuring that they understand that any number in this sequence is a term number squared. Then you should be able to ask for the 20th term: 20^2 (400) followed by others. Get the children to use calculators for this.

Making sure that all children can see, place a tile on the floor marking it with a colour. Next use three more tiles to make the next size square, marking these in a different way. Now make the next. Record the 1 and the number of tiles added each time. Ask the children to copy both the shape and the number pattern on their graph paper and continue to develop both patterns in the same way.

1
1 + 3
1 + 3 + 5
1 + 3 + ... etc

DIFFERENTIATION

More able: After a few minutes of working on the activity individually, work with this group to make general statements such as: 5^2, *the fifth term, is made up from the first five odd numbers $1 + 3 + 5 + 7 + 9$ giving 25,* leading to the idea that any square number can be calculated in this way.

Less able: Help them to make the link between the spatial and the numerical pattern. Work with them, a square at a time, with one child building the spatial development while the others record the number pattern. They may not have time to develop much of the pattern.

PLENARY

Ask children from each group to report what they discovered. Discuss each point made.

RESOURCES

Pegboards and pegs; spotted paper; felt-tipped pens; pencils and paper.

PREPARATION

If you don't have spotted paper, prepare a spotted paper grid (pegboard layout) and photocopy 50 copies. Provide one large pegboard and pegs sorted into colours. Put up to, say, 10 pegs of the same colour, into a triangular arrangement on the board.

LEARNING OUTCOMES

ORAL AND MENTAL STARTER
● Recognise squares of numbers to 12×12.
● Use known number facts and place value to consolidate mental addition/subtraction.

MAIN TEACHING ACTIVITY
● Recognise and extend number sequences, such as the sequence of triangular numbers.
● Make and investigate general statements about numbers and shapes.
● Develop calculator skills and use a calculator effectively.

VOCABULARY

Next,
sequence,
pattern,
continue,
relationship,
rule,
difference,
difference
pattern,
consecutive,
square
number,
triangular
number.

ORAL AND MENTAL STARTER

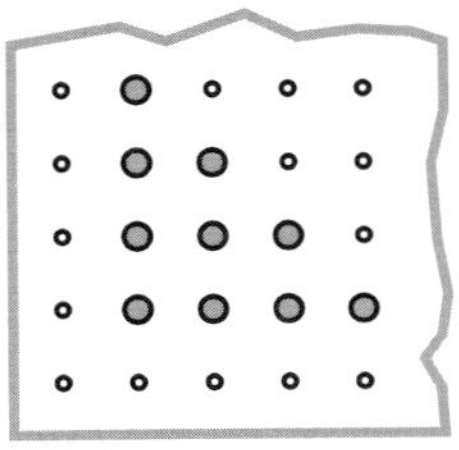

TARGET NUMBERS: Repeat the activity from Lesson 2, but this time extend the targets to beyond 100, eg 125 is $11^2 + 4$, or $11^2 + 2^2$ or $10^2 + 5^2$, 170 is $13^2 + 1$ or $13^2 + 1^2$.

MAIN TEACHING ACTIVITY

TRY TRIANGLES: Tell the children that they are going to build some triangles and investigate the number of pegs (or dots) which are needed to make them. Show them the pegboard with its 10 pegs in a triangular arrangement (see diagram, above). Ask a child to make one like it. Work with them to make the rule that *They are equilateral triangle shapes with the two equal edges parallel to the edges of the pegboard.*

Count the number of pegs used each time and record. Ask them to make other triangles on the spotted paper, using a different colour felt-tipped pen for each triangle. Pull the work together to generate the shape pattern and corresponding number sequence (triangular numbers). Go on to consider the difference pattern. Note that '1' cannot be made spatially and must be created by building 'backwards'.

The children should discover that the sequence can be extended by adding 6, 7, 8 etc and that triangular numbers are formed by adding consecutive counting numbers. *How can we find the third term 6?* (by adding 1 + 2 + 3) *Let's make a pattern to show this.*

I	Ist term	(first number)
I + 2	2nd term	(first 2 numbers)
I + 2 + 3	3rd term	(first 3 numbers)
I + 2 + 3 + 4	4th term	(first 4 numbers)

DIFFERENTIATION

More able: Extend the sequence to find the 10th term etc.
Less able: Check their work to make sure that they have built their triangles correctly. Go around the group orally generating the sequence.

PLENARY

Discuss: *Square numbers can be made by summing consecutive odd numbers 1, 1 + 3, 1 + 3 + 5 etc while triangular numbers come from summing consecutive counting numbers 1, 1 + 2, 1 + 2 + 3 etc.*

LESSON 4

RESOURCES	Pegboard and pegs; spotted paper; felt-tipped pens; pencils and paper.
PREPARATION	Prepare 50 copies of spotted paper (see Lesson 3) and write the square and triangular number sequences on the board.
LEARNING OUTCOMES	**ORAL AND MENTAL STARTER** ● Use known number facts and place value to consolidate mental addition. **MAIN TEACHING ACTIVITY** ● Recognise and extend number sequences. ● Make and investigate a general statement about familiar numbers or shapes. ● Develop calculator skills and use a calculator effectively.
ORAL AND MENTAL STARTER	USE THE FUNCTION: Tell the children that they are going to use the same function on numbers that you will give them, eg the function +13. Start, for example, first with 4 (17) then with 23 (36), then 48 (61), then 179 (192). Use a quick-fire approach.
MAIN TEACHING ACTIVITY	SEQUENCES: Compare some square numbers with pairs of consecutive triangular numbers like 4 (square) with 1 + 3 (triangular), 16 (square) with 6 + 10 (triangular). Ask the children to find out whether this is always true. Afterwards, set up on the pegboard and discuss (see diagram, right):  3+6=10 giving 9, 12, 15, 18... Invite children to the front to try others. Arrange the children into two groups by ability. Get the more able to investigate hollow triangles using dotted paper (see left). giving 8, 12, 16, 20... The other children investigate hollow squares (right):
DIFFERENTIATION	More able: Ask them to consider the hollow triangle numbers coming from the difference of two triangular numbers, 9 coming from 10 (the 4th) – 1 (the 1st); 12 coming from 15 (the 5th) – 3 (the 2nd) etc. Less able: Consider hollow square number links with square numbers
PLENARY	Discuss the outcomes and generalise, eg for the hollow squares: *They go up in fours*; for the hollow triangles: *They are all multiples of three, but 3 and 6 are not included because they make 'solid triangles'.*

LESSON 5

RESOURCES	Copies of the words of 'The 12 Days of Christmas'; calculators; pencils and paper.
PREPARATION	Prepare the photocopies of the songsheet, enough for 1 per pair.
LEARNING OUTCOMES	**ORAL AND MENTAL STARTER** ● Use known number facts and place value to consolidate mental subtraction. **MAIN TEACHING ACTIVITY** ● Recognise and extend number sequences. ● Make and investigate a general statement about familiar numbers or shapes. ● Solve mathematical problems, explain patterns, generalise and predict. Suggest extensions asking: What if...? ● Develop calculator skills and use a calculator effectively.
ORAL AND MENTAL STARTER	USE THE FUNCTION: Repeat the activity from Lesson 4 but this time use subtraction functions instead, eg –29.
MAIN TEACHING ACTIVITY	12 DAYS OF CHRISTMAS: Sing the song. Ask and build up *How many presents did 'My true love' get each day?* (On the first day, 1; On the second, 2 + 1 making 3; On the third, 3 + 2 + 1 making 6) *What is this number sequence called?* (triangular numbers). Let the children use calculators to generate the number of presents received each day. *What other things could we find out?* If they don't suggest similar ideas themselves say: *How many presents would they have after four days?* (1 + 3 + 6 + 10 = 20; summing the triangular numbers). *How many presents did they receive altogether?* (1 + 3 + 6 + 10 + 15 + 21 + 28 + 36 + 45 + 55 + 66 + 78 = 364). Predict and then find out which present they received most of. (A partridge a day for 12 days making 12, 2 turtle doves a day for 11 days making 22, up to 12 lords a-leaping on one day = 12). The number pattern generated gives 12, 22, 30, 36, 40, 42, 42, 40, 36, 30, 22, 12, so the presents that 'My true love' received the most of were swans and geese (42 of each). Set the children to work in pairs on any of the questions listed here.
DIFFERENTIATION	More able: Go on to calculate further, for example, *how many presents would they receive on 10 January if the song continued like this? How many presents would there be altogether by this date?* Less able: Talk over the question the child has chosen to pursue before they start.
PLENARY	Discuss the results of the children's answers.

UNIT 13: Assess & Review

Choose from the activities below. During the group activities, some children can be completing assessment worksheets 2a and 2b (which assess their skills in written addition and subtraction of decimal numbers and solving problems involving numbers and quantities using appropriate operations) while others work with you on practical tasks. The specific assessment criteria for the assessment sheets are given at the bottom of each sheet.

RESOURCES

One set of 0–9 numeral cards per child; prepare and photocopy your own set of angles to be estimated and measured (similar to photocopiable page 72 'Measuring angles', used for Lesson 1 of Units 8–10); copies of photocopiable page 76 ('What's the perimeter?'); protractors (circular if possible); copies of Assessment sheets 2a and 2b (photocopiable pages 91 and 92); pencils and paper.

PREPARATION

Provide the number cards prepared from '1–100 square' (page 13). Photocopy enough copies for one per child of your angles sheet, 'What's the perimeter?' (page 76) and Assessment sheets 2a and 2b (photocopiable pages 91 and 92).

ORAL AND MENTAL STARTER

ASSESSMENT

Can the children:
● Derive quickly: division facts corresponding to tables up to 10×10?

DIVISION FACTS: Ask the children division fact questions. They hold up numeral cards to show their answers. Include questions such as: *Which number when divided by six gives seven?* (42) and *24 when divided by a number gives 3, what's the number?* (8). For the second assessment lesson, repeat the activity but this time dispense with the digit cards and ask questions using a quick-fire approach. Target individuals with some of the questions. Note those who will need more time devoted to division facts.

GROUP ACTIVITIES

ASSESSMENT

Can the children:
● Use a protractor to measure and draw acute and obtuse angles to the nearest degree? Calculate the perimeter of simple compound shapes?

WHAT'S THE ANGLE?: Give out the photocopies you have prepared. For each angle on the sheet, ask the children to name and record the type of angle it is (acute, obtuse or reflex) and to then estimate its size. Ask individuals to justify their estimates: 'It's about 20° more than a right angle, about 110°'. When all the estimates have been made, give out the protractors and ask the children to measure and record the size of each angle. Make a note of any children who are not confident when using a protractor.

ANSWERS:
Assessment 2a 1a) £64.99; b) £13.66; 2a) 51.5 hours; b) 9.6 hours; 3) 151.25; 4a) 13.1; b) 12.42; 5a) 241.21; b) 116.4; c) 20.9; d) 72.72.
Assessment 2b 1) Jane, 0.38m (38cm) above, Simeon, 0.35m (35cm) below; 2a) £9.43; b) Darkly Delicious (£1.85) and a Strawberry and Raspberry Medley (£2.56); 3) Various answers; 4) Various answers.

TERM 2

This term's work reinforces and develops that of Term 1. The Oral and mental activities extend number facts and place value to include higher number and decimal calculations. Practise is given involving division facts corresponding to multiplication tables to 10 × 10, squares of multiples of 10 to 100, work with fractions and timed word problems. Place value develops ordering and finding differences using positive and negative integers. Calculation skills taught are ThHTU × U and short multiplication and division involving decimals. Fractional work blossoms with reducing to simplest form, using a fraction as an 'operator' and converting a fraction to a decimal. Shape work and measures explores making shapes, visualising 3-D shapes from 2-D sketches, reading and plotting co-ordinates in all four quadrants, reflections, calculating areas and converting imperial to metric and vice-versa. Range, mean and median are taught as are distance/time graphs, prime numbers and prime factors. Word problems, 'real world' applications and calculator usage feature throughout the term.

ENLARGE THIS SHEET TO A3 AND USE IT AS YOUR MEDIUM-TERM PLANNING GRID.

ORAL AND MENTAL SKILLS: Use known number facts and place value to consolidate mental addition/ subtraction. **Derive quickly** doubles of multiples of 10 to 1000, doubles of two digit numbers, squares of multiples of 10 to 100, **division facts corresponding to multiplication tables up to 10x10;** use the relationship between multiplication and division. Count on or back in steps of 0.1, 0.2, 0.25, 0.5 etc. Use decimal notation, know what each digit represents and give a decimal fraction lying between two others. Recognise the relationships between fractions; change a fraction to the equivalent mixed number; recognise the equivalence between decimal and fraction forms of simple fractions. Use factors; apply simple tests of divisibility.

Unit	Topic	Objectives: children will be taught to...
1	Place value ordering and rounding. Using a calculator	• Use the vocabulary of estimation and approximation. Consolidate rounding an integer to the nearest 10, 100 or 1000. • (Order a set of numbers to a million and calculate differences). • (Introduce a billion). • Find the difference between a positive and negative integer, or two negative integers, in a context such as temperature or the number line, and order a set of positive and negative integers. • **Solve a problem by** representing and **interpreting data in tables and diagrams.** • Develop calculator skills and use a calculator effectively.
2-3	Understanding × and ÷ Mental calculation strategies (× and÷) Pencil and paper procedures (× and ÷) Money and real life problems Making decisions and checking results including using a calculator	• Understand and use the relationships between multiplication and division. Use brackets. • Use known number facts and place value to consolidate mental multiplication and division. • Approximate first. Use informal pencil and paper methods to support, record or explain multiplications or divisions. • **Extend written methods to:** ThHTUxU (short multiplication); **short multiplication and division of numbers using decimals.** • Develop calculator skills and use a calculator effectively • Check with the inverse operation when using a calculator.
4	Fractions, decimals and percentages Using a calculator	• Change a fraction to the equivalent mixed number and vice-versa. Recognise when two simple fractions are equivalent (Year 5). **Reduce a fraction to its simplest form by cancelling common factors.** • **Use a fraction as an 'operator' to find fractions of numbers or quantities.** • Compare and order fractions by converting them to fractions with a common denominator. • Convert fractions to decimals by using division then compare and order them. • Round a number with one, two or more decimal places to the nearest tenth or whole number. • Use decimal notation for tenths, hundredths and thousandths when recording measurements. Know what each digit represents in a number with up to three decimal places. • Develop calculator skills and use a calculator effectively
5	Shape and space Reasoning about shapes	• Make shapes with increasing accuracy. Visualise 3D shapes from 2D drawings. • Recognise and estimate angles. **Use a protractor to measure** and draw **acute and obtuse angles to the nearest degree.** Calculate angles in a triangle or around a point. • Recognise where a shape will be after a reflection in a mirror line touching the shape at a point; in two mirror lines at right angles. • Describe and visualise properties of solid shapes such as parallel faces or edges... • **Read and plot co-ordinates in all four quadrants.** • Explain methods and reasoning, orally and in writing. • Develop from explaining a generalised relationship in words to expressing it in a formula using letters as symbols. • Express simple fractions as percentages. • Make and investigate a general statement about familiar shapes by finding examples which satisfy it.
6	Assess and review	• **Derive quickly division facts corresponding to tables up to 10x10. Solve a problem by representing, extracting and interpreting data in tables and diagrams. Extend written methods to short multiplication and division of numbers using decimals. Reduce a fraction to its simplest form by cancelling common factors. Use a fraction as an operator to find fractions of numbers or quantities. Use a protractor to measure acute and obtuse angles to the nearest degree. Read and plot co-ordinates in all four quadrants.**

ORAL AND MENTAL SKILLS: Use known number facts and place value to consolidate mental calculations. **Multiply and divide decimals mentally by 10 or 100, and integers by 1000.** Find a difference by counting up. **Derive quickly division facts corresponding to tables up to 10x10.** Use decimal notation; know what each digit represents. **Identify and use appropriate operations (including combinations of operations) to solve word problems involving numbers and quantities. Count on in steps of 0.1, 0.2, 0.25, 0.5.... , and then back.** Use units of time, 24- hour clock notation (Year 5). Recognise squares of numbers to at least 12x12. **Derive quickly** squares of multiples of 10 to 100. Recognise prime numbers to at least 20.

Unit	Topic	Objectives: children will be taught to...
7-8	Measures including problems Handling data	• Use read and write standard metric units (m, mm, m², cm², mm²) including their abbreviations and relationships. Know rough equivalents of lb and kg, oz and g, miles and km, litres and pints or gallons. • Calculate the areas of simple compound shapes that can be split into rectangles. • Make a statement about familiar shapes. Develop from explaining a generalised relationship in words to expressing it in a formula using letters as symbols. • Recognise squares of numbers to 12x12. • Use the vocabulary of estimation and approximation. • Check with an equivalent calculation. • Find the mode and range of a set of data. Begin to find the median and mean of a set of data. • **Solve a problem by** representing **extracting and interpreting data in tables, graphs and charts.** • Develop calculator skills and use a calculator effectively.
9-10	Mental calculation strategies (+ and–) Pencil and paper procedures (+ and –) Money and 'real life' problems Making and checking results, including using a calculator.	• Recognise and extend number sequences. • Consolidate all strategies from previous year, including: finding a difference by adding up; use the relationship between addition and subtraction; add several numbers. • Use known number facts and place value to consolidate mental addition/subtraction. • Recognise and explain patterns and relationships, generalise and predict. • Develop from explaining a generalised relationship in words to expressing it in a formula using letters as symbols. • **Extend written methods to column addition and subtraction of numbers involving decimals.** • Round a number with two decimal places to the nearest tenth or to the nearest whole number. • **Identify and use appropriate operations (including combinations of operation) to solve word problems involving numbers and quantities** based on 'real life', money or measures (including time) using one or more steps. • **Solve a problem by extracting and interpreting data using graphs and charts.** • **Multiply and divide decimals by 10 or 100 and integers by 1000.** • Choose and use appropriate number operations to solve problems and appropriate ways of calculating mental, mental with jottings, written methods. • Develop calculator skills and use a calculator effectively. • Check with an equivalent calculation. • Use knowledge of sums, differences, products of odd/even numbers.
11	Properties of numbers. Reasoning about numbers.	• Recognise prime numbers to at least 20. Factorise numbers into prime factors. • Recognise squares of numbers to at least 12 x 12. • Recognise and explain patterns and relationships, generalise and predict. • Use known number facts and place value to consolidate mental multiplication. • Develop calculator skills and use a calculator effectively. • Use tests of divisibility.
12	Assess and review	• **Derive quickly division facts corresponding to tables up to 10x10. Multiply and divide decimals by 10 or 100 and integers by 1000. Identify and use appropriate operations (including combinations of operation) to solve word problems involving numbers and quantities based on 'real life', money or measures (including time) using one or more steps. Extend written methods to column addition and subtraction of numbers involving decimals. Solve a problem by extracting and interpreting data using graphs and charts. Calculate the perimeters and areas of simple compound shapes that can be split into rectangles.**

UNIT 1

ORGANISATION (3 LESSONS)

	LEARNING OUTCOMES	ORAL AND MENTAL STARTER	MAIN TEACHING ACTIVITY	PLENARY
LESSON 1	● Use the vocabulary of estimation and approximation. ● Consolidate rounding an integer to the nearest 10, 100 or 1000. ● Order a set of integers.	PARTNERS: Adding 2-digit numbers together, and adding their multiples of ten.	LARGER AND LARGER: Ordering numbers to one million. Rounding numbers, estimating differences and then calculating using a calculator.	Introduce and discuss a billion.
LESSON 2	● Find the difference between a positive and negative integer, or two negative integers, in a context such as temperature or the number line, and order a set of positive and negative integers. ● Develop calculator skills and use a calculator effectively.	PARTNERS: Subtracting two 2-digit numbers, together with their multiples of ten.	ON THE LINE: Ordering a set of positive and negative integers. Finding the difference between two of these integers, linking with temperature changes. Using a calculator including the 'sign change' key where appropriate.	Discuss language differences, negative numbers and minus temperatures. Introduce the idea that negative numbers have other 'real life' applications.
LESSON 3	● Find the difference between a positive and negative integer, or two negatives in context. ● **Solve a problem by representing and interpreting data in tables and diagrams.** ● Develop calculator skills and use a calculator effectively.	FOUR DIGITS: Adding two 4-digit multiples of 100.	USING NEGATIVE NUMBERS: Using negative numbers in 'real life' problems.	Mark and discuss children's work.

ORAL AND MENTAL SKILLS Use known number facts and place value to consolidate mental addition/ subtraction (eg from 27 + 34 = 61 to 270 + 340 = 610, from 56 – 32 = 24 to 560 – 320 = 240; together with 3700 + 1200 = 4900).

In Unit 1 Lessons 1 and 2 are shown in full. Lesson 3 is an extension of what has already been taught and is given in outline.

RESOURCES

One calculator per pair; pencils and paper.

LEARNING OUTCOMES

ORAL AND MENTAL STARTER
● Use known number facts and place value to consolidate mental addition (eg from 27 + 34 = 61 to 270 + 340 = 610).

MAIN TEACHING ACTIVITY
● Use the vocabulary of estimation and approximation. Consolidate rounding an integer to the nearest 10, 100 or 1000.
● Order a set of integers (Year 5 revision).

ORAL AND MENTAL STARTER

PARTNERS: Play 'Partners' (as in Lesson 3, Unit 11, Term 1) to practise addition of multiples of 10.

VOCABULARY

Unit, ten, hundred, thousand, million, billion, ascending order, descending order, estimate, approximate, approximately, round.

MAIN TEACHING ACTIVITY

LARGER AND LARGER: Split the class into four groups by ability. Ask the least able to each write on a piece of paper one number that is within the range 0 and 1000. They then as a group arrange them in ascending order. Do the same with the other groups but with greater number ranges; Group 2 1000 – 10 000; Group 3 10 000 – 100 000; Group 4 100 000 – 1 000 000. Bring the class together and, with their help, write all the numbers in order on the board. Ask the children to round some of the 0 – 1000 numbers to the nearest 10, some 1 000 – 10 000 numbers to the nearest 100, some 10 000 – 100 000 numbers to the nearest 1000 and some 100 000 – 1 000 000 numbers to the nearest 10 000. Ask the children, in pairs, to write their estimates for the difference between some rounded numbers selected by you before using their calculators to find the answers. Discuss results, reminding them that an estimate can never be 'wrong', but that some estimates are more reasonable than others. Mention that when estimating the sum of two numbers that have not been rounded, using a rounding strategy first is helpful. Give them some examples to try.

DIFFERENTIATION

More able: Ask for numbers between, say 1000 and 1 000 000, and give situations where they might be used in real life.
Less able: Work with this group and focus on how they went about their estimates. Watch as they check their estimate with the calculator to make sure they are using it correctly. Ask them to read their inputs and outputs to you.

PLENARY

Ask: *What is a billion?* 'It's a very large number, bigger than a million'. Go on to tell them that it is one million million, and write 1 000 000 000 000 on the board. Then explain that the world is now beginning to use the American definition of a thousand million, which is 1 000 000 000. This is important when trading, to ensure that the countries involved are using the same definition. Ask them to listen and note when they hear the word 'billion' used in news items.

RESOURCES

Large floor number line marked from –10 to 10; prepared addition and subtraction calculations; calculators with 'sign change' keys, one per child; pencils and paper.

PREPARATION

Make the floor number line. Write a set of integers –10 to 10 at random on the board. Prepare some addition and subtraction calculations with integers, eg –10 + 11, –7 + 3, 6 – 9, 3 – –5.

LEARNING OUTCOMES

ORAL AND MENTAL STARTER

● Use known facts and place value to consolidate mental subtraction (eg from 56 – 32 = 24 to 560 – 320 = 240).

MAIN TEACHING ACTIVITY

● Find the difference between a positive and negative integer, or two negative integers, in a context such as temperature or the number line, and order a set of positive and negative integers.
● Develop calculator skills and use a calculator effectively.

ORAL AND MENTAL STARTER

PARTNERS: Play 'Partners' (from Lesson 4, Unit 11, Term 1) to practise subtraction of multiples of 10.

VOCABULARY

Integer,
positive,
negative,
above/below
zero, minus,
add, subtract.

MAIN TEACHING ACTIVITY

ON THE LINE: Ask the children to look at the jumbled integers on the board. With their help, put them in order. Seat the children so that they can see the floor number line. Choose children to walk the line for questions such as *What's 3 – 7?, –2 – 7?, –4 + 6?*. Record that 3 – 7 = –4, –2 – 7 = –9 and –4 + 6 = 2. Ask them for descriptions of how these statements would be expressed for temperature, eg *The temperature fell 7°C from 3°C to –4°C; It was –2°C and then fell another 7°C to –9°C; The temperature rose 6°C from –4°C to 2°C.* Go back to the number line and ask one child to stand at 2, and another to stand at –5. *What's the difference between 2 and –5?* Record 2 – 7 = –5. Try, say, the difference between –4 and –6 and –4 + 6. Provide some additions and subtractions and then introduce calculators and talk about the function of the 'sign change' key, for example to calculate –9 – 3. Key [9] [+/–] [–] [3] [=]. Now let them individually find the answers to additions and subtractions using the 'sign change' key where appropriate.

DIFFERENTIATION

More able: Make a set of statements to be marked right or wrong by the other children, for example –1 + 3 = 2 (right); –23 + 7 = 16 (wrong).
Less able: Let these children talk about rises, falls and differences in temperature and calculate answers.

PLENARY

Talk about temperatures of, say –5°C (minus five degrees centigrade) but point out that the integer used is negative five. Go on to say that integers are used in different ways in 'real life' and that some of these will be looked at in the next lesson.

LESSON 3

RESOURCES	Copies of photocopiable page 98 ('Using negative numbers'); golf results (find some or make some up) written on a large sheet of paper; calculators; pencils and paper.
PREPARATION	Photocopy page 98 ('Using negative numbers'), enough for one per child. Write up the golf results.
LEARNING OUTCOMES	**ORAL AND MENTAL STARTER** ● Use known number facts and place value to consolidate mental addition (eg 3700 + 1200 = 4900). **MAIN TEACHING ACTIVITY** ● Find the difference between a positive and negative integer, or two negative integers in a context. ● **Solve a problem by** representing and **interpreting data in tables and diagrams.** ● Develop calculator skills and use a calculator effectively.
ORAL AND MENTAL STARTER	FOUR DIGITS: Tell the children that you are going to give them two 4-digit multiples of 100 to add, such as 2500 + 1200.Try some.
MAIN TEACHING ACTIVITY	USING NEGATIVE NUMBERS: Start with a five-minute recap of the previous lesson. Give out the 'Using negative numbers' sheet and discuss question 1. Explain balance, payments, receipts, direct debit and that cheque payments by Mrs Hawkins are numbered while cheques that are paid into her account are not. Let the children try the examples. **Answers:** 1a) £142.90; 1b) Balances 27.34; –31.88; 19.36; –90.79; –115.79; 142.90; 2b) Julius Caesar 58 years; Augustus Caesar 77 years; 2c) 10 years.
DIFFERENTIATION	More able: Initiate a discussion with them about golf scoring, where the lowest numbered player is the winner, having played the least number of strokes. Less able: Have a group discussion about the questions on the sheet before they start.
PLENARY	Talk about par for the course (say, 72 strokes) with Montgomerie eight strokes under (64) and Lyle four over (76). Use your golf results with them creating questions such as *How far behind the leader is Price?* Mark and discuss the children's work.

Montgomerie	–8
Woods	–6
Langer	Level (Par)
Lyle	+4

Using negative numbers

1.

Date	Description	Payments	Receipts	Balance
5th Jan	*Balance brought forward*			27.34
7th Jan	Cheque 100342	59.22		
7th Jan	Bank Credit		51.24	
10th Jan	Cheque 100343	110.15		
12th Jan	Direct Debit	25.00	258.69	
13th Jan	Cheque			

a) Estimate how much money will be in Mrs Hawkins' account on 13 January.

b) Fill in the Balance column for every line using a calculator to help you (the first one, for 5 January, has been done for you).

2. Julius and Augustus Caesar were both rulers of the Roman Empire.
Julius Caesar was born in 102 BC and died in 44 BC.
Augustus Caesar was born in 63 BC and died in 14 AD.

a) Plot in their births and deaths on the number line.

0

b) How long did each of them live?

c) In 54 BC Julius invaded Britain. Plot this year on the line. How many years was the invasion before he died?
Use a calculator only if you need to.

ORGANISATION (10 LESSONS)

LEARNING OUTCOMES	ORAL AND MENTAL STARTER	MAIN TEACHING ACTIVITY	PLENARY
LESSON 1 +2 • **Extend written methods to:** ThHTU × U (short multiplication). • Estimate by approximating. • Check with the inverse operation when using a calculator. • Make general statements about odd or even numbers, including the outcome of products.	DOUBLES AGAIN: Doubling multiples of 10 to 1000.	MAKE IT SNAPPY 2: Multiplying ThHTU × U.	Discuss strategies and look for real-life applications.
LESSON 3 • Use known number facts and place value to consolidate mental multiplication and division. • Approximate first. Use informal pencil and paper methods to support, record or explain multiplications. • Develop calculator skills and use a calculator effectively.	QUICK BONDS: Making multiplication and division bonds from a given number.	INTO DECIMALS: Using informal approaches and mental methods to solve decimal multiplications.	Discuss results.
LESSON 4 • Approximate first. Use informal pencil and paper methods to support, record or explain multiplications. • Develop calculator skills and use a calculator effectively.	COUNTING ON: Given a starter number, count on in steps of a decimal number.	DECIMALS AGAIN: Using informal written methods to solve decimal multiplications.	Check results. Look for real-life applications.
LESSON 5 +6 • Extend written methods to: short multiplication of numbers involving decimals. • Estimate by approximating then check result. • Develop calculator skills and use a calculator effectively.	DOUBLE DECIMALS: Doubling decimal numbers.	IT'S SNAPPY AGAIN: Calculating short multiplication of decimals.	Finding suitable contexts for maths.
LESSON 7 • Approximate first. Use informal pencil and paper methods to support, record or explain multiplications and divisions.	SQUARES: Squaring multiples of 10 to 100.	FIND THE SIDE: Given the perimeter of a polygon, find its side length.	Discuss strategies used.
LESSON 8 +9 • Extend written methods to: short division of numbers involving decimals. • Express a quotient as a decimal. • Develop calculator skills and use a calculator effectively.	QUICK-FIRE DIVISIONS: Asking and responding to division questions.	DECIMAL DIVISION: Using the short division method for calculations.	Discuss strategies used.
LESSON 10 • Use brackets. • Develop calculator skills and use a calculator effectively.	TELL ME ALL ABOUT IT DECIMALS: Giving facts about a decimal.	CALCULATOR MEMORY: Exploring memory facility on a calculator.	Look for real life applications.

ORAL AND MENTAL SKILLS Derive quickly: doubles of multiples of 10 to 1000. Use the relationship between multiplication and division. **Derive quickly: division facts corresponding to tables up to 10 × 10.** Count on in steps of 0.1, 0.2, 0.3, 0.25, 0.5. **Derive quickly:** doubles of two digit numbers. **Derive quickly:** squares of multiples of 10 to 100. Use decimal notation. Know what each digit represents. Give a decimal fraction lying between two others.

In Units 2–3 Lessons 1, 3–5, 7, 8 and 10 are shown in full. Lessons 2, 6 and 9 are extensions of what has already been taught.

RESOURCES

Copies of photocopiable page 107 ('Multiplying large numbers') for Lesson 2; a four-column board covered with self adhesive plastic; water-based marker; wiper; calculators; pencils and paper.

PREPARATION

Write some multiples of 10 up to 1000 (340, 760 etc) randomly on the board. Photocopy page 107 ('Multiplying large numbers'), one per child.

LEARNING OUTCOMES

ORAL AND MENTAL STARTER
● **Derive quickly:** doubles of multiples of 10 to 1000.

MAIN TEACHING ACTIVITY
● **Extend written methods to** ThHTU × U (short multiplication).
● Estimate by approximating.
● Check with the inverse operation when using a calculator.
● Make general statements about odd or even numbers, including the outcome of products.

VOCABULARY

Multiply, multiplied by, double, divide, divided by, inverse.

ORAL AND MENTAL STARTER

DOUBLES AGAIN: Ask the children to give you quickly the results of doubling each of the numbers on the board. Cross them off as the children tell you the answers and keep a record of the score. See how many they manage in the time available.

MAIN TEACHING ACTIVITY

MAKE IT SNAPPY 2: Tell the children that they are going to continue with some multiplication work that they began last term; short multiplication. Write 367 × 4 on the board and ask for estimates; 'it's about 1200'. Ask the children to remind you how to set this calculation out (see example, right).

$$\begin{array}{r} 367 \\ \times\ 4 \\ \hline \\ \hline \end{array}$$

Tell them to copy this multiplication and then find the answer (1468). Do they all agree? Write 2165 × 3 on the board and ask *What is your estimate?* 'About 6000'. *Could this multiplication with thousands be tackled in the same way as the one you have just done? Try it and see.*
When the children have finished give them the answer (6495) and ask how they did the calculation. Replies may include 'I did it just the same as the hundreds one but included thousands as well'. Set the class the following examples to work on individually: 1738 × 5 (8690); 2943 × 4 (11 772); 3276 × 7 (22 932). Remind them always to estimate first.

DIFFERENTIATION

More able: Challenge them to find a way to check their results on a calculator without inputting the original calculation. Ways of checking for example, 1738 × 5 may include 'I divided my answer, 8690 by 5 and got 1738'; 'I multiplied 1738 by 10 in my head and then put that in the calculator and divided it by 2'.
Less able: Give these children more practise with HTU × U. Let them try, say 516 × 3 (1548) working with you as a group. They then work individually on the following examples: 437 × 2 (874); 618 × 5 (3090); 356 × 7 (2492). Some may also need a column board. Then as a group try 2368 × 3 (7104). Check each result with the calculator.

PLENARY

Ask the children to make general statements about the products of even numbers multiplied by even numbers (even); even multiplied by odd (even) and odd by odd (odd). Point out that these generalisations may be helpful when checking calculations and should be part of their strategies in the future. Discuss the strategies the children used to check their results. Look for real life situations where ThHTU × U occur, such as the distance covered by an aircraft on a return flight to America.

LESSON 2

For the **Oral and mental starter**, repeat DOUBLES AGAIN using different multiples of 10 to 1000. For the **Main teaching activity,** the children work individually to complete photocopiable page 107 ('Multiplying large numbers'). Help the less able where necessary. Question the children about their work and begin to mark it.

RESOURCES

'Answers to multiplication facts' cards from photocopiable page 14; calculators; pencils and paper.

PREPARATION

Place the 'Answers to multiplication facts' cards face down on the table.

LEARNING OUTCOMES

ORAL AND MENTAL STARTER
- Use the relationship between multiplication and division.
- **Derive quickly: division facts corresponding to tables up to 10 × 10.**

MAIN TEACHING ACTIVITY
- Use known number facts and place value to consolidate mental multiplication and division.
- Approximate first. Use informal pencil and paper methods to support, record or explain multiplications.
- Develop calculator skills and use a calculator effectively.

VOCABULARY
Tenth, hundredth, decimal, decimal fraction, decimal place.

ORAL AND MENTAL STARTER

QUICK BONDS: Repeat from Leson 9, Unit 9, Term 1.

MAIN TEACHING ACTIVITY

INTO DECIMALS: Explain to the children that they are going to multiply decimal fractions. Write a multiple of 10 on the board and multiply this by a single digit, for example 40 × 3. Ask the children for the answer (120). *Very easy. How did you do it?* 'I said 4 × 3 is 12, so 40 × 3 is 120 because it's four tens multiplied by 3'. *What if the question was 400 × 3?* 'Then it would be four hundreds multiplied by 3 making 1200'. *What about 4000 × 3?* Lead the children to the idea that *Whatever the power of 10, the calculation always involves 4 × 3 = 12.* Write 0.4 × 3 on the board. Ask the children to tell you about 0.4. They may say: 'It's nearly a half'; 'It's four tenths'. Now ask them to predict the result, hopefully 1.2, and justify this. Ask them to check with the calculator. Write on the board other decimal multiplications, such as 0.6 × 4, 0.5 × 7, 0.3 × 9, 0.05 × 3, 0.08 × 6. Ask the children to give answers verbally and to justify each answer. Now write on the board some decimal multiplications involving two places of decimals, such as 0.34 × 4, 0.62 × 3, 0.85 × 6. Ask all but the least able to write down the answers. Remind them to estimate first, and that they can make jottings if they need to. When they have finished they should check their results with the calculator.

DIFFERENTIATION

More able: Let them make up their own examples to calculate or swap with a partner.
Less able: Work with this group and tackle the multiplications co-operatively. Question them to make sure that they understand the value of the first and second places of the decimal number system.

PLENARY

Discuss results and once again stress the idea of estimating first.

LESSON 4

RESOURCES
Calculators; pencils and paper.

LEARNING OUTCOMES
ORAL AND MENTAL STARTER
● Count on in steps of 0.1, 0.2, 0.3, 0.25, 0.5.

MAIN TEACHING ACTIVITY
● Approximate first. Use informal pencil and paper methods to support, record or explain multiplications.
● Develop calculator skills and use a calculator effectively.

VOCABULARY
Tenth, hundredth, decimal, decimal fraction, decimal place.

ORAL AND MENTAL STARTER
COUNTING ON: Give the children a starter number, say 4, and tell them to count on in 0.3s. Increase the level of difficulty to, say starting with 3.2 and counting on in 0.25s.

$$3 \times 4 = 12$$
$$0.6 \times 4 = 2.4$$
$$0.02 \times 4 = 0.08$$
$$\overline{3.62 \times 4 = 14.4}$$

MAIN TEACHING ACTIVITY
DECIMALS AGAIN: Write on the board 3.62 × 4 and ask the children for estimates. Replies might include 'about 15 or just under 16'. Ask the children to justify their estimate: 'Three multiplied by four is twelve and because there is point six two then it must be more, but under sixteen'. Now ask them to work individually to find a solution to this multiplication. Ask them to record their working. This could be 36 × 4 = 144, so 3.6 × 4 = 14.4 and 0.02 × 4 = 0.08, so 3.62 × 4 = 14.48. If this second recording is not forthcoming, then suggest it as a method. Ask the children to use this method of recording to solve the following multiplications, remembering to estimate first: 2.74 × 5; 3.83 × 6; 6.48 × 7; 9.25 × 8; 4.67 × 9.

DIFFERENTIATION
More able: May go on to consider 4-digit examples such as 15.37 × 4.
Less able: May need help with layout.

PLENARY
Ask the children to check their results using a calculator. Discuss real life applications of multiplication of decimals. For example, *I'm buying each of my 3 aunts a tin of biscuits for Christmas. Each tin costs £3.65, so the total cost will be £3.65 × 3, which is £10.95.*

LESSON 5 + 6

RESOURCES
A large four-column board covered with self-adhesive plastic; water-based marker; wiper; a small piece of card; calculators; copies of photocopiable page 108 ('Multiplying decimals') for Lesson 6; pencils and paper.

PREPARATION
Provide the column board. Write the '×' operator on the card. Find some examples of multiplication of decimals in textbooks. Photocopy page 108, one per child.

LEARNING OUTCOMES
ORAL AND MENTAL STARTER
● **Derive quickly:** doubles of two digit numbers.

MAIN TEACHING ACTIVITY
● **Extend written methods to:** short multiplication of numbers involving decimals.
● Estimate by approximating then check result.
● Develop calculator skills and use a calculator effectively.

VOCABULARY

Tenth;
hundredth;
decimal;
decimal
fraction;
decimal place.

ORAL AND MENTAL STARTER

DOUBLE DECIMALS: Give the children a decimal number, say 6.3 or 0.72, and ask them to double it and give the answer. How many can they do in five minutes? Keep score.

MAIN TEACHING ACTIVITY

IT'S SNAPPY AGAIN: Write 4.38×6 on the board and ask for an estimate: 'About 26 because 6×4 is 24 and 0.3×6 is 1.8 and there is a bit more'. Use the column board and discuss with the children how to record 4.38 on it. *To use the column board to help us to do this multiplication we must first label the columns and show where the decimal point will be. If we label the first column tens, then what will the other column headings be?* Suggest shading the line dividing ones and tenths. Using the column board ask one child to write the digits where they belong, and place the 'x' symbol by the side of the board. Remind the children of last term's work on short multiplication and tell them to use the same ideas to help you solve this multiplication.

10s	1s	$\frac{1}{10s}$	$\frac{1}{100s}$
	4	3	8
	6		
2	6	2	8
	2	4	

Say, *Let's begin with the hundredths; 8 multiplied by 6 is 48. We leave 8 in the hundredths column and carry the 4 to the tenths column. Let's write it underneath so that we don't forget. Now on to the tenths. Who can carry on?*

Let a volunteer complete the recording and ask another child to check the result with the calculator. Ask the children to work individually to calculate 3.79×4. Then give them other suitable examples. Remind them that the decimal points should always line up under each other.

DIFFERENTIATION

More able: Make up patterns for their partner to try.
Less able: Work with this group and use the column board together to tackle 3.79×4.

PLENARY

Ask the children to find suitable contexts for the multiplication. For example, 3.79 might give 'What is the perimeter of a square whose sides are 3.79cm?'

LESSON 6

Repeat the **Oral and mental starter** from Lesson 5, this time using other 2-digit decimals. For the **Main teaching activity,** the children work individually to complete page 108 ('Multiplying decimals'). Question individuals about their work and give help to the less able children. Discuss methods and answers in the **Plenary.**

RESOURCES

An equilateral triangle large enough for the class to see; one large sheet of paper; shapes to use as templates (square, regular hexagon, regular pentagon, regular octagon); felt-tipped pen; calculators; paper and pencils.

PREPARATION

Write some multiples of 10 to 100 randomly on the board. Provide the equilateral triangle. On the large sheet of paper, draw round each of the shapes using the felt-tipped pen. In the centre of each shape write its perimeter, for example: square 25.2cm, regular hexagon 44.4cm, pentagon 41.5cm, octagon 75.2cm. The shapes are only illustrative and the measurements need not be to scale. Display the sheet for all to see.

LEARNING OUTCOMES
ORAL AND MENTAL STARTER
● **Derive quickly:** squares of multiples of 10 to 100.

MAIN TEACHING ACTIVITY
● Approximate first. Use informal pencil and paper methods to support, record or explain multiplications and divisions.

Divide,
divided by,
divided into,
inverse,
remainder,
perimeter,
equilateral
triangle.

ORAL AND MENTAL STARTER

SQUARES: Ask the children to choose one of the numbers on the board and give you the square of that number. See how many the children can do in the time allowed.

MAIN TEACHING ACTIVITY

FIND THE SIDE: *If you were given the perimeter of a regular shape, how would you calculate the length of the sides?* Answers will hopefully include, 'I would divide the perimeter by the number of its sides'. *This equilateral triangle has a perimeter of 14.1 centimetres. With your partner, find a way to calculate the length of one edge. Record your working.* After a few minutes, ask pairs to describe their methods. These may include, 'We estimated first, just under 5, because there are three sides and 3 × 5 is 15. Then we said 3 × 4 = 12, with 2.1 remaining and 3 × 0.7 = 2.1, so the sides are all 4.7 centimetres'. Record this method on the board as shown, right:

$$3 \times 4 = 12$$
$$3 \times 0.7 = 2.1$$
$$3 \times 4.7 = 14.1$$

In pairs, the children then find the lengths of the sides of the shapes you have drawn, with the perimeter written in the centre of the shape.

DIFFERENTIATION

More able: Go on to other perimeters of other shapes, eg a heptagon with a perimeter of 92.4cm, a nonagon with a perimeter of 132.3cm.
Less able: Work with this group to find the side lengths of the square then let the group split into pairs, each pair finding the side length of one of the shapes.

PLENARY

Go through the calculations and discuss the strategies used.

LESSON 8 + 9

RESOURCES

Copies of photocopiable page 109 ('Division of decimals') for Lesson 9; examples of division of a 2-digit decimal by a single-digit whole number, pencils and paper.

PREPARATION

Prepare some divisions questions such as 13.8 ÷ 2, 72.3 ÷ 3 and 29.2 ÷ 4 for the less able, and 93.6 ÷ 4, 242.2 ÷ 7 and 114.3 ÷ 9 for the more able. Photocopy page 109 ('Division of decimals'), one per child.

LEARNING OUTCOMES

ORAL AND MENTAL STARTER
● **Derive quickly:** division facts corresponding to tables up to 10 × 10.

MAIN TEACHING ACTIVITY
● **Extend written methods to: short division of numbers involving decimals.**
● Express a quotient as a decimal.
● Develop calculator skills and use a calculator effectively.

Divide, divided
by, divisible
by, times,
multiplied by,
inverse.

ORAL AND MENTAL STARTER

QUICK-FIRE DIVISIONS: Ask each child to jot down one division fact corresponding to multiplication tables up to 10 × 10, eg 56 ÷ 7 = 8. They then take turns to ask the class their question. Record how many questions are answered in the time available.

MAIN TEACHING ACTIVITY

DECIMAL DIVISION: Ask the children to tell you the result of 72 ÷ 4, working mentally (18). Ask them to explain how they did this; 'I said 4 × 10 is 40, that leaves 32 and 4 × 8 is 32 so the answer is 18'; 'I said 4 × 20 is 80 and 72 is 8 less, that's 2 × 4, so that's 18'. *So you did your division by multiplication. Do we do all our divisions this way?* Discuss the idea

```
        4.7
3) 14.1
  -12.0
    2.1
   - 2.1
      0
```

3) 14.1
  -12.0   4 × 3
    2.1   then
   - 2.1   0.7 × 3
      0

Answer 4.7

that, just as addition and subtraction are inverses, so are multiplication and division. In fact, we can do all our divisions by multiplication. Write 14.1 ÷ 3 on the board as 3) 14.1. Tell them that today they are going to set these divisions as they did last term, using multiplication to help. Ask for estimates; 'nearer 4 than 3'. Work through the division together. *What do we do first? 3 multiplied by 4 is 12 and there is 2.1 left.* Record this and then ask them to carry on, recording as they tell you '3 multiplied by 0.7 is 2.1, so the answer is 4.7'.

Set the class to work individually on the examples. Once complete, they can use a calculator to check their results.

DIFFERENTIATION

More able: Make up their own divisions involving 3- or 4-digit numbers divided by a single-digit number for their partner to try.

Less able: Go through another example before letting them work individually.

PLENARY

Mark the exercise and begin to question the children about any problems they have.

LESSON 9

For the **Oral and mental starter**, repeat 'Quick-fire divisions', and challenge the children to beat yesterday's score. For the **Main teaching activity,** let the children work individually on page 109 ('Division of decimals'), while you continue to question individuals about their work and any problems they may have.

LESSON 10

RESOURCES

Calculators with the following memory facilities:

[MR]	[M+]	[M–]	[CM]	[MC] or [AC]
memory recall	add to memory	subtract from memory	clear memory	memory clear

(Beware that some calculators have all clear rather than memory clear.)

PREPARATION

Write on the board: [35] [+] [16] [M+] [+] [12] [+] [13] [MR] (Answer: 51)
Prepare other examples such as: [71] [M+] [25] [M-] [MR] (Answer: 46),
or [41] [×] [3] [M+] [22] [M–] [MR] (Answer: 101).

LEARNING OUTCOMES

ORAL AND MENTAL STARTER
● Use decimal notation. Know what each digit represents. Give a decimal fraction lying between two others.

MAIN TEACHING ACTIVITY
● Use brackets.
● Develop calculator skills and use a calculator effectively.

ORAL AND MENTAL STARTER

TELL ME ALL ABOUT IT DECIMALS: Give the children a number with one decimal place, say 6.4, and ask them to say as much as they can about the number. For example 'It's nearer 6 than 7'; 'It lies between 6.3 and 6.5'; 'It lies between 6.39 and 6.41'; 'It's half of 12.8'.

MAIN TEACHING ACTIVITY

CALCULATOR MEMORY: Give out the calculators and explain that there are three keys for controlling the memory; [M+] add to memory, [M–] subtract from memory and [MR] recall memory. *Find these on your calculators.* Ask the children to work in pairs and put any two digit number into their calculator, say 46 and press [M+]. *What do you notice?* 'The number 46 stays in the display and a little M appears in the corner'. *Put another two digit number in, say, 23 and then press [M+]. Now press [MR]. What happens?* 'The numbers have been added together in the memory and by pressing [MR] we have got the answer.' Remind the children that the small M is still present so the numbers will still be in the memory and will stay there until the [MC] (or [AC]) key is pressed. Tell them to press [MC].

Now ask the children to follow the first set of key instructions you have written on the board and notice what happens. *35 + 16 stayed in the memory even though you pressed other keys.* The children then work in pairs on the examples you prepared – remind them to always press [MC] to cancel the memory between sums.

DIFFERENTIATION

More able: Work with the more able group on using brackets. Write on the board a calculation such as (43 × 8) + (27 × 9) and ask the group how they would do this without a calculator. Replies should include, 'I would do 43 × 8 and write down the answer, then do 27 × 9 and then add the two answers together'. Ask the group to work in pairs and find the answer (587). Now ask them if they can find a way of doing this calculation using the memory keys on the calculator. Tell them to record the keys used: [43] [×] [8] [M+] [27] [×] [9] [M+] [MR].

Less able: Work with the less able group on using brackets, but this time give them simpler calculations to solve using memory such as 45 + (16 + 7) and 63 – (14 × 3).

PLENARY

Discuss when the memory function on a calculator might be used in real life applications. For example, when shopping: 6 bottles of lemonade @ 67p a bottle, 3 bags of sugar @ 38p a bag and 2 packs of margarine @ 83p a pack.

Name

Multiplying large numbers

1. Sam is going to Italy for his holiday this year. His gran has given him £5. His sister has just returned from Italy and given him her remaining 17 070 lire. There are 2845 lire to the pound. How much money has Sam been given in total, worked out:

   a) in lire? 　　　　　　　　　　　b) in £s?

2. My dad has just won £3679.32 on the lottery. He is part of a syndicate of 7 workmates. What was the total won?

3. The manufacturer says that the large size pack of Woof holds more than four times the amount of the small size. Is this true?

4. 4122 ÷ ☐ = 687. Fill in the box.

5. Do these as short multiplications:
   a) 2961 × 7 　　　　　b) 3758 × 6 　　　　　c) 1924 × 8

6. Make up 'real life' contexts for the multiplications in question 5.

Multiplying decimals

1. The school disco raised £200.00. With the money, the headteacher would like to buy 6 footballs and 6 netballs. Footballs cost £15.99 and netballs cost £17.45. Is there enough money to buy them?

2.

Mr Todd has made a patio (above) and covered it with square slabs of side length 61 cm. What is the perimeter of the patio in metres?

3. My gran made some lemonade. She used an old recipe and made 6 pints. I used a new recipe and made 4 litres. Who made the most and by how much? (1 pint = 0.568 litres)

4. Do these multiplications:

a) 1.46 × 5   b) 3.97 × 8   c) 8.546 × 7

5. Make up 'real life' contexts for the multiplications in question 4.

Division of decimals

1. Video tapes cost £21.48 for a pack of 6 tapes, or £3.76 each. I bought a pack of 6. How much did I pay for each tape and how much did I save by buying the pack?

2. I want to make 4 bookshelves, all the same length and as long as possible. I have a piece of wood 3.46m. How long will each of my shelves be?

3. I think of a number, subtract 2.6 from it and then multiply the result by 6. The answer is 19.2. What was the original number?

4.

How much do the shoes, shirt and sweater now cost each?

5. Do these divisions:

   a) 36.9 ÷ 4   b) 2.61 ÷ 6   c) 62.64 ÷ 8

6. Make up 'real life' contexts for the divisions in question 5.

UNIT 4

ORGANISATION (5 LESSONS)

	LEARNING OUTCOMES	ORAL AND MENTAL STARTER	MAIN TEACHING ACTIVITY	PLENARY
LESSON 1	• Change a fraction to the equivalent mixed number and vice versa. • Recognise when two simple fractions are equivalent (Y5 revision). **• Reduce a fraction to its simplest form by cancelling common factors.** **• Use a fraction as an 'operator' to find fractions of numbers or quantities.**	BITS: Stating how many fractional parts there are in a mixed number.	OPERATORS: Changing a fraction to an equivalent mixed number and vice-versa, recognising equivalent fractions and using fractions as operators.	Mark children's work with them, using calculators. Rectify problems that arise.
LESSON 2	• Round a number with one, two or more decimal places to the nearest tenth or whole number. • Know what each digit represents in a number with up to three decimal places. **• Order a mixed set of numbers with up to three decimal places.** • Use decimal notation for tenths, hundredths and thousandths when recording measurements. • Round up or down after division. • Develop calculator skills and use a calculator effectively.	ADD THEM: Adding two simple fractions and giving the answer as a mixed number.	ROUND IT: Rounding decimal numbers to the nearest tenth or whole number and using calculators to give answers to divisions and rounding.	Discuss 'real life' applications where we have to round to the nearest tenth or whole number.
LESSON 3	• Order fractions by converting them to fractions with a common denominator. • Convert a fraction to a decimal using division.	ADD WHAT?: Rounding up to the next whole number with one and then two places of decimals.	WHAT'S THE ORDER?: Comparing and ordering fractions by finding a common denominator and converting to a decimal using a calculator.	Emphasise the approach used when comparing and ordering decimals.
LESSON 4	• Convert a fraction to a decimal using division. • Express simple fractions such as one half, one quarter, three quarters, one third, two thirds... and tenths as percentages. • Develop calculator skills and use a calculator effectively.	ADD WHAT?: Adding from a number with one decimal place to the next 'ten' number.	ON AND ON: Investigating infinite and recurring decimals.	Discuss some of the children's comments.
LESSON 5	• Convert a fraction to a decimal using division. • Express simple fractions such as one half, one quarter, three quarters, one third, two thirds... and tenths as percentages. • Develop calculator skills and use a calculator effectively.	FRACDECS: giving decimal equivalents to simple fractions and vice-versa. Employing equivalent fractions.	ON AND ON: Continuing the work from Lesson 4 on recurring decimals.	Pull together the work and share discoveries.

ORAL AND MENTAL SKILLS Recognise relationships between fractions. Change a fraction to the equivalent mixed number. Use known number facts and place value to consolidate mental addition/ subtraction. Recognise the equivalence between the decimal and fraction forms of one half, one quarter, three quarters, one eighth...and tenths, hundredths and thousandths.

In Unit 4, Lessons 1, 2, 3 and 4 are shown in full. Lesson 5 is an extension of what has already been taught and is given in outline.

RESOURCES

Number cards 1 to 100, prepared from photocopiable resource sheet 13; prepared question sheet; calculators; measure equipment (rulers, scales etc); pencils and paper.

PREPARATION

Produce six sets of 1 to 100 number cards. Provide suitable examples for using fractions as operators, eg $^1/_3$ of 9, $^3/_{10}$ of 40, leading on to $^2/_5$ of 30cm, $^1/_{10}$ of 2m, and including other measures, then photocopy one copy per child.

LEARNING OUTCOMES

ORAL AND MENTAL STARTER
- Recognise relationships between fractions.

MAIN TEACHING ACTIVITY
- Change a fraction to the equivalent mixed number and vice-versa.
- Recognise when two simple fractions are equivalent. (Y5 revision)
- **Reduce a fraction to its simplest form by cancelling common factors.**
- **Use a fraction as an 'operator' to find fractions of numbers or quantities.**

VOCABULARY

Numerator, denominator, equivalent fractions, cancel, simplest form, operator.

ORAL AND MENTAL STARTER

BITS: Sit the children in mixed ability groups around six tables, each table with a set of the 1 to 100 number cards and a 'Captain'. Ask how many fractional parts there are in a mixed number, eg *How many quarters in $2^1/_4$?* (9). The children work it out, agree, and the 'captain' displays the number. Later, ask individual children selected questions.

MAIN TEACHING ACTIVITY

OPERATORS: Revise previous fractional work involving changing a fraction to the equivalent mixed number and vice-versa, recognising equivalent fractions and reducing a fraction to its simplest form, eg $^{60}/_{100}$ is $^6/_{10}$ by cancelling common factors in the numerator and denominator. Do this by asking questions such as *How many equivalent fractions can we think of for $^2/_5$?; Does $^3/_4 = ^9/_{12}$?* Ask how in all the examples.

Discuss, say, an eating survey of vegetables in a class of 24 children, where $^1/_3$ liked cabbage, $^2/_3$ liked cauliflower, $^5/_8$ liked carrots etc. *How many children in each case? How are you finding out?* (For carrots $(24 \div 8) \times 5 = 15$). Hand out written examples for the children to work on individually. Mention that fractions are being used as operators in the questions, eg $^1/_3$ of...

DIFFERENTIATION

More able: Can go on to produce their own 'real life' situations.
Less able: Give help by showing the group the measurement examples using equipment.

PLENARY

Mark the examples with the children using calculators to check. Rectify any difficulties.

RESOURCES

A height measure, or two metre sticks with centimetre graduations taped together to make one; prepared sheet of whole number divisions; calculators; pencils and paper.

PREPARATION

Write a set of numbers with one or two decimal places at random on the board. Set up the height measure. Write the division examples, the first set with answers involving up to two decimal places, eg $18 \div 5$, $14.7 \div 6$; the second set with answers involving a string of decimals, eg $47 \div 7$, $158 \div 3$ then photocopy one per child.

LEARNING OUTCOMES

ORAL AND MENTAL STARTER
- Recognise relationships between fractions.
- Change a fraction to the equivalent mixed number.

MAIN TEACHING ACTIVITY
- Round a number with one, two or more decimal places to the nearest tenth or whole.
- Know what each digit represents in a number with up to three decimal places.
- **Order a mixed set of numbers with up to three decimal places.**
- Use decimal notation for tenths, hundredths and thousandths when recording measurements.
- Round up or down after division.
- Develop calculator skills and use a calculator effectively.

ORAL AND MENTAL STARTER

ADD THEM: Give children two simple fractions to add and to give you the answer as a mixed number, eg $^5/_8 + {}^5/_8 = 1^1/_4$; $1^5/_6 + {}^1/_6 = 2$; $2^1/_2 + 1^3/_4 = 4^1/_4$.

MAIN TEACHING ACTIVITY

ROUND IT: Ask the children to help you to order the numbers you have written on the board. Ask them to write each number in two ways; first rounded to the nearest tenth, then to the nearest whole number. Mention that *The 5 hundredths of 6.25 makes it 6.3 to the nearest tenth, and the 5 tenths of 9.5 makes it 10 to the nearest whole number.* Discuss, say, the mass of a suitcase being 16kg to the nearest kg. *What could it actually weigh?*

Measure some children's heights to the nearest centimetre. *This answer is good enough even if she actually measures, say, 165.38421cm. If only I could find a piece of equipment which would measure to this degree of accuracy.*

Let the children work individually using calculators to find answers to the set of divisions you prepared, eg 18 ÷ 5 (3.6), 14.7 ÷ 6 (2.45), but giving the answers to the nearest whole number. Move on to provide other examples that have a string of decimal digits. Round these to the nearest tenth, eg 47 ÷ 7 (6.7142857), 158 ÷ 3 (52.666666).

DIFFERENTIATION

More able: Encourage them to talk with you and then with each other about practical applications of rounding and approximating, eg a ribbon 56cm long cut into 6 equal lengths each 9.3333333cm long is 9.3cm to the nearest mm (ie one decimal place).
Less able: Spend time with this group clarifying any problems they may have.

PLENARY

Discuss one or two of the 'real life' problems generated by the more able group.

RESOURCES

Calculators; pencils and paper.

PREPARATION

Distribute calculators one between two.

LEARNING OUTCOMES

ORAL AND MENTAL STARTER
- Use known number facts and place value to consolidate mental addition/subtraction.

MAIN TEACHING ACTIVITY
- Order fractions by converting them to fractions with a common denominator.
- Convert a fraction to a decimal using division.

VOCABULARY

Numerator, denominator, equivalent, decimal fraction.

ORAL AND MENTAL STARTER

ADD WHAT?: Give the children a number with one decimal place and ask them for the number that, when added to this, rounds it up to the next whole number. For example, 3.4 gives 0.6. Increase difficulty to giving a number with two decimal places, eg 6.82 gives 0.18. Discuss strategies, leading to links with complements to 10 for the one-place decimal numbers and complements to 100 for the two-place decimal numbers.

MAIN TEACHING ACTIVITY

WHAT'S THE ORDER?: Tell the children that they are going to compare and order fractions using various approaches. Compare, for example, $\frac{1}{4}$ and $\frac{3}{8}$ by converting them to fractions with a common denominator ($\frac{2}{8}$, $\frac{3}{8}$). So $\frac{1}{4}$ *is smaller than* $\frac{3}{8}$. Try others. Now order a set, eg $\frac{1}{4}$, $\frac{3}{4}$, $\frac{5}{8}$, $\frac{7}{8}$, $\frac{1}{2}$ by first writing down the $\frac{1}{4}$, $\frac{1}{2}$, $\frac{3}{4}$, and then inserting the other fractions from the set by comparing as above ($\frac{1}{4}$, $\frac{1}{2}$, $\frac{5}{8}$, $\frac{3}{4}$, $\frac{7}{8}$).*What about another approach? Let's change them all to decimal fractions.* Give out the calculators. Talk about $\frac{1}{8}$ being $1 \div 8$, which is 0.125. Ask the children in pairs to calculate the decimal answers for the other fractions and order them, giving the same order as before. Remind them that to change a common fraction to a decimal fraction all they have to do is divide the numerator by the denominator. Then let them order a set of fractions, such as $\frac{7}{13}$, $\frac{16}{31}$, $\frac{1}{2}$, $\frac{3}{7}$, $\frac{8}{14}$. Mention that for this work, the calculator is essential. They then invent their own sets for ordering.

DIFFERENTIATION

More able: Challenge them to invent sets of common fractions that are very nearly the same value (as was the case for $\frac{1}{2}$, $\frac{16}{31}$, $\frac{7}{13}$, $\frac{8}{14}$), using their decimal equivalences to decide which fractions to include.

Less able: Let them order other sets of fractions invented by themselves.

PLENARY

Emphasise the careful approach used when comparing and ordering the sets of decimals. Consider tenths first, and if they are the same, consider hundredths etc. Mention that for some decimals the numbers after the decimal point will go on forever (infinite decimals).

RESOURCES

Copies of photocopiable page 115 ('Investigating fractions and decimals'); calculators; pencils and paper.

PREPARATION

Photocopy page 115 ('Investigating fractions and decimals') and distribute with calculators, one of each per pair.

LEARNING OUTCOMES

ORAL AND MENTAL STARTER
● Use known number facts and place value to consolidate mental addition.

MAIN TEACHING ACTIVITY
● Convert a fraction to a decimal using division.
● Express simple fractions such as one half, one quarter, three quarters, one third, two thirds... and tenths as percentages.
● Develop calculator skills and use a calculator effectively.

ORAL AND MENTAL STARTER

ADD WHAT?: Repeat the activity from Lesson 3, but this time give the children a number with one decimal place and ask them for the number to be added to reach the next ten, eg 6.3 (3.7), 15.8 (4.2). Ask for and discuss strategies used. These should include calculating up to the next whole number and then up to the next ten number.

VOCABULARY

Numerator, denominator, equivalent, decimal fraction, recurring decimal.

MAIN TEACHING ACTIVITY

ON AND ON: Remind the children of the work covered in Lesson 3, including infinite decimals. Try working out $^1/_3$ using calculators (0.3333333). *This is another infinite decimal, but it's a special one with the 3 digit in every place, on and on. We say 0.3 recurring and that $^1/_3$ gives a recurring decimal.* Ask them what they think $^2/_3$ will give (0.6666666; 0.6 recurring). Give out the 'Investigating fractions and decimals' sheet and talk through what the children are to do. Mention that they may wish to consider percentage equivalents to simple fractions, eg $^1/_2$ is 50%, $^1/_3$ is $33^1/_3$%. Let them work through the questions on the sheet in pairs.

DIFFERENTIATION

More able: Encourage them to extend their thinking, eg $^{10}/_9$ gives $^1/_9 \times 10$, or $0.1111111 \times 10 = 1.1111111$, so $^{20}/_9$ will give 2.2222222.
Less able: Will need pointers from you.

PLENARY

Discuss some of the children's comments on the earlier fractions on the sheet. Ask the children to explain their thinking. They will continue with the sheet in the next lesson.

LESSON 5

RESOURCES	As Lesson 4.
LEARNING OUTCOMES	**ORAL AND MENTAL STARTER** ● Recognise the equivalence between the decimal and fraction forms of one half, one quarter, three quarters, one eighth... and tenths, hundredths and thousandths. **MAIN TEACHING ACTIVITY** ● Convert a fraction to a decimal using division. ● Express simple fractions such as one half, one quarter, three quarters, one third, two thirds...and tenths as percentages. ● Develop calculator skills and use a calculator effectively.
ORAL AND MENTAL STARTER	ON AND ON: Ask the children to give you decimal equivalents of simple fractions and vice-versa. Use equivalent fractions as well, eg $^{300}/_{1000} = ^{30}/_{100} = ^3/_{10} = 0.3$.
MAIN TEACHING ACTIVITY	ON AND ON: Recap the work from Lesson 4, discussing any common problems that occurred. The children then carry on with the 'Investigating fractions and decimals' worksheet. Those children who complete the work should search for other recurring decimals, considering possibilities before trying out their ideas using a calculator, eg '$^1/_9$ is 0.1111111 recurring, so perhaps $^1/_{18}$ is as well. $^2/_{18}$ must be because it's equivalent to $^1/_9$. Yes $^1/_{18}$ is, it's 0.0555555'. The answers for the questions on the worksheet are below.
DIFFERENTIATION	More able: When these children go on to search for other recurring decimals, work with them to establish sound investigational approaches. For example, working through all the 'teen' fractions might lead to statements like $^1/_{16}$ is half of $^1/_8$, giving $0.125 \div 2$, which is 0.0625. Less able: Give help where needed.
PLENARY	Discuss the work and let the children share any exciting discoveries about recurring decimals that have been made.

Common fraction	Decimal equivalent	Is it a recurring decimal?	If it recurs, how?	Any comments
$\frac{1}{2}$	0.5	no	–	I know this and I know it's equivalent to 50%.
$\frac{1}{3}$	0.3333333	yes	Every decimal place has a '3' digit in it.	We did this together as a class, it's point three recurring.
$\frac{2}{3}$	0.6666666	yes	Every decimal place has a '6' digit in it.	
$\frac{1}{4}$	0.25	no		
$\frac{2}{4}$	0.5	no		$^2/_4$ is equivalent to $^1/_2$ and is $^1/_4 \times 2$ or $0.25 \times 2 = 0.5$.
$\frac{1}{5}$	0.2	no		
$\frac{1}{6}$	0.1666666	yes	The digit '6' recurs from the second place of decimals.	
$\frac{1}{7}$	0.1428751	no		
$\frac{1}{8}$	0.125	no		
$\frac{1}{9}$	0.1111111	yes	Every decimal place has a '1' digit in it.	
$\frac{5}{9}$	0.5555555	yes	Every decimal place has a '5' digit in it.	
$\frac{10}{9}$	1.1111111	yes	Every decimal place has a '1' digit in it.	
$\frac{1}{10}$	0.1	no		
$\frac{1}{11}$	0.090909	yes	The digits '0' and '9' recur.	
$\frac{1}{12}$	0.083333	yes	The digit '3' recurs from the third place of decimals.	
$\frac{3}{12}$	0.25	no		
$\frac{1}{16}$	0.0625	no		
$\frac{1}{20}$	0.05	no		

Investigating fractions and decimals

Change these common fractions to decimal fractions using a calculator. Some have been done for you.

Common fraction	Decimal equivalent	Is it a recurring decimal?	If it recurs, how?	Any comments
$\frac{1}{2}$	0.5	no	–	I know this and I know it's equivalent to 50%.
$\frac{1}{3}$	0.3333333	yes	Every decimal place has a '3' digit in it.	We did this together as a class, it's point three recurring.
$\frac{2}{3}$				
$\frac{1}{4}$				
$\frac{2}{4}$	0.5	no		$\frac{2}{4}$ is equivalent to $\frac{1}{2}$ and is $\frac{1}{4} \times 2$ or $0.25 \times 2 = 0.5$
$\frac{1}{5}$				
$\frac{1}{6}$				
$\frac{1}{7}$				
$\frac{1}{8}$				
$\frac{1}{9}$				
$\frac{5}{9}$				
$\frac{10}{9}$				
$\frac{1}{10}$				
$\frac{1}{11}$				
$\frac{1}{12}$				
$\frac{3}{12}$				
$\frac{1}{16}$				
$\frac{1}{20}$				

UNIT 5

ORGANISATION (8 LESSONS)

LEARNING OUTCOMES	ORAL AND MENTAL STARTER	MAIN TEACHING ACTIVITY	PLENARY
LESSON 1 • **Explain methods and reasoning**, orally and in writing. • Develop from explaining a generalised relationship in words to expressing it in a formula using letters as symbols.	MULTIPLES OF 10, ADDITION: Quickly adding two multiples of 10, such as 360 + 250.	ROUND AND ROUND: Exploring the relationship between the circumference and diameter of circles.	Discuss measurements and lead to a general statement.
LESSON 2 • Make shapes with increasing accuracy. • Calculate angles in a triangle or around a point. • **Use a protractor to measure** and draw **acute and obtuse angles to the nearest degree.**	FINISH THE DIVISION: Completing a division statement.	DRAWING POLYGONS: Constructing regular polygons.	Discuss results.
LESSON 3 • Describe and visualise properties of solid shapes such as parallel or perpendicular faces or edges.	FINISH THE DIVISION: Completing a division statement.	THINK THE ATTRIBUTE: Playing a game using attributes of shapes.	Discuss strategies used.
LESSON 4 • Visualise 3–D shapes from 2–D drawings. • Recognise and estimate angles. • **Use a protractor to measure** and draw **acute and obtuse angles to the nearest degree.**	MULTIPLES OF 10, DIFFERENCE: Quickly finding the difference between two multiples of 10.	NETS AGAIN: Visualising 3–D shapes from 2–D sketches and drawing their net.	Discuss and compare sketches.
LESSON 5 • **Read and plot co-ordinates in all four quadrants.**	QUICK BONDS: Making multiplication and division bonds from three given numbers.	CO-ORDINATES: Making designs using co-ordinates.	Display and discuss designs.
LESSON 6 • **Read and plot co-ordinates in all four quadrants.** • Recognise where a shape will be after reflection in two mirror lines at right angles.	FACTOR LOOPS: Finding factors from given numbers.	CO-ORDINATES AGAIN: Labelling reflections using co-ordinates.	Discuss results and make general statements.
LESSON 7 + 8 • Recognise where a shape will be after reflection in a mirror line touching the shape at a point; in two mirror lines at right angles.	DOUBLE DECIMALS: Doubling decimal numbers.	REFLECTIONS: Constructing reflections.	Discuss methods of construction.
ORAL AND MENTAL SKILLS Recognise relationship between fractions. Change a fraction to the equivalent mixed number. Use known number facts and place value to consolidate mental addition/ subtraction. Recognise the equivalence between the decimal and fraction forms of one half, one quarter, three quarters, one eighth… and tenths, hundredths and thousandths.			

Lessons 1–3, 5 and 6 are shown in full. Lessons 4, 7 and 8 are extensions of what has already been taught and are shown in outline.

RESOURCES

Circular objects; string; cotton; thin strips of paper; rulers; compasses; a large sheet of paper; smaller sheets of paper for tables of results; pencils and paper.

PREPARATION

Ask each child to bring to school one circular object, such as a plate or jar, to measure. Also have some circular objects such as container lids in reserve for those who forget. Each table should have a selection of circular objects of different sizes, one for each child, and some measuring instruments. Draw a circle on the large sheet of paper for labelling.

LEARNING OUTCOMES

ORAL AND MENTAL STARTER

● Use known number facts and place value to consolidate mental addition/subtraction

MAIN TEACHING ACTIVITY

● Explain methods and reasoning, orally and in writing.
● Develop from explaining a generalised relationship in words to expressing it in a formula using letters as symbols.

VOCABULARY
Circle, circular, radius, diameter, circumference, pi.

ORAL AND MENTAL STARTER

MULTIPLES OF 10, ADDITION: Ask the children to quickly jot down an addition of two numbers that are both multiples of 10, eg 360 + 250, and then jot down the answer. The children take turns to ask their addition to the class. Aim to give each child a turn.

MAIN TEACHING ACTIVITY

ROUND AND ROUND: Ask the children for words associated with circles, such as radius and diameter, and to define the words they give. Label these words on your diagram of a circle. Introduce the word circumference if it is not forthcoming, asking for a definition.

Shape	diameter	circumference
jam jar	6 cm	20.5 cm
coin	2.2 cm	

Answers may include; 'It's the perimeter of a circle'; 'It's the measurement around the outside'. Explain that they are going to try to find a relationship between the diameter and the circumference of all circles. Split the class into groups of about 4 or 5 and say: *I want you to decide on a way of measuring the diameter of each object and a way of measuring the circumference. Prepare a table of results and record your measurements. Be ready to tell me if you notice anything about your results.*

DIFFERENTIATION

More able: Question them about their ideas and the accuracy of their results.
Less able: Spend time with these children, making sure they understand the task and if necessary offer ideas on how to measure.

PLENARY

Discuss how different groups tackled the problem of measuring. Display and discuss the tables of results. *Did you notice anything about your results?* Hopefully, 'Our circumferences were always about three times the length of our diameters'. *Look at other results; do they agree? Check measurements if some do not.* Lead to the idea that the circumference of any circle is always about three times its diameter. Tell the children that, however accurate the measurements are, no-one has been able to find the exact value. *Usually we say that it is 3.14 or the fraction $^{22}/_{7}$, and we give this value the name pi.* Write both the word pi and the symbol π on the board. Ask the children if they can put this into a formula: 'If c is the circumference and d is the diameter then c = 3 × d or, more accurately, c = π × d.'

LESSON 2

RESOURCES

'Answers to multiplication facts' cards from photocopiable page 13; copies of photocopiable page 123 ('Polygons'); compasses; protractors; pencils and paper.

PREPARATION

Photocopy and cut out photocopiable page 13 ('Answers to multiplication facts') – you may have these from last term, and photocopiable page 123 ('Polygons'), enough for one per child; have ready your recording sheet ('Making polygons') from Lesson 8, Unit 9, Term 1.

LEARNING OUTCOMES

ORAL AND MENTAL STARTER
● **Derive quickly division facts corresponding to tables up to 10 × 10.**

MAIN TEACHING ACTIVITY
● Make shapes with increasing accuracy.
● Calculate angles in a triangle or around a point.
● **Use a protractor to measure** and draw **acute and obtuse angles to the nearest degree.**

VOCABULARY
Triangle, pentagon, hexagon, heptagon, octagon, isosceles triangle, regular, irregular.

ORAL AND MENTAL STARTER

FINISH THE DIVISION: Place the 'Answers to multiplication facts' cards face down on the table. Turn over one card and say the number on it. The children then complete the division fact 'sentence'. For example, if you turn over 28 then they must say 'divided by 7 is 4', or 'divided by 4 is 7'. See how many they can do in a given time and keep the score.

MAIN TEACHING ACTIVITY

DRAWING POLYGONS: Remind the children of the work they did last term (Lesson 8, Unit 9, Term 1) when they found the sum of the angles in polygons by building them with triangles. Tell them that in this lesson they are going to find ways of constructing regular polygons. *What is a regular polygon?* 'A polygon with all its sides and all its angles the same'. Look at a regular pentagon. *What is the sum of the internal angles?* Remind the children of the triangle investigation. Replies may include; 'It was three triangles, that's 540°'. *So can you tell me what each angle will be?* 108°. Ask each child to construct a regular pentagon with sides of length 4cm. Now give out page 123 ('Polygons'). *Can you explain how the regular pentagon has been constructed?* If answers are not forthcoming lead the children towards the idea that the circle was drawn first then the centre was split into five equal angles (each 72°), and five radii were then drawn to the circumference. Ask them to draw the other polygons in this way to find out if this idea will work for any regular polygon.

DIFFERENTIATION

More able: Go on to try other polygons.
Less able: Help them with their constructions. Let them use calculators to calculate the angles of the polygons.

PLENARY

Discuss the polygons drawn. *Could you draw irregular polygons in this way?*

LESSON 3

RESOURCES

'Answers to multiplication facts' cards, as prepared for Lesson 2, one large single loop Venn diagram and one set of different 3–D shapes per group of four.

PREPARATION

On each table place a Venn diagram in the centre and the shapes around the edge. Group the children in to fours by ability.

LEARNING OUTCOMES

ORAL AND MENTAL STARTER

● Derive quickly division facts corresponding to tables up to 10 × 10.

MAIN TEACHING ACTIVITY

● Describe and visualise properties of solid shapes such as parallel or perpendicular faces or edges.

UNIT 5

VOCABULARY

Venn diagram, face, side, edges, base, square-based, vertex, right-angled.

ORAL AND MENTAL STARTER

FINISH THE DIVISION: Repeat the activity from Lesson 2. Try to beat your previous score.

MAIN TEACHING ACTIVITY

THINK THE ATTRIBUTE: Explain to the children that today they are going to play a game called 'Think the attribute'. *What does the word attribute mean?* Replies may include: 'It's something that the shape has, like square faces'. Select a shape and ask one child to talk about it. For example, 'All the faces of this shape are regular pentagons. There are 12 of them. I don't know its name' (dodecahedron), or 'This is a hexagonal prism. All its faces except two are rectangles'. Choose one child from each group to think of one attribute that some of the shapes have, such as 'triangular faces'. The rest of the group take turns to select a shape and place it on the Venn diagram in either of the two regions, in the loop if they think the shape has the attribute, outside if they think it hasn't. Each time, the class says 'yes' or 'no' depending on whether the shape has been placed in the correct region or not. If not then the shape is removed and placed in the other region. Play continues in this way until one child challenges when they think they know the attribute. If they are correct then they take a turn to think of an attribute. If they are incorrect then they do not have another turn until the next round.

DIFFERENTIATION

More able: Think of two attributes or use a two loop diagram and think of a single attribute for each loop. When using two loops it is helpful for the child thinking the attributes to make a quick sketch and record the attributes in the regions.
Less able: Discuss strategies used and go on to think of two attributes using a single loop.

PLENARY

Discuss the strategies used when playing the game.

LESSON 4

RESOURCES	Copies of photocopiable page 124 ('3–D shapes'); 3–D shapes corresponding to those on the photocopy; sheets of thin card; Sellotape; compasses; rulers; protractors; pencils.
PREPARATION	Photocopy page 124 ('3–D shapes'), enough for one per child.
LEARNING OUTCOMES	**ORAL AND MENTAL STARTER** ● Use known number facts and place value to consolidate mental addition/ subtraction. **MAIN TEACHING ACTIVITY** ● Visualise 3–D shapes from 2–D drawings. ● Recognise and estimate angles. ● **Use a protractor to measure** and draw **acute and obtuse angles to the nearest degree.**
ORAL AND MENTAL STARTER	MULTIPLES OF 10, DIFFERENCE: Repeat from Lesson 1, but this time find the difference between two multiples of 10.
MAIN TEACHING ACTIVITY	NETS AGAIN: Give out photocopiable page 124 ('3–D shapes'). Briefly discuss the components of each shape. For example, *Number 1 has 3 squares and 2 equilateral triangles.* Ask for the name of the shape; 'A triangular prism'. The children work on their own to sketch the nets of each shape on the sheet before drawing them on card and constructing the shape.
DIFFERENTIATION	More able: Go on to sketch the planes of symmetry on each shape on the sheet. Less able: These children may need solid shapes to aid their visualisation.
PLENARY	Discuss the net sketches and compare them. Display completed models.

RESOURCES

'Answers to multiplication facts' cards from Lesson 2; a large sheet of cm squared graph paper; a large sheet of card; self-adhesive covering; cm squared graph paper; water based felt-tipped marker; wiper; metre rule; rulers; pencils.

PREPARATION

Mount the large sheet of graph paper on to the card. Using the felt-tipped marker, draw and label axes for a single quadrant graph showing values 0 to 10 on both axes in the top right-hand corner. Leave room for four other quadrants. Using the self-adhesive plastic, cover the graph. This 'covered graph' may be wiped clean after use to be used again (see example, right).

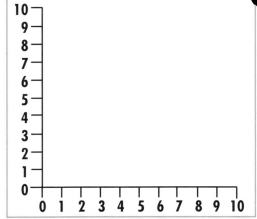

LEARNING OUTCOMES

ORAL AND MENTAL STARTER

● **Derive quickly division facts corresponding to tables up to 10 × 10.**

MAIN TEACHING ACTIVITY

● **Read and plot co-ordinates in all four quadrants.**

VOCABULARY

Quadrant, x axis, y axis, co-ordinates.

ORAL AND MENTAL STARTER

QUICK BONDS: Repeat the activity from Lesson 9, Unit 9, Term 1.

MAIN TEACHING ACTIVITY

CO-ORDINATES: Refer to the covered graph and ask individuals to plot points, say (3,8), making sure that they consider the x co-ordinate first. Ask another child if they can plot say (–5,9). When the answer is 'No', ask what alteration will be necessary so that co-ordinates such as (–5,9), (6,–7), (–3,–4) can be plotted. 'You will need to make the axes longer so that they are like number lines with negative numbers as well'. Using the felt-tipped marker, draw the two remaining axes to create a four quadrant graph. Ask two children to label each axis for you. Now ask individuals to come and plot co-ordinates that you give verbally. The other children check that the points are correctly positioned. If incorrect, wipe them off and position them correctly. Give out the sheets of graph paper, one to each child. Ask them to draw and label both axes as you have done. They should then draw a simple design using the intersections of the squares as vertices and write on another sheet of paper the co-ordinates of the vertices of the design. Once complete, they give the co-ordinates to their partner who uses them to duplicate their design.

DIFFERENTIATION

More able: Encourage them to make complicated designs.
Less able: Let them work in pairs.

PLENARY

Display the designs and use this time to look at individual's work and answer any queries.

RESOURCES

Wipe-clean graph board from Lesson 5; felt-tipped marker; wiper; metre rule; graph paper; rulers; pencils.

LESSON 6

PREPARATION

On the graph axes prepared for Lesson 5, draw the axes for a four quadrant graph. Give each child a sheet of graph paper.

LEARNING OUTCOMES
ORAL AND MENTAL STARTER
- Use factors.
- Use tests of divisibility.

MAIN TEACHING ACTIVITY
- **Read and plot co-ordinates in all four quadrants.**
- Recognise where a shape will be after reflection in two mirror lines at right angles.

VOCABULARY

Quadrant,
x-axis, y-axis,
reflect,
reflection,
mirror line,
position.

ORAL AND MENTAL STARTER
FACTOR LOOPS: Repeat from Lesson 1, Unit 8, Term 1.

MAIN TEACHING ACTIVITY

CO-ORDINATES AGAIN: Ask the children to draw and label the axes for a four quadrant graph on their sheet of graph paper. They should make each axis from −10 to 10. Tell them to draw a square with one vertex at (2, 3) and another at (2, 7). Select two children to mark these points on your graph and join them. Now ask the class to tell you the possible co-ordinates of the other vertices of the square (either (6, 7) and (6, 3) or (−2, 7) and (−2, 3)) and how they found them. 'I counted 4 squares up from (2, 3) to (2, 7) so that's how long each side is. I counted 4 squares along from (2, 7), that was (6, 7) and then 4 squares down, that's (6, 3)'. Tell the children to work individually and draw an oblong with co-ordinates (4, 5), (4, 8) and (9, 8) for three of its vertices. When they have completed the task, ask for the fourth vertex (9, 5). While they are working, wipe the square from your grid and draw the oblong. *We're now going to reflect this oblong into the other quadrants, what does reflect mean?* 'It's like a mirror being put along an axis and seeing a reflection'; 'All the sides are the same distance from the mirror line'; 'It's symmetrical about the mirror line'. Label the quadrants 1, 2, 3, and 4. *Now let's reflect the oblong into the second quadrant, how can I do this?* Replies may include; 'One side of the oblong is four squares from the y axis, so two of the co-ordinates will be on the line where x is always −4'. The children should now carry on and reflect their oblongs into the four quadrants, labelling each vertex as they do so.

DIFFERENTIATION

More able: Go on to draw a right-angled triangle with edges parallel to the axes. Reflect this.
Less able: Let them work in pairs. Check that they are coping and if possible work with them.

PLENARY

Discuss results, noting any patterns in the co-ordinates. For example, 'In the second quadrant all the co-ordinates have the same numbers as the first quadrant except that the x values are all negative'.

LESSON 7 +8

RESOURCES

Copies of photocopiable page 125 ('Reflections'); a large sheet of paper; a large sheet of card; self-adhesive covering; felt-tipped marker; wiper; metre rule; paper and pencils. For Lesson 8; suitable textbook pages or prepared designs of simple reflections; protractors; set squares; compasses; rulers; paper and pencils.

PREPARATION

Photocopy page 125 ('Reflections'), one per child. Mount the large sheet of paper on the card and cover with self-adhesive covering. Draw a design and draw a dotted line to represent the mirror line that touches the shape at a vertex. Prepare further designs on plain paper or on a grid of simple reflections. These may be both mathematical and non-mathematical.

LEARNING OUTCOMES
ORAL AND MENTAL STARTER
- **Derive quickly** doubles of two-digit numbers.

MAIN TEACHING ACTIVITY
- Recognise where a shape will be after reflection in a mirror line touching the shape at a point; in two mirror lines at right angles.

ORAL AND MENTAL STARTER

DOUBLE DECIMALS: Repeat from Lesson 5, Unit 2.

MAIN TEACHING ACTIVITY

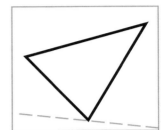

REFLECTIONS: Explain to the children that they are going to look at reflecting shapes again but this time they are not using a grid. Ask the children to remind you about reflecting patterns or shapes in a mirror line.'The reflected shape is exactly the same size as the original, it's congruent, and every vertex of the reflected shape is the same distance from the mirror line'. Show the children your prepared design and ask them to help you to sketch its reflection. Ask them to justify their instructions. The children then work on their own to complete page 125 ('Reflections').

DIFFERENTIATION

More able: Make up designs for their partner to complete using two mirror lines.
Less able: Question these children about their sketches. Encourage them to justify the position of the reflection.

PLENARY

Discuss the sketches and rectify any errors.

LESSON 8

Repeat the **Oral and mental starter** from Lesson 7. For the **Main teaching activity**, prepare some more reflections questions, this time involving reflections in more than one axis. Copy these and hand them out to the children who should work through the questions, moving on to reflecting in two axes as appropriate. Ask the children to use drawing instruments and find ways of constructing their shape reflections as accurately as possible. More able can compare ways of constructing reflections with a partner. Give less able children further designs to sketch. These designs may be on plain paper or on a grid and may be both mathematical or non-mathematical. In the **Plenary**, discuss strategies with both groups.

Polygons

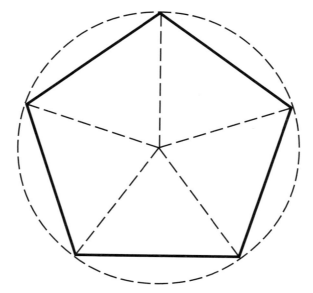

Draw a regular polygon with 8 edges.

Now find some paper and draw a polygon with:

1. 3 edges

2. 10 edges

3-D shapes

1.

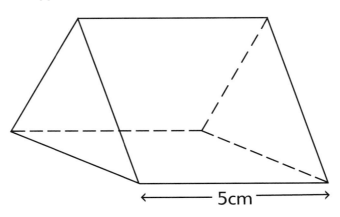

5cm

2.

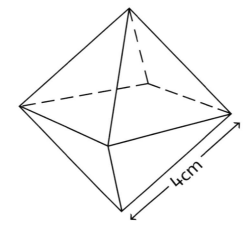

4cm

3.

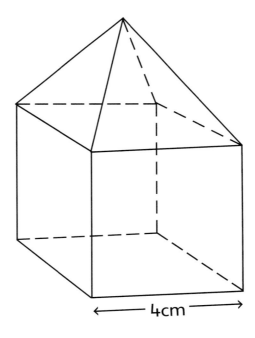

4cm

Reflections

Sketch reflections of the following shapes.

1.

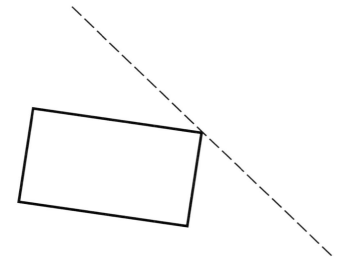

2.

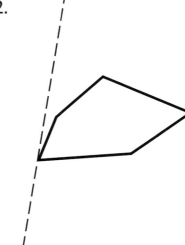

4.

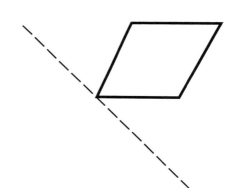

3.

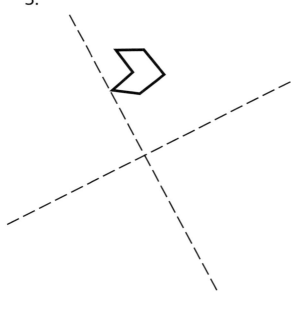

5.

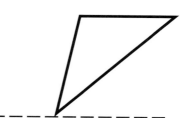

UNIT 6: Assess & Review

Choose from these activities. During the group activities, some children can be completing assessment worksheets 3a and 3b, which assess their skills with multiplication and division of decimal fractions, solving problems involving numbers and quantities using appropriate operations, reducing a fraction to its simplest form, using a fraction as an 'operator' to find fractions of numbers or quantities and ordering a mixed set of numbers with up to three decimal places, while others work with you on practical tasks. The specific criteria for the assessment sheets are to be found at the bottom of each sheet.

RESOURCES

Photocopiable page 13 ('Answers to multiplication facts'); sheets of 1cm graph paper; sheets of plain paper; compasses; set squares; protractors; rulers; paper; pencils; photocopies of Assessment sheets 3a and 3b.

ORAL AND MENTAL STARTER

ASSESSMENT

Can the children:
● Derive quickly division facts corresponding to tables up to 10×10?

DERIVING DIVISION FACTS: Play 'Finish the division' (Lesson 2, Unit 5). Note specific problems experienced by individuals. In the second starter assessment, dispense with the 'Answers to multiplication facts' cards and ask questions using a quickfire approach. Target individuals with some of the questions. Note those who will need more time devoted to division facts.

GROUP ACTIVITIES

ASSESSMENT

Can the children:
● Read and plot co-ordinates in all four quadrants? Use a protractor to measure and draw acute and obtuse angles? Solve a problem by interpreting data in tables and diagrams?

REFLECTING A TRIANGLE: Give each child a sheet of graph paper and ask them to draw a four quadrant grid showing values −10 to 10 for each axis. In the first quadrant they should plot the values (3, 1), (6, 2) and (5, 7), and join these points to form a triangle. Now tell them to reflect this triangle about the axes into quadrants 2 and 4 and record each set of co-ordinates.

HEXAGONS: Ask the children to construct regular hexagons in as many different ways as they can and be prepared to tell you each of the different ways.

TRIPLE JUMP: Give each child a copy of Assessment sheet 3a and explain that in a triple jump event it was thought that any competitor jumping 17m 50cm stood a good chance of winning. The results are shown in cm, using positive integers for jumps more than 17m 50cm and negative integers in cm for jumps less than this distance. Ask the children to complete the table for the event.

ANSWERS:
Assessment 3a 1) 17.78cm; 2) 19p; 3a) 9.48; b) 24.92; c) 73.44; d) 1.34; e) 1.8; f) 12.82.
Assessment 3b 1a) $^1/_2$; b) $^3/_5$; c) $^2/_9$; d) $^3/_7$; e) $^4/_7$; 2a) $1^1/_4$; b) $2^1/_5$; c) $4^1/_3$; 3a) 4; b) 12; c) 28; d) 2cm; e) 15g; f) $15^3/_4$; g) 50cm; h) 750g; 4) 0.612, 0.613, 0.625, 0.65.

Assessment sheet 3a

UNIT 6

Do not use a calculator.

1. 1 inch is 2.54cm. How many cm are there in 7 inches?

2. If a 'six' pack of crisps costs £1.14, what is the cost of 1 bag?

3. Do these multiplications and divisions:

   a) 2.37 × 4   b) 3.56 × 7   c) 9.18 × 8

   d) 6.7 ÷ 5   e) 5.4 ÷ 3   f) 51.28 ÷ 4

4. Make up real life number stories about three of the calculations in Question 3.

TRIPLE JUMP

| −12cm | −6cm | 17.50m | +2cm | +23cm | +27cm |

| C. Friedek | R. Dimitriv | J. Edwards | P. Camossi | D. Kapustin |

Position	Name	Length of jump
5	C. Friedek	
4	R. Dimitriv	
3	J. Edwards	
2	P. Camossi	
1	D. Kapustin	

How much further did P. Camossi jump than C. Friedek ?

• Extend written methods to: short multiplication of numbers involving decimals and short division of numbers involving decimals.

Assessment sheet 3b

Name

1. Reduce these fractions to their simplest form by cancelling common factors.

   a) $\dfrac{4}{8}$

   b) $\dfrac{6}{10}$

   c) $\dfrac{4}{18}$

   d) $\dfrac{21}{49}$

   e) $\dfrac{24}{42}$

2. Now change these to mixed numbers in their simplest form.

   a) $\dfrac{10}{8}$

   b) $\dfrac{33}{15}$

   c) $\dfrac{52}{12}$

3. Find:

   a) $\dfrac{1}{3}$ of 12

   b) $\dfrac{3}{4}$ of 16

   c) $\dfrac{7}{10}$ of 40

   d) $\dfrac{1}{4}$ of 8cm

   e) $\dfrac{3}{4}$ of 20g

   f) $\dfrac{3}{4}$ of 21

   g) $\dfrac{1}{4}$ of 2m

   h) $\dfrac{1}{4}$ of 3kg

4. Use a calculator to find the answer to these divisions:

   $5 \div 8$

   $4.904 \div 8$

   $4.55 \div 7$

   $3.672 \div 6$

   Write the answers in order with the smallest first.

- Reduce a fraction to its simplest form by cancelling common factors
- Use a fraction as an 'operator' to find fractions of numbers or quantities
- Order a mixed set of numbers with up to three decimal places.

UNITS 7-8

ORGANISATION (10 LESSONS)

LEARNING OUTCOMES	ORAL AND MENTAL STARTER	MAIN TEACHING ACTIVITY	PLENARY
LESSON 1 • Make a general statement about familiar shapes. Develop from explaining a generalised relationship in words to expressing it in a formula using letters as symbols. • **Solve a problem by representing and interpreting data in charts.** • Use, read and write standard metric units (m, cm, mm, m, cm, mm) including their abbreviations. • Recognise squares of numbers to 12 × 12. • Use the vocabulary of estimation and approximation. • Develop calculator skills and use a calculator effectively.	USE THE FUNCTION: Using an addition and subtraction function on 2- and 3-digit numbers.	WHAT'S THE AREA?: Calculating areas of rectangles using flow charts, words and letters as symbols.	Estimate, measure and calculate larger areas.
LESSON 2 • Express a relationship in a formula using letters as symbols. • Use, read and write standard metric units, including their abbreviations. • **Calculate the area of simple compound shapes that can be split into rectangles.** • Check with an equivalent calculation.	USE THE FUNCTION: Using an addition and subtraction function on 2- and 3-digit numbers.	ADDING AREAS: Calculating the areas of simple shapes by splitting them into rectangles.	Mark work and discuss strategies.
LESSON 3 • Express a relationship using letters as symbols. • Use, read and write standard metric units, including abbreviations and relationships between them. • **Calculate the area of simple compound shapes that can be split into rectangles.**	TEN UP: Multiplying or dividing decimals involving tenths by 10 or 100.	SURFACE AREA: Calculating the surface areas of cubes and cuboids and finding quicker methods	Find how many mm² in a cm² and cm² in a m².
LESSON 4 + 5 • Use, read and write standard metric units, including their abbreviations. • Know rough equivalents of lb and kg, oz and g, miles and km, litres and pints or gallons. • **Solve a problem by representing and extracting data in tables and charts.** • Develop calculator skills and use a calculator effectively.	TRIPLES: Multiplying and dividing integers by 10, 100 and 1000.	CONVERTING: Creating and using conversion line charts for km to miles, cm to inches, l to gallons, g to ounces.	Discuss real life applications.
LESSON 6 • Find the mode and range of a set of data.	GOING UP AND DOWN: Finding the difference between a decimal and a whole number.	LOOKING BACK: Recapping mode and range.	Discuss situations where mode is used.
LESSON 7 • Begin to find the median and mean of a set of data. • Develop calculator skills and use a calculator effectively.	FINISH THE DIVISION: Completing a division statement.	AVERAGE: Exploring mean.	Discuss results.
LESSON 8 + 9 • Find the mode and range of a set of data. • Begin to find the mean of a set of data. • Develop calculator skills and use a calculator effectively.	GOING UP AND DOWN: As Lesson 6. TELL ME ALL ABOUT IT – DECIMALS: Giving facts about a decimal.	AVERAGE AGAIN: Exploring range and median.	Discuss results.
LESSON 10 • **Solve a problem by extracting and interpreting data in tables and graphs.** • Develop calculator skills and use a calculator effectively.	ON AND ON: Finding differences.	DISTANCE/TIME GRAPHS: Interpreting and drawing graphs.	Discuss strategies used and graphs drawn.

In Units 7–8, lessons 1, 2, and 4–10 are shown in full. Lesson 3 is an extension of what has already been taught and is given in outline.

RESOURCES

A large rectangle of card (50cm × 25cm) with 1cm graph paper glued on one side; metre stick; two charts written on the board; area of rectangle examples; calculators; pencils and paper.

PREPARATION

Prepare the rectangle. Write the two charts side by side on the board:

How to find the area of a rectangle

Write down the number of centimetres in the length and do the same for the breadth.	Write down the values of l and b.
Multiply the two numbers.	
Write down the area of the rectangle in square centimetres (cm²).	

Provide some 'area of rectangle' examples. Use situations involving m, cm and mm and have some squares involved. For example, the length of a playground is 52m, its breadth is 36m, what is its area? ($1872m^2$); a book's length is 23.5cm, and its breadth 17cm (area = $399.5cm^2$); a stamp measures 25mm by 21mm, what is the area approximately (area = $525mm^2$); a square has a length of side of 12mm (area = $144mm^2$).

LEARNING OUTCOMES

ORAL AND MENTAL STARTER
- Use known number facts and place value to consolidate mental addition/subtraction.

MAIN TEACHING ACTIVITY
- Make a general statement about familiar shapes. Develop from explaining a generalised relationship in words to expressing it in a formula using letters as symbols.
- **Solve a problem by** representing **and interpreting data in charts.**
- Use read and write standard metric units (m, cm, mm, m², cm², mm²) including their abbreviations.
- Recognise squares of numbers to 12 × 12.
- Use the vocabulary of estimation and approximation.
- Develop calculator skills and use a calculator effectively.

ORAL AND MENTAL STARTER

USE THE FUNCTION: Play 'Use the function' for addition and subtraction from Lesson 4, Unit 1, Term 1.

MAIN TEACHING ACTIVITY

WHAT'S THE AREA?: Show the plain side of the large rectangle. Run the palm of your hand across it and say that the word area means the space covered by its surface. Turn the rectangle over to reveal the squared surface. Talk about how the area can be calculated by counting the number of squares. Say that this would take a long time and is not practical. Suggest counting the number in a row (50) and multiplying this by the number of rows (25),

VOCABULARY

Area, covers, surface, surface area, distance, square, metres (m), square centimetres (cm²), square millimetres (mm²), edge, edge length, chart, formula.

giving 50 × 25 (1250). Say that the area is therefore 1250 square centimetres and write on the board 1250cm². Talk about how this method can be made even quicker by measuring the length and the breadth. Ask a child to check this for you by measuring the blank side of the rectangle. Point to the charts on the board. Explain that they show each step you take in order. First, use the left-hand one to give a formula in words, then move to the right-hand one to give the formula using letters as symbols.
Fill in the two blank boxes on this chart:

Multiply the two numbers (l × b)
Write down a in cm² (a = l × b)

The children then work on their own to complete your prepared examples.

DIFFERENTIATION

More able: Begin to calculate the length of an oblong if its breadth is 10cm and its area is 150cm². Let them make up some 'real life' examples for others to try.
Less able: May need help in understanding area and its measurement. Go back over the start of the lesson with them.

PLENARY

Ask the children to estimate and write down on scrap paper the area of the classroom, the hall, the playground, the football pitch. Ask them how they went about it. Find an opportunity for children to measure the various lengths required so that areas can be found and compared with the estimates. *Were these estimates accurate?*

RESOURCES

Copies of photocopiable page 139 ('Areas from rectangles'); a simple compound shape drawn on the board; metre stick; centimetre rulers with halves marked or millimetre rulers; centimetre squared paper; pencils and paper.

PREPARATION

Photocopy page 139 ('Areas from rectangles'), enough for one between two. Draw the shape below on the board, without showing the dimensions or the dotted lines.

LEARNING OUTCOMES

ORAL AND MENTAL STARTER
● Use known number facts and place value to consolidate mental addition/subtraction.

MAIN TEACHING ACTIVITY
● Express a relationship in a formula using letters as symbols.
● Use, read and write standard metric units, including their abbreviations.
● **Calculate the area of simple compound shapes that can be split into rectangles.**
● Check with an equivalent calculation.

VOCABULARY

Area, covers, surface, surface area, distance, square metres (m²), square centimetres (cm²), square millimetres (mm²), edge, edge length, flow chart, formula, split.

ORAL AND MENTAL STARTER

Repeat 'Use the function' from Lesson 1, this time using harder functions, eg + 37, – 54.

MAIN TEACHING ACTIVITY

ADDING AREAS: Explain to the children that they are going to calculate areas of more difficult shapes by splitting them into rectangles, measuring the length of their sides, and calculating their areas (using l × b), then adding the values of these areas. Try this out using the example shape on the board. Ask the children how to split it into rectangles. Insert the one dotted line inside the shape. Now let a child make the necessary measurements while you add them to the diagram. Make the area calculations with them (50 × 20) + (30 × 10) = 1300cm². Try splitting the shape in other ways, eg into two squares (30 × 30) + (20 × 20) = 1300cm², or (50 × 30) − (20 × 10) = 1300cm². Each time, rub out the dotted lines and insert new ones. In pairs, the children then complete the 'Areas from rectangles' sheet. Make it clear that they must show how they are splitting the shapes and the measurements they use, as well as how the calculation was made.

ANSWERS:
1) 65cm²; 2) 14.5cm²; 3) 20cm²; 4) 14.5cm²; 5) 66cm².

DIFFERENTIATION

More able: Encourage them to check their work by splitting each shape into different rectangles. In question 5 they may well think of each 'tab' filling a corner of the shape, creating one rectangle 11cm by 6cm.
Less able: Work with them, discussing the shapes before they start in pairs.

PLENARY

Mark the work with the children discussing the different strategies used.

RESOURCES	A collection of cubes and cuboids made up from Multilink and/or centicubes; centimetre or millimetre rulers; pencils and paper.
PREPARATION	Split the children into four ability groups. Make and set out cubes and cuboids on each of the four tables.
LEARNING OUTCOMES	**ORAL AND MENTAL STARTER** ● **Multiply and divide decimals mentally by 10 or 100.** **MAIN TEACHING ACTIVITY** ● Express a relationship using letters as symbols. ● Use, read and write standard metric units, including their abbreviations and relationships between them. ● **Calculate the area of simple compound shapes that can be split into rectangles.**
ORAL AND MENTAL STARTER	TEN UP: Give children numbers involving up to one decimal place and ask for the result of multiplying or dividing by 10 or 100.
MAIN TEACHING ACTIVITY	SURFACE AREA: Show a cuboid and talk about its surfaces and total surface area. Run your hand over each face to make the total surface area clear. Describe how to calculate its value by adding the values of the areas of the six faces, ie *The value of a long face × 2, a short face × 2 and the top × 2 all added together.* Ask a child to measure the length (l), breadth (b) and height (h) of the cuboid while you draw a sketch on the board and insert the dimensions. Calculate the surface area with the children. The children then work in pairs to calculate the surface areas of the cubes and cuboids on their table. Let them discover that with cubes the value of the area of one face is simply multiplied by 6 to find the total surface area.
DIFFERENTIATION	More able: Ask them to develop a formula for surface areas. For a cube, if the edge length is l, the surface area, S, is l × l × 6, and for cuboids with edge lengths of l, b and h, the surface area, S, is (l × h) × 2 + (b × h) × 2 + (l × b) × 2 or S = 2(l × h) + 2(b × h) + 2 (l × b). Less able: Give help with the points mentioned at the end of the **Main teaching activity**. Discuss and work through the shapes if necessary.
PLENARY	Discuss how many square millimetres there are in a square centimetre. Ask for possible answers and how they were calculated. For example, 'A square of 1cm side length gives an area of 1cm². If measured in mm the area is 10 × 10 = 100mm², so 1cm² = 100mm². *What about the number of square centimetres in a square metre?* (100 × 100 = 10 000, so 1m² = 10 000cm²).

RESOURCES

Distance chart on board; road atlas of Europe; 1cm graph paper; calculators; sharp pencils; scrap paper.

PREPARATION

LESSON 4 + 5

Draw this distance chart on the board:

Amsterdam					Distance chart in km:
1585	Barcelona				
653	1886	Berlin			
210	1384	773	Brussels		
509	1114	1047	307	Paris	
1413	2066	877	1368	1494	Budapest

LEARNING OUTCOMES

ORAL AND MENTAL STARTER
- **Multiply and divide integers mentally by 10, 100 and 1000.**

MAIN TEACHING ACTIVITY
- Use, read and write standard metric units, including their abbreviations.
- Know rough equivalents of lb and kg, oz and g, miles and km, litres and pints or gallons.
- **Solve a problem by** representing **and extracting data in tables and charts.**
- Develop calculator skills and use a calculator effectively.

VOCABULARY

Kilometre (km), metre (m), centimetre (cm), millimetre (mm), kilogram (kg), gram (g), litre (l), convert, conversion charts, equivalent to, is about, is approximately, represents.

ORAL AND MENTAL STARTER

TRIPLES: Put the children into threes of mixed ability and tell them that you are going to give them a whole number which they must multiply by 10, by 100 and by 1000. They must not reply until they are ready with all three results. Each child gives one answer to the class. Extend to ÷10, ÷100 and ÷1000.

MAIN TEACHING ACTIVITY

CONVERTING: Point out the distance chart and explain that it can be used to find out how far it is in kilometres between capital cities in Europe. Show how to use it, and ask individuals to give the distances between cities selected first by you and then by other children. Build up a conversion table, kilometres to miles, on the board:

1km is about 0.62 miles
10km is about 6.2 miles
100km is about 62 miles
1000km is about 620 miles

Let them use calculators to give approximate distances between cities, rounded to the nearest mile using the kilometre distance chart and multiplying the readout by 0.62. For example, *Amsterdam to Paris is 509 km, or 315.58 miles, so it's 316 miles.* Then give them other examples to try individually. Say that every mile is equal to about 1.6km, and show them how to construct a conversion line chart of miles and kilometres using graph paper. Draw a line, say 16cm long, and on one side of it construct a kilometre scale with 1cm representing 1 km. On the same line mark a mileage scale with each 1.6cm representing a mile. Ask them to convert some kilometre readings to miles and vice-versa. Make sure they realise that the answers will be approximate.

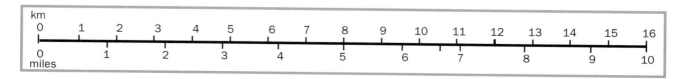

DIFFERENTIATION

More able: Find other cities on a road atlas and use its distance chart for more kilometre to mile calculations.

Less able: Give help with constructing and reading the chart.

PLENARY

Talk about the work and go on to introduce other conversion information which will be worked on during the next lesson. For example: 2.54cm = 1 inch, about 4.55l = 1 gallon, and about 28g = 1 ounce. Discuss real life uses of these conversions, as in woodwork, buying petrol, cooking.

LESSON 5

Repeat the **Oral and mental starter** from Lesson 4. For the **Main teaching activity**, have a five minute recap of yesterday's work before splitting the children into three ability groups. In pairs within their groups, they create line charts for other imperial to metric unit conversions. They should try some conversions before passing their chart to children in other groups to use. Less able children should work on centimetres to inches, constructing a line marked in centimetres with inches marked every 2.54cm. Other children can move on to work on converting litres to gallons with a line marked in litres (1l represented by 1cm), and gallons marked every 4.5cm. More able children can work on grams to ounces conversions, using 28g to 1 ounce (10g represented by 1cm) and ounces marked every 2.8cm. In the **Plenary**, discuss possible real life contexts for these conversions.

LESSON 6

RESOURCES

Mode and range questions; copies of class shoe size sheet; pencils and paper; numeral cards 1–10.

PREPARATION

On the day before this lesson, ask the children to record their shoe size on a sheet of paper prepared by you (no names are necessary). Photocopy this sheet for each group of 4–5 children of mixed ability. Write on the board:

> Number of copies sold for each of 10 records in one week:
> 178, 192, 134, 168, 178, 168, 166, 174, 137, 168

Provide textbook problems involving finding the mode and range of data sets, or provide appropriate questions of your own.

LEARNING OUTCOMES

ORAL AND MENTAL STARTER

- Consolidate all strategies from previous year, including find a difference by counting up.
- Use known number facts and place value to consolidate mental addition/subtraction.

MAIN TEACHING ACTIVITY

- Find the mode and range of a set of data.

VOCABULARY

Mode, range, average, statistics, most common, most popular.

ORAL AND MENTAL STARTER

GOING UP AND DOWN: Place the numeral cards face down on the table. Give the children a decimal, say 3.4, turn over a digit card, say 8, and the children must find the difference between the two (4.6). Later, go on to two decimal places, eg 2.57, turn over 9 (6.43).

MAIN TEACHING ACTIVITY

LOOKING BACK: Begin by recapping the meaning of range and mode. Do this by explaining that the data on the board represents the number of copies sold for different pop songs. Ask the class to tell you the range of these copies sold; 'It's the difference between 134 and 192, which is 58'. *What does this mean?* 'The most popular song sells 58 more copies than the least popular.' *What does mode mean?* 'Most common or most popular item'. *What is the mode of this set of data?* (168). Ask the children to suggest occasions when the mode would be used. These may include a shop ordering clothes or shoes where more of the popular sizes will be needed. Give out photocopies of the shoe sizes sheet and ask each group to find the range and mode of this data. They then work on the textbook examples.

DIFFERENTIATION

More able: Work individually on the textbook examples.
Less able: Work with this group, asking questions about their work and rectifying any misconceptions they may have.

PLENARY

Check results and discuss other situations where mode is appropriate. Tell the children that mode is just one form of average.

RESOURCES

Copies of photocopiable page 140 ('Averages'); pencils.

PREPARATION

Write on the board: 'Buy the new VW Golf for excellent fuel consumption! It will average 42 miles to the gallon'. Photocopy page 140 ('Averages'), one per child.

LEARNING OUTCOMES

ORAL AND MENTAL STARTER
● **Derive quickly division facts corresponding to tables up to 10 × 10.**

MAIN TEACHING ACTIVITY
● Begin to find the median and mean of a set of data.
● Develop calculator skills and use a calculator effectively..

VOCABULARY
Mean, range, average, statistics.

ORAL AND MENTAL STARTER

FINISH THE DIVISION: Repeat the activity from Lesson 2, Unit 5 of Term 2.

MAIN TEACHING ACTIVITY

AVERAGE: Discuss the statement written on the board. Ask for an explanation of the word 'average' in this context. Build on statements such as: 'It means that if the car travels a long way, sometimes it does more than 42 miles to a gallon and other times it does less. If you add all the miles the car travels and then divide by the number of gallons used then the answer will be about 42'. Ask the children when they have seen or heard the word average used. Replies may include batting averages in cricket, the number of cars travelling along a road in an hour, the rainfall for a particular month over many years etc.

Give out the photocopiable page 140 ('Averages') and tell the children to look at the first example, hours of sunshine. Ask them what the data tells them. *Tuesday wasn't very nice, Friday was the best day.* Explain that you want to know the range of hours of sunshine. *To do this we need to find the difference between the least and most hours of sunshine, that is the difference between Tuesday (1.8) and Friday (9.9), giving 8.1.* Ask the children to use calculators to find the average number of hours of sunshine for the week and discuss the calculator result (7.357142857 rounding to 7.4 hours). Tell the children *We call this result the mean, another type of average.* The children then work individually to complete the sheet.

ANSWERS:
2a) 36; b) 47.5; c) 51.5; d) 45.9; 3) 348; 4a) 11 (9–20); b) 16.2; c) 18.

DIFFERENTIATION

More able: Go on to gather their own data such as cricket scores, football attendances etc.
Less able: Explain the calculator display when several places of decimals are shown.

PLENARY

Discuss the results from the questions, in particular the decimal answer to question 4b. Is this result sensible?

RESOURCES

Suitable textbook examples or simple computer database; calculators; pencils and paper.

PREPARATION

Write on the board:

> Jay's timings for swimming one length, in seconds
> 28.3, 27.9, 27.5, 26.9, 27.3, 34.5, 27.6, 27.8, 28.0

Copy the table below on to a large sheet of paper:
  For Lesson 9, prepare a simple database. You may choose to use information about the children themselves, such as numbers of brothers and sisters; number of pets; the way they journey to school; time spent watching television; time taken to perform certain tasks such as running around the playground etc.

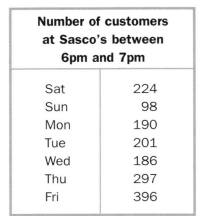

Number of customers at Sasco's between 6pm and 7pm	
Sat	224
Sun	98
Mon	190
Tue	201
Wed	186
Thu	297
Fri	396

LEARNING OUTCOMES

ORAL AND MENTAL STARTER

● Consolidate all strategies from previous year, including find a difference by counting up.
● Use known number facts and place value to consolidate mental addition/subtraction.

MAIN TEACHING ACTIVITY

● Find the mode and range of a set of data.
● Begin to find the mean of a set of data.
● Develop calculator skills and use a calculator effectively.

ORAL AND MENTAL STARTER

GOING UP AND DOWN: Repeat the activity from Lesson 6.

MAIN TEACHING ACTIVITY

AVERAGE AGAIN: Point to the data on the board and tell the children *The last time that Jay went to coaching she swam nine separate lengths and her coach recorded the time for each length. What they you tell about the times taken and their range?* Replies may include; 'The range was 7.6 seconds'; 'Her fastest time was 26.9 seconds'; 'She had one slow length, 34.5'. Discuss what might have caused this one slow length; 'Perhaps someone got in her way'. *If we wanted to find her average time for swimming a length it would not be sensible to include 34.5 seconds as this time is not representative of her overall timings. We would have to include it if finding the mean. Instead, we can find a different type of average called median. To find the median we must first put all the timings in ascending order.* With their help, record the nine times in order:

26.9, 27.3, 27.5, 27.6, 27.8, 27.9, 28.0, 28.3, 34.5

The median is the middle time in the nine given, so the fifth timing will be the median, 27.8 as there are four faster and four slower times. This method will discount her unusually slow length. Ask the children how they think they would find the median if there were 10 timings instead of nine? (Add together the fifth and sixth timings and halve them to find the median). Display the Sasco's supermarket data. In pairs, the children find the range, mean and median of this data.

DIFFERENTIATION

More able: Let them think up contexts when the median may be used as an average.
Less able: May need help with the calculations.

PLENARY

Return to the chart showing the number of customers at Sasco's and discuss the data. Which type of average do you think is the most appropriate?

LESSON 9

For the **Oral and mental starter**, repeat the activity from Lesson 10 of Unit 3. In the **Main teaching activity**, set the children to work on a suitable textbook exercise or making a simple computer database as suggested in *The National Numeracy Strategy*, page 117, involving range, mode mean, median. In the **Plenary**, discuss the results.

RESOURCES

Number cards 11–99 prepared from resource page 13 (1–100 square); copies of photocopiable page 141 ('Distance/time graphs'); rulers; calculators; pencils and paper.

PREPARATION

Place the number cards face down on your table. Photocopy page 141 ('Distance/time graphs') enough for one per pair.

LEARNING OUTCOMES

ORAL AND MENTAL STARTER
● Consolidate all strategies from previous year, including find a difference by counting up.

MAIN TEACHING ACTIVITY
● **Solve a problem by extracting and interpreting data in tables and graphs.**
● Develop calculator skills and use a calculator effectively.

ORAL AND MENTAL STARTER

ON AND ON: Give the class a two digit number, say 24, and turn over one of the number cards, say 71. The children must quickly tell you the difference between these two numbers (47). Now turn over another card, say 29, and the children must tell you the difference between this number and 47 (18). Once you have used a card, leave it face up so that at the end of the session you can count how many cards have been used. Record this so that the class can try to better their score in the future.

MAIN TEACHING ACTIVITY

DISTANCE/TIME GRAPHS: Explain to the children that in this lesson they are once again going to explore graphs, this time using time and distance. Remind the class of the work they did on average, using mean. They were asked to find the average speed of a car if it travelled say, 180 miles in 5 hours and they found that it was 36mph. *Does this mean that the car travelled for 5 hours at a constant speed of 36mph?* Replies will hopefully include, 'No it means that sometimes the car went slower than 36mph, like when starting and sometimes it went faster, like on a straight road, but if you take all its different speeds add them then divide by the time taken the answer is 36'. Give out photocopiable page 141 ('Distance/time graphs') and ask the class to look at question 1. Explain that *Mr Brand works for a builder's merchant and that he has a delivery to make. What does the graph tell us about his journey?* 'It took him 2 hours 30 minutes, he travelled 60 miles, he stopped for 30 minutes'. Ask the children to justify their statements, then ask about his average speed for the journey. Let the children work in pairs to find this, having first decided if his stop should be included. 'I think it should because he probably has to stop at traffic lights and we include that, it's just the same!' Set the children to work in pairs on the other questions on the sheet.

ANSWERS
2) 214 miles; 3) Children's own answers.

DIFFERENTIATION

More able: Go on to make up their own distance/time graphs, problems and contexts. For example, going shopping on Saturday, air travel etc.
Less able: Gather this group together and discuss each question with them before they work in pairs to answer the questions.

PLENARY

Discuss the strategies used to answer the questions on the sheet. If any pairs have made up their own graphs then discuss these and their contexts.

Name

Areas from rectangles

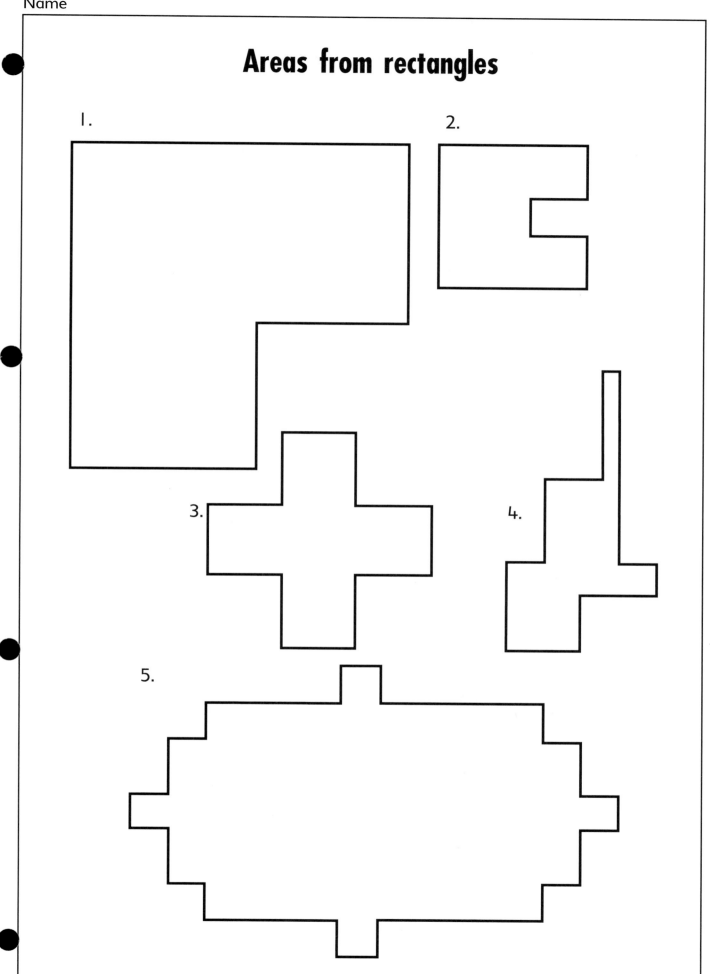

1.

2.

3.

4.

5.

Name

Averages

Hours of sunshine at Sidmouth	
Sat	8.4
Sun	9.1
Mon	7.8
Tues	1.8
Wed	5.9
Thu	8.6
Fri	9.9

1. What is the average amount of sunshine for the week?

2. What is the average (mean) speed of a car if it travels:
   a) 180 miles in 5 hours?
   b) 380 miles in 8 hours?
   c) 463.5km in 9 hours?
   d) 321.3km in 7 hours?

3. John scored an average of 58 runs per innings when playing cricket. He has had 6 completed innings. Approximately how many runs did he score in total?

4. These are the marks gained by 10 children in a spelling test:

   14, 18, 16, 9, 18, 17, 15, 18, 20, 17

What is the:
a) range of the marks?
b) mean of the marks?
c) mode of the marks?

Distance/time graphs

1. Mr. Brand's journey

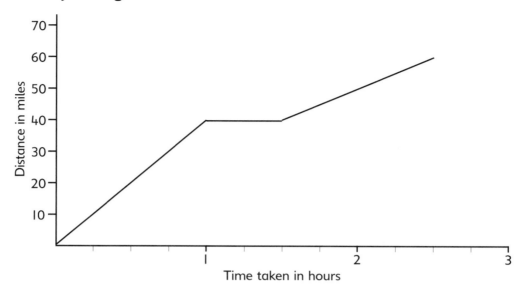

2. Jane and her aunt are going to Cruft's Dog Show in Birmingham. They leave home at 5am, and after 2 hours they have travelled 106 miles. They decide to stop for breakfast, which takes 35 minutes. Jane and her aunt arrive at Cruft's at 9.50am. The average speed for the last part of their journey was 48 miles an hour. How far did they travel?

3. The Pope family is going to London. Graph A shows their outward journey. Mr Pope decides to come home a different way, and Graph B shows the homeward journey. Write some questions about the journey for your partner to answer.

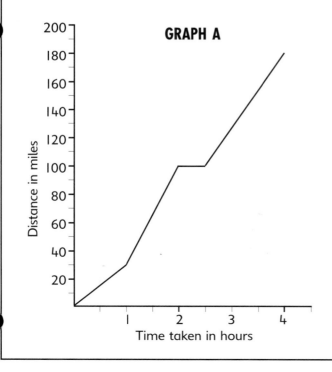

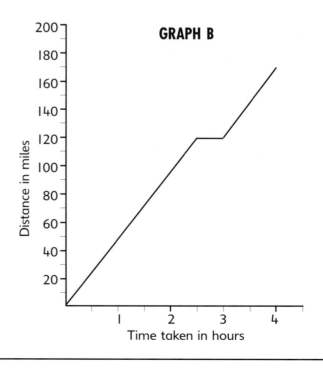

UNITS 9–10

ORGANISATION (10 LESSONS)

LEARNING OUTCOMES	ORAL AND MENTAL STARTER	MAIN TEACHING ACTIVITY	PLENARY
LESSON 1 + 2 • Recognise and extend number sequences.	FUNCTION STRINGS: Using two functions on single digit numbers.	REPEATING FUNCTIONS: Recognising and extending number sequences involving addition, subtraction, multiplication and division.	Mark work. Discuss difficulties and strategies used, including 'trial and improvement' ideas.
LESSON 3 + 4 • Recognise and explain patterns and relationships, generalise and predict. • Develop from explaining a generalised statement in words to expressing it in a formula using letters as symbols.	FIVE SECONDS: Answering addition and subtraction questions based on 'real life' contexts within five seconds.	FIND THE FUNCTIONS: Working out the functions used. Expressing the relationships in words and then by formulae.	Discuss interesting games that have arisen.
LESSON 5 + 6 • Consolidate all strategies from previous year, including: find a difference by counting up; use the relationship between addition and subtraction; add several numbers. • Use known number facts and place value to consolidate mental addition/subtraction. • Extend written methods to column addition and subtraction of numbers involving decimals. • Choose and use appropriate number operations to solve problems, and appropriate ways of calculating: mental, mental with jottings, written methods. • Round a number with two decimal places to the nearest tenth.	DECIMAL 'POINTS': Counting on and back in steps of 0.1, 0.2, 0.25, 0.5 etc from various starting numbers.	STRATEGIES: Using appropriate ways of calculating, including some rounding of numbers with two decimal places to the nearest tenth.	Explore useful strategies used.
LESSON 7 • **Identify and use appropriate operations (including combinations of operations) to solve word problems involving numbers and quantities** based on 'real life', money or measures (including time) using one or more steps. • Develop calculator skills and use a calculator effectively. • Use knowledge of sums, differences, products of odd /even numbers. • Check with an equivalent calculation. • Check with the inverse operation when using a calculator.	FOUR DIGITS: Adding two 4-digit multiples of 100.	REAL LIFE CALCULATIONS: Solving word problems involving all four operations, sometimes using a calculator (including the memory function). Creating number stories involving decimals.	Mark the work and discuss different number stories.
LESSON 8 • **Identify and use appropriate operations (including combinations of operations) to solve word problems involving numbers and quantities.** • **Solve a problem by extracting and interpreting data using graphs and charts.** • Develop from explaining a relationship in words to expressing it in a formula using letters as symbols. • Round a decimal to the nearest whole number. • Develop calculator skills and use a calculator effectively.	TIMES: Converting 12-hour pm time to 24-hour time.	TEMPERATURE CONVERSIONS: Converting from Celsius to Fahrenheit and vice-versa, using flow charts, formulae and a temperature scale. Rounding decimal answers to the nearest whole number. Using a calculator including the 'sign change' key.	Discuss weather forecasting and dual temperature statements.

LEARNING OUTCOMES		ORAL AND MENTAL STARTER	MAIN TEACHING ACTIVITY	PLENARY
LESSON 9 +10	• **Identify and use appropriate operations (including combinations of operations) to solve word problems involving numbers and quantities.** • **Solve a problem by extracting and interpreting data using graphs and charts.** • Develop from explaining a relationship in words to expressing it in a formula using letters as symbols. • Round a decimal to the nearest whole number. • Develop calculator skills and use a calculator effectively. • **Multiply and divide decimals mentally by 10 or 100 and integers by 1000.** • Develop calculator skills and use a calculator effectively. • Check with an equivalent calculation.	TIMES: Converting 12-hour pm time to 24-hour time and vice-versa.	CONVERTING CURRENCY: Converting pounds to different foreign currencies and vice-versa, both mentally and using a calculator. Reading and creating conversion tables and solving word problems.	Mark the children's work.

ORAL AND MENTAL SKILLS Use known number facts and place value to consolidate mental calculations. **Identify and use appropriate operations to solve word problems involving numbers and quantities** based on 'real life', money or measures (including time). Count on or back in steps of 0.1, 0.2, 0.3, 0.25, 0.5 etc and then back. Use units of time; use 24-hour clock notation (Year 5).

In Units 9 and 10, Lessons 1–6 and 8–10 are shown in full. Lesson 7 is provided as an outline to develop what has been taught in Lessons 5 and 6.

LESSON 1 +2

RESOURCES

Addition and subtraction sequence examples; pencils and paper.

PREPARATION

Prepare addition and subtraction sequence examples for two levels of ability and photocopy as required for the class. Organise the children into two corresponding ability groups.

LEARNING OUTCOMES

ORAL AND MENTAL STARTER
• Use known number facts and place value to consolidate mental calculations.

MAIN TEACHING ACTIVITY
• Recognise and extend number sequences, mentally.

VOCABULARY

Sequence, function, positive and negative.

ORAL AND MENTAL STARTER

FUNCTION STRINGS: Write a pair of functions on the board, such as × 2 and + 5. Give the children a single digit number on which to operate these two functions, × 2 then + 5. Repeat with other numbers and encourage a quick-fire response. After several numbers, change to another pair of functions, eg × 7 followed by – 6, or – 4 followed by ÷ 2.

MAIN TEACHING ACTIVITY

REPEATING FUNCTIONS: Tell the children that they are going to work out some sequences using addition and then subtraction functions. Try one on the board, for example: 5, 20, ❏, ❏, 65, ❏, ❏. Ask them how they completed the sequence. 'From 5 up to 20 is + 15, so I kept doing this.'

Try others involving subtraction and negative integers, for example: 55, 38, ❏, ❏, ❏, or 7, ❏, ❏, ❏, 43, ❏. Ask for their strategies: '55 – 38 is 17, so I subtracted 17 each time'; 'I had to get from 7 to 43 in four equal jumps. It's 36 divided by 4 giving 9, so each time I used + 9'. Go on to try some decimal sequences, for example + 1.2, – 0.9. Mix and match where the empty boxes occur. The children should then work individually on your prepared examples within their ability group.

DIFFERENTIATION

More able: Once they complete your examples, let them invent their own number sequences for their friends to try.

Less able: Give help on problems where needed.

PLENARY

Mark the children's work. Discuss any difficulties that may have arisen, such as in, say, 2, ❏, ❏, 8, a child may mistakenly think that they should make two 'jumps' from 2 to 8, not three. *2 to 8 in two jumps doesn't work, it's 6 divided by 2 giving 3. When I add 3 each time I get 2, 5, 8, 8, which is wrong!*

LESSON 2

Repeat the **Oral and mental starter** from Lesson 1. In the **Main teaching activity**, use the same ideas from Lesson 1, increasing the scope to include multiplication, division and two functions at once, for example: 1, 3, ❏, ❏, 81, ❏, ❏... (× 3); 128, 32, ❏, ❏, 0.5... (÷ 4); 1, 5, 17, ❏, 161 (× 3 followed by + 2). Make sure the photocopied sheets of examples you provide are again differentiated for the two ability groups. Let the more able children devise some of their own examples. Use the **Plenary** to discuss the strategies used for the two-function questions, emphasising 'trial and improvement' ideas, such as in the last example above: *× 2 followed by + 3 will go from 1 to 5, but when used on 5 will give 13 which is undershooting. Trying × 4 followed by + 1 once again will go from 1 to 5, but when used on 5 will give 21, which is overshooting. Trying × 3 followed by + 2 works.*

LESSON 3 + 4

RESOURCES

Prepared questions for 'Five seconds' mental work; A3 paper; felt-tipped pens; calculators (for Lesson 4 only); pencils and scrap paper.

PREPARATION

Write addition and subtraction questions for 'Five seconds', some presented in words and some involving 'real life' contexts such as money or measures: *What is 250 + 70?; Add 5.3 to 6.1; Subtract 60 from 130; How much change from £10 if I spend £4.35?; What's the cost of two articles if one is £15.90 and the other £2.32?; How many centimetres will be left if I cut 247cm from a plank of wood 4 metres long?; The clock reads 16.28, how many minutes to 18.00 hours?*

LEARNING OUTCOMES

ORAL AND MENTAL STARTER

● Use known number facts and place value to consolidate mental calculations.

● **Identify and use appropriate operations to solve word problems involving numbers and quantities** based on 'real life', money or measures (including time).

MAIN TEACHING ACTIVITY

● Recognise and explain patterns and relationships, generalise and predict.

● Develop from explaining a generalised statement in words to expressing it in a formula using letters as symbols (Lesson 4).

VOCABULARY

Relationship, pattern, input, output, function, generalise, predict, equation.

ORAL AND MENTAL STARTER

FIVE SECONDS: The children have five seconds to answer each question. Ask the questions you have prepared. Repeat each question clearly twice and wait five seconds. The children put their hands up, waiting until, after five seconds, you ask for the answer.

MAIN TEACHING ACTIVITY

FIND THE FUNCTIONS: Tell the children that they will choose a number, the input, you will write it on the board, use one function or perhaps two functions on it and give them the output. They must find out what function or functions you are using. Start with something straightforward, like + 6. Write *What's the function?*, 'Input', and 'Output' on the board as column headings. Write the first input yourself as an example, say 2, and the output, 8. When a child responds with + 6, say that this is right but ask whether it could have been anything else, maybe × 4. *It may be better to wait for other inputs and outputs to make sure of the function before you answer, because from now on we are going to play this as a game and if you give the wrong answer you are out.* Try another with two functions. Ask for inputs from the children, apply your functions and give outputs. For example × 2 followed by – 6 could build up as shown (see diagram, right) until a child challenges and predicts the correct functions.

Input	Output
7	8
10	14
0	– 6
4	2
1	– 4

Divide the class into three ability groups to play the functions game between themselves. Choose a child to start the first game in each group. They write the column headings on the A3 paper. They then secretly write down their functions on scrap paper and hide it, recording each input that they are given by others in the group along with the resulting output. When a child gives the correct functions this is verified from the scrap paper. No negative integer inputs are allowed and you should discourage high input numbers.

DIFFERENTIATION

More able: Encourage the children to try more difficult functions, eg × 7 followed by + 13.
Less able: Work with them using single functions only.

PLENARY

Talk over any interesting games that occurred. For example, a group may have tried, say – 4 followed by × 6. 'Vaughan said input 1, I subtracted 4 and got –3. I wasn't sure how to multiply by 6 so we had to stop that game and start a new one. We didn't choose subtraction functions first any more!' Division functions may also cause problems eg inputting 3 and applying ÷ 7 gives what output? Point this out if it hasn't arisen.

LESSON 4

Repeat Lesson 3's **Oral and mental starter**. Spend a few minutes in the **Main teaching activity** reminding children of work covered in Lesson 3. Try a squaring function with them on the board, eg square and + 1. Let them play 'Find the functions' again in their groups, using the types of function used in Lesson 1 and perhaps introducing squaring functions. Calculators may be needed if larger inputs are given. Introduce the idea that generalised statements can be expressed as a formula using letters as symbols (see figure, left). In the **Plenary,** let children describe and show the recordings of their games.

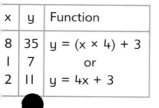

x	y	Function
8	35	y = (x × 4) + 3
1	7	or
2	11	y = 4x + 3

LESSON 5 + 6

RESOURCES

Prepared addition and subtraction number problems; scrap paper; pencils and paper.

PREPARATION

Compile number problems appropriate for different ability levels then photocopy two different sheets per child. Pages 35 and 37 of 'Supplement of examples: Years 4, 5 and 6' in the *NNS Framework for teaching mathematics* are a helpful guide. Include questions involving rounding two decimal place answers to the nearest tenth. Do not ask questions that need a calculator.

LEARNING OUTCOMES

ORAL AND MENTAL STARTER
● Count on or back in steps of 0.1, 0.2, 0.3, 0.25, 0.5 etc and then back.

MAIN TEACHING ACTIVITY
● Consolidate all strategies from previous year, including: find a difference by counting up; use the relationship between addition and subtraction; add several numbers.

- Use known number facts and place value to consolidate mental addition/subtraction.
- **Extend written methods to column addition and subtraction of numbers involving decimals.**
- Choose and use appropriate number operations to solve problems, and appropriate ways of calculating: mental, mental with jottings, written methods.
- Round a number with two decimal places to the nearest tenth.

ORAL AND MENTAL STARTER

DECIMAL 'POINTS': Repeat the activity from Lesson 6, Unit 5, Term 1.

MAIN TEACHING ACTIVITY

STRATEGIES: Write 40 + 20 + 60 + 90 on the board. Ask for the answer and the strategies used. 'I said 40, 60, 120, 210'; '4 + 2 + 6 + 9 is 21, so 40 + 20 + 60 + 90 is 210'. Now try another, say 6 + 4 + 17 and ask *What number should be added to make 49?* The children will probably use an 'add up to' strategy. Try another, say 47 + 217 + 250. Ask for estimates around the class before suggesting a mental calculation with jottings, perhaps 250 + 217 giving 467 (jotted down) + 47, which is 514. Try adding 4.8, 5.7, 1.92 and 0.04 with the problem of finding three more numbers to give a total of 23. Here, a written addition could be used, followed by mental calculations with jottings. *12.46 up to 13 is 0.54, then up to 20 is 7, then up to 23 is 3, which gives 0.54, 7 and 3 as the three additional numbers.*

The children now work individually on the question sheets you have provided. Explain that they should use an appropriate strategy each time, sometimes calculating mentally, sometimes mentally with jottings, sometimes using written methods involving columns. Do not allow them to use calculators.

DIFFERENTIATION

More able: Select some of your questions for only these children to try.
Less able: Some questions might only be presented to these children.

PLENARY

Mark the questions with the children, picking out any useful strategies that may have arisen. For example, the question 24 + 25 + 26 + 27 might have been tackled as (20 × 4) + (4 + 5 + 6 + 7), giving 102 as the answer.

LESSON 6

In the **Oral and mental starter**, remind the children of the work of Lesson 5. In particular, emphasise that they should use appropriate strategies, eg if the question can be tackled entirely mentally they should do this. Provide today's number problems, following on from the previous lesson for the **Main teaching activity**; mark and discuss the questions with the children in the **Plenary**.

LESSON 7

RESOURCES

Prepared addition, subtraction, multiplication and division word problems involving both single- and two-step calculations; calculators; pencils and paper.

PREPARATION

Prepare the examples, indicating those that require a calculator. Include some that involve using the memory key. Ideas for questions involving calculator usage can be found on pages 71 and 75 of 'Supplement of examples: Years 4, 5 and 6' in the *NNS Framework for Teaching Mathematics*. Provide different questions for the different ability groups, then photocopy one per child.

LEARNING OUTCOMES

ORAL AND MENTAL STARTER
● Use known number facts and place value to consolidate mental subtraction
(eg 2500 – 1300 = 1200).

MAIN TEACHING ACTIVITY
● **Identify and use appropriate operations (including combinations of operations) to solve word problems involving numbers and quantities** based on 'real life', money or measures (including time) using one or more steps.
● Develop calculator skills and use a calculator effectively.
● Use knowledge of sums, differences, products of odd/even numbers.
● Check with an equivalent calculation.
● Check with the inverse operation when using a calculator.

ORAL AND MENTAL STARTER

FOUR DIGITS: Use the activity from Lesson 3, Unit 1, Term 2, moving on this time to subtraction examples.

MAIN TEACHING ACTIVITY

REAL LIFE CALCULATIONS: Give an example of a real life calculation: *Mum and Dad have saved up for a holiday. They saved £34 a month for seven months and £67 for four months. How much did they save?* (34 × 7) + (67 × 4) = £506. The children work individually on your prepared examples. Say that some will need a calculator and may involve using the memory. Encourage them to check their calculations by using their knowledge of sums, differences and products of odd and even numbers together with equivalent operations for the mental calculations, and by using inverse operations for those questions requiring a calculator.

DIFFERENTIATION

More able: Go on to make up number stories from statements involving decimals, eg '62.47 – 59.85 = 2.62: In the second lap of the track the athlete was 2.62 seconds faster than in her first lap.'
Less able: Include more questions that involve using the calculator.

PLENARY

Mark the work with the children and discuss different number stories generated from number statements.

RESOURCES

Copies of photocopiable page 150 ('Converting temperature'); calculators, some with a 'sign change' key; pencils and paper.

PREPARATION

Photocopy page 150 ('Converting temperature'), one per child. Prepare conversion questions for the different abilities. For the less able group, keep the questions simple for them to solve using the appropriate formula, eg convert 10°C to °F, 59°F to °C. For the rest of the class prepare questions involving using the scale and then checking with the appropriate formula. They may need a calculator for these questions.

LEARNING OUTCOMES

ORAL AND MENTAL STARTER
● Use units of time; use 24-hour clock notation (Year 5 revision).

MAIN TEACHING ACTIVITY
● **Identify and use appropriate operations (including combinations of operations) to solve word problems involving numbers and quantities.**

- **Solve a problem by extracting and interpreting data using graphs and charts.**
- Develop from explaining a relationship in words to expressing it in a formula using letters as symbols.
- Round a decimal to the nearest whole number.
- Develop calculator skills and use a calculator effectively.

VOCABULARY

Convert, conversion chart, scale, degrees Celsius (°C), degrees Fahrenheit (°F), is equivalent to, is about, is approximately, represents, 'sign change' key.

ORAL AND MENTAL STARTER

TIMES: Give the children a 12-hour pm time and ask them to give you its equivalent 24-hour time, for example 4.20pm (16.20), or 25 minutes to 8 (19.35).

MAIN TEACHING ACTIVITY

TEMPERATURE CONVERSIONS: Remind the children that temperatures are sometimes given in degrees Celsius and sometimes in degrees Fahrenheit. Write the words on the board with their symbols, °C and °F. Say that we are going to convert temperatures from Celsius to Fahrenheit and vice-versa. Give out the 'Converting temperature' photocopies and tell the children the flow charts show how to convert temperatures. Talk about boiling point (100°C) and work through the left-hand chart, using a calculator to convert 100°C to the output of 212°F. Try 20°C (68°F) and talk about a sunny day in early summer. Build on the flow chart second from the left to develop a formula using letters for converting from c, where ultimately $f = ((c \times 9) \div 5) + 32$. Use the °F to °C chart with a °F input.

Then ask the children to fill in the boxes on the empty flow chart to produce the formula, building up from f; $f - 32$; $(f - 32) \times 5$; $c = ((f - 32) \times 5) \div 9$. When they have finished, talk about the similarities between the two flow charts and the formulae, ie their use of inverse (opposite) functions. Talk about how the temperature scale on the photocopy enables an approximate answer when converting from °C to °F or vice-versa. The children then work individually on the prepared conversion questions. Tell them to round any decimal answers to the nearest whole number where necessary.

DIFFERENTIATION

More able: Go on to consider temperatures below freezing point involving negative integer readings on the scale and in the formula. They will need a calculator with a 'sign change' key. Let them talk about the work and then try their own examples.
Less able: Work with easier questions.

PLENARY

Discuss weather forecasts on the television or radio and how and why temperatures in both Celsius and Fahrenheit are stated. Ask if they think this is sensible and why.

RESOURCES

Copies of photocopiable page 151 ('Converting currency'); calculators; pencils and paper.

PREPARATION

Photocopy page 151 ('Converting currency'), one per child.

LEARNING OUTCOMES

ORAL AND MENTAL STARTER
- Use units of time; use 24-hour clock notation (Year 5).

MAIN TEACHING ACTIVITY
- **Identify and use appropriate operations (including combinations of operations) to solve word problems involving numbers and quantities.**
- **Solve a problem by extracting and interpreting data using graphs and charts.**
- Develop from explaining a relationship in words to expressing it in a formula using letters as symbols.

- Round a decimal to the nearest whole number.
- Develop calculator skills and use a calculator effectively.
- **Multiply and divide decimals mentally by 10 or 100 and integers by 1000.**
- Develop calculator skills and use a calculator effectively.
- Check with an equivalent calculation.

VOCABULARY

Currency, how many...?, is equivalent to, about, approximately, total, amount, value, exchange rate.

ORAL AND MENTAL STARTER

TIMES: Repeat the activity from Lesson 8 and extend to giving a 24-hour time and asking for the 12-hour time, eg 13.42 (1.42pm).

MAIN TEACHING ACTIVITY

CONVERTING CURRENCY: *Why is it useful to be able to convert pounds to different foreign currencies and vice-versa?* Replies might include: 'I would want to know how much things cost if I was on holiday abroad'; 'When I went to Italy, a cup of coffee cost 5000 lire'. From an exchange rate of, say £1 being equivalent to 9.5 French francs, draw up a table on the board with the children's help (see diagram, right). Let them work mentally.

Pounds	French francs
1	9.5
2	19.0
5	47.5
10	95.0
100	950.0

Using their calculators, ask them to use the table to find out how many French francs you would get for £15. ((9.5 × 10 = 95) + (9.5 × 5 = 47.5) = 142.5 francs, checking by 9.5 × 15.) Try £112 (1064 francs). Ask the children the approximate value of 1 French franc (about 10p). What about if we divide 1 by 9.5? (calculator answer: £0.11 rounded to the nearest penny). Give out 'Converting currency' (page 151) for the children to work on individually. Tell them to solve questions 1 and 2 without using a calculator.

DIFFERENTIATION

More able: Stop this group 10–15 minutes from the end of the Main teaching activity time and ask them to develop formulae for the currency conversions. Say, *If the number of pounds is p and the number of francs is f, then to change pounds to francs use f = 9.5 × p (f = 9.5p). To change francs to pounds use p= f ÷ 9.5 and round to the nearest penny.* Let them give each other amounts of money to convert.
Less able: May need help with the mental conversions in question 1 and the place value in question 2.

PLENARY

Mark questions 1 and 2 together. Talk about how difficult it is for us to use lire because of the high numbers involved. Explain that they will continue working on the examples during the next lesson.

LESSON 10

Spend a minute or two recapping on Lesson 9's work for the **Oral and mental starter**. The children then continue with the Converting currency examples for the **Main teaching activity**. Ask the more able children to find the price of a house which costs £80 000 in England in Italian lire and express it in words (224 000 000 lire, two hundred and twenty-four million lire). A calculator attempting 80 000 × 2800 will display 'error', so the children must use a place value strategy, perhaps 8000 × 280 and then mentally multiplying by 100. Work as much as you can with the less able group, helping them with any problems that arise. Check answers in the **Plenary** and discuss any problems encountered

ANSWERS:

1) 0.22 (22p); 0.55 (55p); 1.1 (£1.10); 11.0 (£11); 110.0 (£110); 2) £2, 5600; £5, 14 000; £10, 28 000; £100, 280 000; £1000, 2 800 000; 3a) 538 Swiss francs; b) £258; c) Total £13.46, £1.91 cereal, £5.43 lamb, 8.7 francs change; 4) 228 000 Deutschmarks; 872 000 Danish krône.

Converting temperature

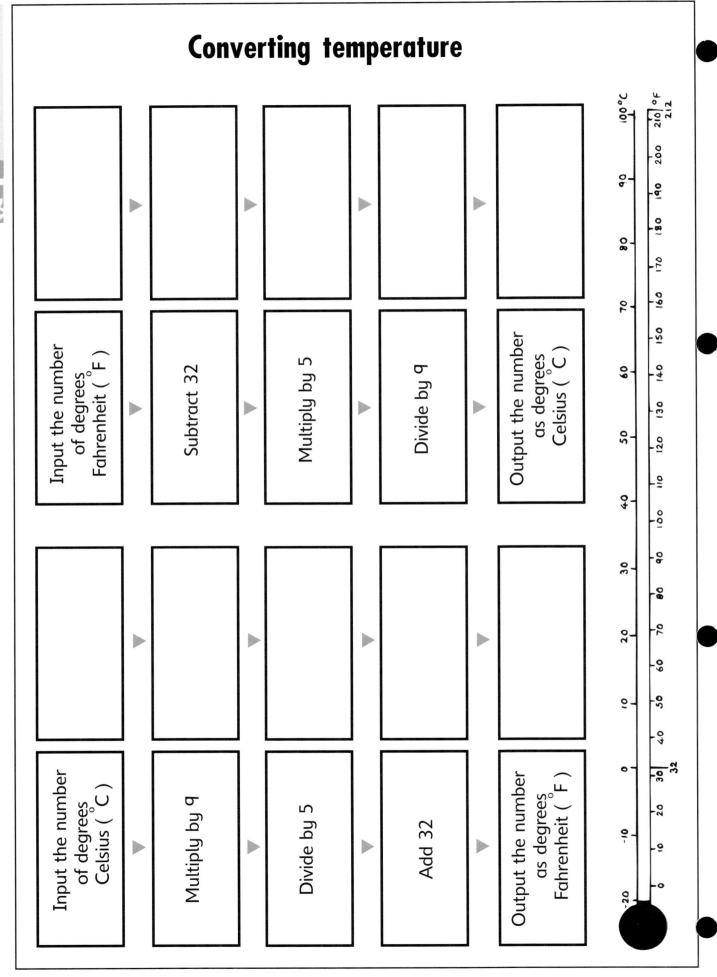

Input the number of degrees Fahrenheit (°F) ▶ Subtract 32 ▶ Multiply by 5 ▶ Divide by 9 ▶ Output the number as degrees Celsius (°C)

Input the number of degrees Celsius (°C) ▶ Multiply by 9 ▶ Divide by 5 ▶ Add 32 ▶ Output the number as degrees Fahrenheit (°F)

Converting currency

1. Without using a calculator, complete this currency exchange table.

French francs and their approximate value in pounds	
French francs	Pounds
1	0.11(11p)
2	
5	
10	
100	
1000	

2. There are about 2800 Italian lire to the pound. Make up the table showing pounds to lire.

Pounds	Italian lire
1	2800
2	
5	
10	
100	
1000	

You may now use a calculator.

3. There are 2.34 Swiss francs to the pound.

a) This summer, the Benson family is going on holiday to Switzerland.
Mr Benson exchanged £230 for Swiss francs.
How many did he get, rounded down to the nearest franc?
1 Swiss franc is worth approximately £0.43.

b) If Mr Benson had wanted 600 francs how much, in pounds, would he have changed?

c) Mrs Benson looked at her till slip for food:

Check that the total is correct and then convert it into pounds and pence.
How much, in English money did the cereal cost? What about the lamb?
How much change did she get from 40 francs?

	Swiss Francs	Pounds
Fromage (cheese)	5.80	
Thé (tea)	6.32	
Céréal (cereal)	4.45	
Jus d'orange (orange juice)	2.11	
Agneau (lamb)	12.62	
Total	31.30	

4. Currency exchange rates for £1 are 2.85 Deutschmarks and 10.90 Danish krone. Find the price of a house that costs £80 000 in England in each of the two currencies.

UNIT 11

ORGANISATION (5 LESSONS)

	LEARNING OUTCOMES	ORAL AND MENTAL STARTER	MAIN TEACHING ACTIVITY	PLENARY
LESSON 1 + 2	● Recognise prime numbers to at least 20. ● Recognise and explain patterns and relationships, generalise and predict. ● Use tests of divisibility.	FIVE SECONDS: Answering multiplication and division questions based on 'real life' contexts within five seconds.	PRIMES: Finding prime numbers, investigating and making generalisations.	Draw together what has been found out. Talk about Eratosthenes.
LESSON 3	● Factorise numbers into prime factors.	FIVE SECONDS: Answering addition, subtraction, multiplication and division questions based on 'real life' contexts within five seconds.	PRIME FACTORS: Factorising a number, extending to factorising into prime factors.	Mark and rectify errors.
LESSON 4 + 5	● Recognise squares of numbers to at least 12 × 12. ● Use known number facts and place value to consolidate mental multiplication. ● Develop calculator skills and use a calculator effectively.	SQUARING: Squaring numbers, including squares of multiples of 10 to 100. IT'S NOT PRIME: Saying whether given numbers are prime, and if not giving two of its factors.	SQUARE ROOTS: Introducing the idea of a square root. Finding square roots of numbers mentally or using a calculator involving estimating and using 'trial and improvement' strategies.	Discuss strategies and, in Lesson 5, introduce the square root sign √ and the square root key [√] on a calculator. Find and discuss answers that the calculator gives.

ORAL AND MENTAL SKILLS Use known number facts and place value to consolidate mental addition, subtraction, multiplication and division. **Identify and use appropriate operations to solve word problems involving numbers and quantities** based on 'real life', money or measures (including time). Recognise squares of numbers to at least 12 × 12. Derive quickly squares of multiples of 10 to 100 (eg 60 × 60). Recognise prime numbers to at least 20.

In Unit 11, Lessons 1 and 4 are shown in full. Lessons 2, 3 and 5 are extensions of what has already been taught and are shown in outline.

RESOURCES

Questions for 'Five seconds' mental work; copies of photocopiable page 13 (1 to 100 square); sets of different colours of felt-tipped pens for each child; pencils and paper.

PREPARATION

Write questions for 'Five seconds', but limited this time to multiplication and division. Photocopy page 13 ('1 to 100 square'), one per child.

LEARNING OUTCOMES

ORAL AND MENTAL STARTER
● Use known number facts and place value to consolidate mental multiplication and division.
● **Identify and use appropriate operations to solve word problems involving numbers and quantities** based on 'real life', money or measures (including time).

MAIN TEACHING ACTIVITY
● Recognise prime numbers to at least 20.
● Recognise and explain patterns and relationships, generalise and predict.
● Use tests of divisibility.

ORAL AND MENTAL STARTER

FIVE SECONDS: Repeat the activity from Lesson 3, Unit 9 with prepared questions.

MAIN TEACHING ACTIVITY

PRIMES: Write a number on the board and ask the children for pairs of factors. Record these. For example:

```
    24
    1   ×   24
    2   ×   12
    3   ×   8
    4   ×   6
8 factors altogether
An even number of factors
Now try a square number say 16:
16
    1   ×   16
    2   ×   8
    4   ×   4
  5 factors altogether
  An odd number of factors
```

Ask the children to try all the square numbers up to 100. When they have finished, ask what they notice from the results. 'All these square numbers have an odd number of factors'. Ask whether this will always be true; 'Well, factors of a number can usually be linked in pairs but with square numbers there is always one factor that is multiplied by itself, so you get an odd number of factors. I think numbers that are not square numbers will always have an even number of factors'. Give out the 1 to 100 squares and tell the children to use a felt-tipped pen to make a dot by all the multiples of 2 except 2 itself. Continue up to 100.

Now ask them to dot all the multiples of 3, except 3 itself, using a different colour. Let them dot all the multiples of 4, except itself with a third colour. Ask what they notice; 'They've all been marked before because all the multiples of 4 must be multiples of 2.' Leave them to continue for 5 and 6, asking them to write down all they find out, for example the multiples of 6 already have two dots because they are all multiples of 2 and 3.

DIFFERENTIATION

More able: Let them go on to try multiples of 7, 8, 9 and 10. (For possible comments and other ideas, see Lesson 2.)
Less able: Check over their work to ensure that they are progressing satisfactorily.

PLENARY

Discuss the work, emphasising that if a number is a multiple of 4 it must also be a multiple of 2, and if a number is a multiple of 6 it must also be a multiple of both 2 and 3. Ask about other multiples, say 12: 'If a number is a multiple of 12 it must also be a multiple of 2, 3, 4 and 6.'

LESSON 2

Repeat Lesson 1's **Oral and mental starter**. When introducing the **Main teaching activity**, tell the children that they are to continue Lesson 1's work. Let them continue dotting multiples of 7, then 8, 9 and 10 using different colours. Ask them to write down their comments. These might include; 'Up to 70, 49 was the only multiple of 7 not dotted'; 'The multiples of 8, 9 and 10 all had dots before. This was because the multiples of 8 are all multiples of 2 and 4, multiples of 9 are all multiples of 3 and multiples of 10 are all multiples of both 2 and 5'. Talk with pairs or groups of children about their comments. *A prime number can be described as a number that is divisible only by itself and 1, but these two numbers must be different.* Pick out some numbers on their 100 squares that have no marks and check that they are prime. Discuss the fact that 1 is not a prime number. *It is divisible by itself, 1, and also by 1. The numbers are not different, so 1 is not prime, so we must dot it.* Also make the connection that the prime numbers all have only two factors, themselves and 1, eg 19 has factors of 19, 1 and no others and is therefore prime. Ask less able children to try other unmarked numbers on the grid to check that they are prime. More able children can find prime numbers to, say, 120 using their own strategies. For example, by using tests of divisibility, 101, 103, 107 and 109 are the prime numbers between 100 and 120. For the **Plenary**, mention that this mathematical work was first done by a Greek mathematician named Eratosthenes who lived from 275 BC to 194 BC.

It is known as the Sieve of Eratosthenes, because the prime numbers can be thought of as passing through the sieve, while the non-primes do not. Go over the prime numbers up to 20 again.

RESOURCES

Questions for 'Five seconds' mental work involving all four operations; examples for 'Prime factors' activity divided into three ability levels, limiting numbers to 100; pencils and paper.

PREPARATION

Write questions for 'Five seconds', but this time involving all four operations. Prepare and write on the board the numbers to be factorised into prime factors. Numbers for the less able might be 8, 11, 20 etc, for the average ability level 28, 36, 47 etc, and for the more able 56, 64, 85 etc.

LEARNING OUTCOMES

ORAL AND MENTAL STARTER
● Use known number facts and place value to consolidate mental addition, subtraction, multiplication and division.
● **Identify and use appropriate operations to solve word problems involving numbers and quantities** based on 'real life', money or measures (including time).

MAIN TEACHING ACTIVITY
● Factorise numbers into prime factors.

VOCABULARY
Factorise, factor, product.

ORAL AND MENTAL STARTER

FIVE SECONDS: Repeat the activity from Lesson 2 using your prepared questions.

MAIN TEACHING ACTIVITY

PRIME FACTORS: Tell the children they are going to learn how to factorise a number, ie express it as a product of its factors. Give an example, say 32, which can be factorised as 8×4 or 16×2. Try others such as 48, becoming 8×6, 12×4, 16×3, 24×2 or $8 \times 3 \times 2$. Go on to factorise into prime factors only. *A prime factor is a factor that is a prime number.* Try an example, say 80. 80 could be expressed as 2×40, $2 \times 2 \times 20$, $2 \times 2 \times 2 \times 10$ or $2 \times 2 \times 2 \times 2 \times 5$. Both 2 and 5 are prime numbers.

Now try another, say 26. 26 can be expressed as 2×13. Both 2 and 13 are prime numbers. *What about 45? 45 can be written as 3×15, or $3 \times 3 \times 5$. Both 3 and 5 are prime numbers. 37 is a prime number and cannot be factorised.*

Split the class into the three ability groups and set them to work on the prepared examples you have provided.

DIFFERENTIATION

More able: Let them try higher numbers.
Less able: Work with them on, say, 16 (4×4, then $2 \times 2 \times 2 \times 2$), or 18 ($9 \times 2$, then $3 \times 3 \times 2$).

PLENARY

Mark the work, rectifying any misconceptions or errors.

RESOURCES

Calculators; pencils and paper.

PREPARATION

Split the class into two ability groups. Write two groups of numbers on the board. For the average and above group: 324, 441, 625, 676, 1156, 1225, 1849, 2401, 9604, 12 321. For the average and below group: 81, 100, 121, 144, 169, 225, 289, 400, 900, 1600, 2500.

GROUP 1	GROUP 2
324	81
441	100
625	121
676	144
1156	169
1225	225
1849	289
2401	400
9604	900
12321	1600

LEARNING OUTCOMES

ORAL AND MENTAL STARTER

● Recognise squares of numbers to at least 12 × 12.
● **Derive quickly** squares of multiples of 10 to 100 (eg 60 × 60).
● Recognise prime numbers to at least 20.

MAIN TEACHING ACTIVITY

● Recognise squares of numbers to at least 12 × 12.
● Use known number facts and place value to consolidate mental multiplication.
● Develop calculator skills and use a calculator effectively.

ORAL AND MENTAL STARTER

SQUARING: Ask the children to square some numbers. *What is 6 squared? What is 11 squared?* Specifically ask the more able *What is 13 squared? What is 15 squared?* Go on to questions involving squares of multiples of 10 to 100, eg 20 squared, 50 squared.

MAIN TEACHING ACTIVITY

SQUARE ROOTS: Ask the children the number which, when multiplied by itself gives an answer of 25. Write on the board ❑ × ❑ = 25. Say and write *Five squared* (5^2) *is 25,* and introduce *The square root of 25 is 5.* Point out that squaring and finding a square root are inverse operations, like adding and subtracting or multiplying and dividing. Ask for the square root of say, 64 or 100.

Give some tenths, in decimal form, to be squared using calculators. For example, 0.5 (0.25), 0.3 (0.09). Discuss the fact that the one place of decimal input gives two places of decimals as an output. Let them try others. Ask whether they think that this will always happen. Record answers from 0.1 (0.01) to 0.9 (0.81) on the board. Ask the children to use their calculators to find the square root of, say 256. Tell them to estimate first and then use 'trial and improvement' strategies; 'I estimate 14. 14 × 14 is 196. I need it to be higher so I'll try 18, giving 324. I need it to be lower than that, so I'll try 16, giving 256'.

The children then work on their own to find the square roots of numbers in their group. Ask them to do this mentally if possible, or if the number is too difficult by using a calculator to help.

DIFFERENTIATION

More able: Work on more complex numbers, including decimals.
Less able: Work on less complex numbers.

PLENARY

Discuss any problems that have arisen. Mention strategies. For example: *For 529, if a number multiplied by itself gives an answer of 529, the unit digit must either be a 3 or a 7 (3 × 3 = 9 or 7 × 7 = 49, each giving 9 in the units column). 20² is 400, so the answer is likely to be 23 or 27. Trying 23 gives 529. The square root of 529 is 23.* Ask if any children used this strategy and for which examples. Say that they will be carrying on with this work tomorrow.

LESSON 5

For the **Oral and mental starter**, play IT'S NOT PRIME: Ask a child for the lowest prime number (2) and then ask other children to give the other primes in order up to 20 (2, 3, 5, 7, 11, 13, 17, 19). Give numbers asking if they are prime. If the answer is no, they must give two of its factors. For example 24, not prime, 2 and 12. Try numbers up to 100. In the **Main teaching activity**, recap on Lesson 5's search for square roots. Emphasise the importance of a good 'starter' estimate. The children then carry on with the examples. If less able children finish their work, let them try the numbers from the other group. More able children could go on to try some decimal examples, eg finding the square root of 0.25, 0.64, 6.25 and then 10. For the square root of 10, let them take their answer to as many decimal places as they wish, recording their attempts and comparing their results with others (to six decimal places, the answer is 3.162277). In the **Plenary,** introduce the square root sign with $\sqrt{25}$ (the square root of 25). Then show them the square root key, $[\sqrt{\ }]$, on the calculator. Let them try some square roots of numbers and discuss the results, including the 'strings' of decimal digits, which may well go on infinitely.

UNIT 12: Assess & Review

Choose from these activities. During the group activities, some can complete assessment worksheets 4a and 4b (which assess children's skills with written addition and subtraction, multiplication and division of decimal fractions, solving problems involving numbers and quantities using appropriate operations, and calculating the perimeter and area of simple compound shapes), while others work with you on practical tasks. The specific assessment criteria for the assessment sheets are to be found at the bottom of each sheet.

RESOURCES

Questions for 'Five seconds'; copies of photocopiable page 158 ('Shopping'), one per group; pencils and paper; assessment photocopiables 4a and 4b.

ORAL AND MENTAL STARTER

ASSESSMENT
Can the children:
● Derive quickly division facts corresponding to tables up to 10×10
● Multiply and divide decimals mentally by 10 or 100, and integers by 1000, and explain the effect
● Identify and use appropriate operations (including combinations of operations) to solve word problems involving numbers and quantities?

HERE'S THE ANSWER: Tell the children that the answer to several division facts is 9, and ask them to quickly give you facts which have this answer ($63 \div 7$, $36 \div 4$, $18 \div 2$ etc.) Notice particularly those children who do not seem to be responding.

FIVE SECONDS: Repeat the activity from Lesson 3, Unit 9, but use all four operations and include questions involving multiplication and division of decimals by 10 or 100. For example, *If £1 is 8.9 French francs, what is £10, £100 worth in French francs? If £1 is 2.5 Swiss francs then how many francs will I get for 10p? If £10 is 28 000 lire then what is 1p worth in lire?*

GROUP ACTIVITIES

ASSESSMENT
Can the children:
● Identify and use appropriate operations (including combinations of operations) to solve word problems involving numbers and quantities based on 'real life', money or measures, including converting pounds to foreign currency, or vice-versa
● Solve a problem by extracting and interpreting data in tables, graphs and charts?

SHOPPING: Show the children the photocopy of page 158 ('Shopping') and ask them what they can say about buying clothes and food in the various countries (they should have paper available for jottings, and calculators to use if they need help). 'We could convert the USA cost of the Khosi Jeans, $35.6, to pounds and see if they are cheaper in the USA.' Then go on to try other countries: *Could we find out whether the country selling the cheapest Khosi Jeans also sells the cheapest Café Coffee?*

ANSWERS:

Assessment 4a 1a) 9.92 seconds; b) 0.16 seconds; c) 9.92, 9.93; 2) Many answers are possible, eg 1.4 and 2.1; 1.5 and 2; 1.6 and 1.9 etc; 3a) 10.5; b) 64.26; c) 7.3.
Assessment 4b 1) 15.2cm, 16.6cm; 2a) 1.54cm; b) 3.4cm; 3) p = 23cm, a = 28.32cm²; 4) 230.64cm².

Shopping

KHOSI JEANS

£35

CAFÉ COFFEE

£2·36

Exchange rate	Cost of Khosi Jeans	Café Coffee
United States $1.685	$35.6	$4.5
Portugal 326.48 Esc	97944 Esc	816.2 Esc
Japan 206.10 Yen	8656.2 Yen	824.4 Yen
Denmark 12.14Kr	437.04Kr	36.42Kr
Switzerland 2.633Fr	131.65Fr	10.532Fr

Name

Assessment sheet 4a

Do not use a calculator.

1. Here are some Olympic runners' times for the 100 metres race, given in seconds:

   9.92
   9.85
   10.01
   9.89
   9.93

   Find the

   a) average time.

   b) difference between the fastest and the slowest times.

   c) times above 9.9 seconds and below 10.0 seconds.

2. At the local horticultural show Mr Dart entered four marrows. Their total weight was 7kg. The lightest marrow weighed 1.3kg, and the heaviest 2.2kg. Give some possible weights of the other two marrows.

3. Find the answer and write a real life context for each of the following:

   a) 3.08 + 4.89 + 2.53 =

   b) 67.1 – 2.84 =

   c) 2.93 + 0.86 + 1.5 + 2.01 =

● Extend written methods to column addition and subtraction of numbers involving decimals.
● Identify and use appropriate operations (including combinations of operations) to solve word problems involving numbers and quantities.

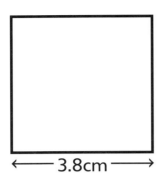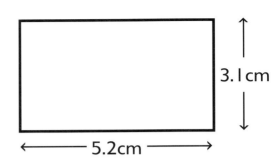

Assessment sheet 4b

1. Find the perimeter of these shapes:

2. a) What is the length of an edge of a square if the perimeter is 6.16cm?
   b) What is the length of an edge of a regular pentagon with a perimeter of 17cm?

3. Find the perimeter and area of this shape:

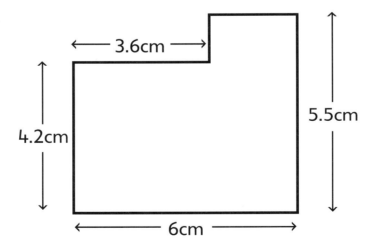

4. Use a calculator to find the surface area of a cube with an edge length of 6.2cm.

• Calculate the perimeter and area of simple compound shapes that can be split into rectangles.

This term's work builds on Term 2. Known number facts and place value are used to extend and apply mental facility together with division facts to 10 × 10, doubling multiples of 10 and 100 and the corresponding halves. Mental calculations include finding simple percentages and solving problems involving proportion. Fractional, decimal and percentage relationships are consolidated, and squaring multiples of 10, prime numbers, prime factors and extending number sequences are practised. Relationships involving metric units and converting imperial to metric units also feature. Multiplying and dividing decimals by 10 or 100 and integers by 1000, rounding, approximating and links with accuracy, are developed. Calculations extend to long multiplication and division and word problems are widely used. Proportion, common factors, decimals and percentages are linked to simple pie charts. Probability and graphing number facts and equations are taught. Rotations and translations feature, as do height, sampling, time zones and calculating and comparing perimeters and areas of rectangles. Common multiples and number sequences are investigated, calculator skills used and extended.

ENLARGE THIS SHEET TO A3 AND USE IT AS YOUR MEDIUM-TERM PLANNING GRID.

ORAL AND MENTAL SKILLS: Use known number facts and place value to consolidate mental addition, subtraction, multiplication and division. **Derive quickly:** doubles of ; two digit numbers; multiples of 10 to 100; **division facts corresponding to tables up to 10 × 10.** Consolidate all strategies from previous year, including add several numbers, use the relationship between multiplication and division. **Identify and use appropriate operations (including combinations of operations) to solve word problems involving numbers and quantities** based on 'real life', money or measures (including time). **Understand percentages as the number of parts in every 100; find simple percentages of smal whole number quantities.** Solve simple problems involving proportion.

Unit	Topic	Objectives: children will be taught to...
1	Place value ordering and rounding Using a calculator	● **Multiply and divide decimals mentally by 10 or 100 and integers by 1000 and explain the effect.** ● Use the vocabulary of estimation and approximation. Consolidate rounding an integer to the nearest 10, 100 or 1000. ● Round a number with two decimal places to the nearest tenth or to the nearest whole number. ● **Solve a problem by** representing, **extracting and interpreting data in tables.** ● Check with the inverse operation, when using a calculator.
2-3	Understanding × and ÷ Mental calculation strategies (× and ÷) Pencil and paper procedures, money and 'real life' Making decisions and checking results, including using a calculator.	● Understand and use the relationships between the four operations and the principles of the arithmetic laws. Use brackets. ● Use related facts and doubling or halving. ● Use factors. ● Use closely related facts. ● Partition. ● Use the relationship between multiplication and division. ● Use known number facts and place value to consolidate mental multiplication and division. ● Consolidate all strategies from previous year. ● Extend written methods to: **long multiplication of a three-digit by a two-digit integer;** division of HTU by TU. ● Choose and use appropriate number operations to solve problems and appropriate ways of calculating. ● **Explain methods and reasoning.** ● Solve mathematical problems or puzzles. ● Make and investigate a general statement about familiar numbers or shapes by finding examples which satisfy it. ● Develop calculator skills and use a calculator effectively.
4-5	Fractions, decimals and percentages Ratio and proportion	● Change a fraction to the equivalent mixed number and vice- versa. Recognise relationships between fractions. ● **Reduce a fraction to its simplest form by cancelling common factors** in the numerator and the denominator. ● Order fractions by converting them to fractions with a common denominator. ● Convert a fraction to a decimal using division. ● Give a decimal fraction lying between two others. ● **Order a mixed set of numbers.** ● **Understand percentages as the number of parts in every 100**. ● Express simple fractions as percentages. ● **Find simple percentages of small whole number quantities.** ● **Solve simple problems involving ratio and proportion.** ● Solve a problem by representing, **extracting and interpreting data in tables, graphs and charts.** ● Round an integer to the nearest 100. ● **Use a protractor to measure** and draw **angles to the nearest degree.** ● Recognise and extend number sequences and make general statements . ● Develop calculator skills and use a calculator effectively.
6	Handling data Using a calculator	● Use the language associated with probability to discuss events, including those associated with probability. ● **Solve a problem** by representing, **extracting and interpreting data in tables and graphs.** ● **Read and plot co-ordinates in all four quadrants.** ● Develop calculator skills and use a calculator effectively.
7	Assess and review	● **Multiply and divide decimals mentally by 10 or 100 and integers by 1000 and explain the effect. Find simple percentages of small whole number quantities.. Solve a problem by representing, extracting and interpreting data in tables, charts and diagrams. Read and plot co-ordinates in all four quadrants. Solve simple problem involving ratio and proportion. Understand percentages as the number of parts in every 100. Use a protractor to measure** and draw **angles to the nearest degree. Extend written methods to: long multiplication of a three-digit by a two-digit integer.**

ORAL AND MENTAL SKILLS: Use known number facts and place value to consolidate mental addition/subtraction. **Derive quickly** doubles of: two digit numbers; multiples of 10 to 100; **division facts corresponding to tables up to 10x10.** Express simple fractions as percentages (and vice- versa). **Find simple percentages of small whole number quantities.** Recognise the equivalence between decimal and fraction forms. Recognise prime numbers to at least 20. Factorise numbers to 100 into prime factors. Calculate angles in a triangle or around a point. Convert smaller to larger units and vice-versa; know rough equivalents(metric to imperial). **Calculate the perimeter and area of simple shapes.** Recognise and extend number sequences.

Unit	Topic	Objectives: children will be taught to...
8-10	Shape and space Reasoning about shapes Measures including problems	● Make shapes with increasing accuracy. ● **Use a protractor to measure** and draw **acute and obtuse angles to the nearest degree.** ● **Read and plot co-ordinates in all four quadrants.** ● Recognise where a shape will be after a rotation through 90° about one of its vertices. ● Recognise where a shape will be after two translations. ● Solve mathematical problems, recognise and explain patterns and relationships, generalise and predict. Suggest extensions asking "What if...?" ● Explain methods and reasoning orally and in writing. ● Make and investigate a general statement about familiar shapes by finding examples which satisfy it. ● Use read and write centimetres including their abbreviation cm. ● Record estimates and readings from scales to a suitable degree of accuracy. ● Calculate the perimeter and area of simple shapes that can be split into rectangles. ● Appreciate different times around the world.
11	Mental calculation strategies (+ and −) Pencil and paper procedures (+ and −) Money and 'real life' problems. Making decisions and checking results, including using a calculator	● **Solve a problem by** representing, **extracting and interpreting data in charts, tables,** diagrams **and graphs;** frequency tables and bar charts with grouped discrete data. ● Develop calculator skills and use a calculator effectively. ● Use known number facts and place value to consolidate mental addition/ subtraction. ● Use informal pencil and paper methods to support, record or explain addition and subtractions. ● **Identify and use appropriate operations to solve word problems** involving quantities based on 'real life' money , using one or more steps, and calculating percentages such as VAT (and discounts). ● Know (and use) equivalents (of oz and lbs to g, pints to ml, tablespoons to ml, inches to cm, °F to °C). ● **Solve a problem by** representing, **extracting and interpreting data in charts, tables,** diagrams **and graphs** eg a conversion graph. ● Express a generalised relationship in a formula using letters as symbols. ● Solve mathematical problems or puzzles and explain patterns and relationships. ● Recognise and extend number sequences. ● Round a decimal number to the nearest whole number or ten. ● Develop calculator skills and use a calculator effectively.
12	Properties of numbers Reasoning about numbers	● Find simple common multiples. ● Recognise and extend number sequences, such as the sequence of square numbers or the sequence of triangular numbers. ● Make and investigate a general statement about familiar numbers. Develop from explaining a generalised relationship in words to expressing it in a formula using letters as symbols. ● **Solve a problem** by representing and **interpreting data** in diagrams. ● Develop calculator skills and use a calculator effectively.
13	Assess and review	● **Derive quickly division facts corresponding to tables up to 10 × 10.** ● **Calculate the perimeter and area of simple shapes that can be split into rectangles.** ● **Read and plot co-ordinates in all four quadrants.** ● **Identify and use appropriate operations to solve word problems** involving quantities based on 'real life' money, using one or more steps, and calculating percentages such as VAT (and discounts). ● **Use a protractor to measure** and draw **acute and obtuse angles to the nearest degree. Solve a problem by** representing, **extracting and interpreting data in charts, tables,** diagrams **and graphs.**

UNIT 1

ORGANISATION (3 LESSONS)

LEARNING OUTCOMES		ORAL AND MENTAL STARTER	MAIN TEACHING ACTIVITY	PLENARY
LESSON 1	• **Multiply and divide decimals mentally by 10 or 100, and integers by 1000, and explain the effect.** • Check with the inverse operation when using a calculator.	USE THE FUNCTION: Using the functions × 3, × 4 and × 5 on whole numbers up to 100.	DIGIT MOVEMENTS: Multiplying and dividing numbers by 10, 100 or 1000 and explaining the effects.	Check answers using calculators and inverse operations.
LESSON 2 + 3	• Use vocabulary of estimation and approximation. Consolidate rounding to the nearest 10, 100, 1000. • Round a number with two decimal places to the nearest tenth or whole number. • **Solve a problem by interpreting data in tables.**	USE THE FUNCTION. HIT THE TARGET: Doubling 2-digit numbers with one decimal place.	ORDERING AND ROUNDING: Ordering and rounding integers and decimal numbers. Considering approximations and accuracy.	Mark the examples and discuss the mathematical points which arise.

ORAL AND MENTAL SKILLS Use known number facts and place value to consolidate mental multiplication. **Derive quickly** doubles of two-digit numbers.

Lessons 1 and 2 are shown in full. Lesson 3 extends the work of Lesson 2 and is shown afterwards.

RESOURCES

Copies of photocopiable page 166 ('Digit movements'); calculators; pencils and paper.

PREPARATION

Photocopy page 166 ('Digit movements'), one per child.

LEARNING OUTCOMES

ORAL AND MENTAL STARTER
● Use known number facts and place value to consolidate mental multiplication.

MAIN TEACHING ACTIVITY
● **Multiply and divide decimals mentally by 10 or 100, and integers by 1000, and explain the effect.**
● Check with the inverse operation when using a calculator.

VOCABULARY

Unit, ten, hundred, thousand, ten thousand, hundred thousand, million, billion, ascending/ descending order.

ORAL AND MENTAL STARTER

USE THE FUNCTION: Choose a function, say × 3, and ask the children to use it on whole numbers up to 100. Take care to differentiate questions according to the varying abilities of the children. Now try other functions, such as × 4 and then × 5.

MAIN TEACHING ACTIVITY

DIGIT MOVEMENTS: Write a single digit number on the board, say 5, and ask the effect of multiplying by 10 (the 5 digit moves one place to the left and a nought is inserted in the units column: 50). Then try × 100 and × 1000. Next try ÷ 10. *The 5 digit moves one place to the right and we write 0.5.* Next try ÷ 100 and then ÷ 1000. Discuss how × 1000 is equivalent to multiplying by 10 and then by 100. Try some larger numbers and then some decimal inputs. The children move on to work individually to complete 'Digit movements'.

DIFFERENTIATION

More able: Let them go on to work in pairs, making up questions for each other to answer.
Less able: Spend time giving help to this group where needed.

PLENARY

Mark the examples with the children, letting them use calculators to check the answers. For 4c), d), e) and f), check the answers using inverse operations. In question 4c), for example, 46 000 ÷ 46 = 1000. Give the answers to 2c) and 2d).

RESOURCES

Copies of photocopiable page 167 ('Ordering and rounding'), one per child; world atlas; scrap paper; pencils and paper.

PREPARATION

Photocopy page 167 ('Ordering and rounding'). Write on the board these river lengths:

River length (in km)					
Nile	6 695	Amazon	6 570	Yangtze	6 380
Missouri	3 969	Zambesi	2 650	Rhine	1 320

LEARNING OUTCOMES

ORAL AND MENTAL STARTER
● Use known number facts and place value to consolidate mental multiplication.
● **Derive quickly** doubles of two-digit numbers (Lesson 3).

MAIN TEACHING ACTIVITY
● Use the vocabulary of estimation and approximation. Consolidate rounding an integer to the nearest 10, 100, 1000.
● Round a number with two decimal places to the nearest tenth or to the nearest whole number.
● **Solve a problem by** representing, **extracting and interpreting data in tables.**

ORAL AND MENTAL STARTER

USE THE FUNCTION: Repeat the activity from Lesson 1

MAIN TEACHING ACTIVITY

ORDERING AND ROUNDING: Discuss the river lengths written on the board. Bring out the fact that they are in order and are very accurately stated (to the nearest kilometre). Ask the children to round the lengths to the nearest hundred kilometres. Write their answers on the board and say that these approximate lengths might well be quoted when discussing rivers. *The Nile is approximately (about) 6700 km long.* Ask for the approximate difference in length between some of the rivers, eg Nile and Rhine (5400km). The children then start work on the 'Ordering and rounding' worksheet.

DIFFERENTIATION

More able: Ask this group to discuss population statistics from a world atlas. They might say that the data has been rounded to the nearest 100 000, for example. Ask them to quote some of the populations to the nearest million.
Less able: Discuss the first two examples with this group before setting them to work.

VOCABULARY

Unit, ten, hundred, thousand, ten thousand, hundred thousand, million, billion, ascending/ descending order, estimate, approximate, approximately, round to the nearest ten/ hundred/ thousand/ tenth/whole number.

PLENARY

Mark the first two examples with the children. Discuss, in question 1, 1528 and 1650 (giving 1500 and 1700 respectively to the nearest 100 miles, and both giving 2000 to the nearest 1000 miles). Mention that in the Olympic Games the results are now given to two decimal places. Ask why: 'It's now possible to measure the times more accurately'; 'Athletes' times are so close that a second place of decimals (one hundredth of a second) is needed to 'split' them'.

LESSON 3

For the **Oral and mental starter**, play HIT THE TARGET: Tell the children that you are going to give them numbers with one decimal place which they will double (eg 1.7 × 2 = 3.4). Ask them to write down five numbers that could be answers to the questions you are going to ask. Children score a point each time the answer corresponds to one of the numbers they have written on their paper. Each time they score a point they must record the input which gave it to them (if the answer was 5.8 they record 2.9 beside it). See who can be first to cross off all their numbers. For the **Main teaching activity**, the children continue from where they left off in Lesson 2. More able children can go on to consider multiplication or divisions that would give answers which are the numbers appearing in question 4. They must use a different function each time. For example, they cannot say 33.44 ÷ 2 = 16.72 and then say 272.96 ÷ 2 = 136.48. Discuss any problems encountered with less able children. Finish marking the work in the **Plenary**, and discuss question 4d), where the answer is the same for both parts of the question.

ANSWERS:

1a) 78 506, 17 941, 17 216, 10 050, 4414, 1650, 1528; b) 78 500, 17 900, 17 200, 10 100, 4400, 1700, 1500; c) 79 000, 18 000, 17 000, 10 000, 4000, 2000, 2000; 2) No, 1920 was slower than 1904 and 1900; 10.4 seconds; 3) Everest 8850m; K2 8610m; Rakaposhi 7780m; Bonete 6870m; Logan 6050m; Ben Nevis 1340m (all to the nearest 10 metres); 4a) 16.7, 17; b) 136.5, 136; c) 0.1, 0; d) 42.0, 42

UNIT 1

Digit movements

Work out all the questions mentally.

1. Multiply each number by 10, then multiply by 100, then multiply by 1000.
a) 6   b) 73   c) 314   d) 1829   e) 23 429   f) 104 371

a)

b)

c)

d)

e)

f)

Write the answers to c) and d) in words.

c) _____

d) _____

2. Divide each number by 10, then by 100.
a) 370   b) 0.8   c) 105.04

a)

b)

c)

3. Divide each number by 1000.
a) 220 000   b) 10 400   c) 974

a)

b)

c)

4. Try these

a) 0.3 × 10 = ☐   c) 46 × ☐ = 46 000   e) 0.79 × ☐ = 79

b) 17 ÷ 0 = ☐   d) 120 000 ÷ ☐ = 120   f) 8 ÷ ☐ = 0. 08

Ordering and rounding

1. a) Put these car milometer readings in descending order:

    10 050,   17 216,   4414,   78 506,   17 941,   1528,   1650

Round each reading: b) to the nearest 100 miles. c) to the nearest 1000 miles.

a) _____   b) _____   c) _____

_____   _____   _____

_____   _____   _____

_____   _____   _____

_____   _____   _____

_____   _____   _____

_____   _____   _____

2. Here are some Olympic champions' times for the 400 metres between 1896 and 1968 (not all the Olympic Games are shown):

1896 T.E. Burke (USA) 54.2 sec   1900 M.W. Long (USA) 49.4 sec
1904 H.L. Hillman (USA) 49.6 sec   1920 B.G.D. Rudd (S. Africa) 43.6 sec
1964 M.D. Larrabee (USA) 45.1 sec   1968 L. Evans (USA) 43.8 sec

Did the athletes always get faster? If not, say when they didn't. _____

What is the difference between the times taken in 1896 and 1968? _____

3. Put these mountain heights in order with the highest first:

Rakaposhi   7780 metres   _____

Bonete   6870 metres   _____

K2   8610 metres   _____

Logan   6050 metres   _____

Ben Nevis   1340 metres   _____

Everest   8850 metres   _____

How accurate are the heights, do you think? _____

4. Round each of these decimals to the nearest tenth and to the nearest whole number. a) 16.72   b) 136.48   c) 0.134   d) 41.95

a) _____   b) _____   c) _____   d) _____

a) _____   b) _____   c) _____   d) _____

UNITS 2-3

ORGANISATION (10 LESSONS)

LEARNING OUTCOMES	ORAL AND MENTAL STARTER	MAIN TEACHING ACTIVITY	PLENARY
LESSON 1 +2 • Understand and use the relationships between the four operations, and the principles (not the names) of the arithmetic laws. Use brackets. • Use related facts and doubling or halving. • Use factors. • Use closely related facts. • Partition. • Develop calculator skills and use a calculator effectively.	AND THE ANSWER IS: Given an answer, finding divisions that satisfy it.	EXPLORING MULTIPLICATION: Using informal methods of longer multiplication.	Check results and explore methods.
LESSON 3 +4 • **Extend written methods to long multiplication of a 3-digit by a 2-digit integer.**	BONDS AGAIN: Giving the number bonds for three numbers involving multiplication and division and introducing decimals.	LONG MULTIPLICATION: Multiplying 3-digit numbers by 2-digit numbers.	Give answers and discuss contexts.
LESSON 5 +6 • **Extend written methods to** division of HTU by TU.	DOUBLE DECIMALS: Doubling decimal numbers with 1 and 2 decimal places.	LONG DIVISION: Leading to a standard written method.	Give answers discuss remainders and contexts.
LESSON 7 • **Extend written methods to: long multiplication of a 3digit by a 2-digit integer;** division of HTU by TU. • Develop calculator skills and use a calculator effectively.	AS NEAR AS YOU CAN: Using digits and operations to reach a target number.	PROBLEMS: Solving problems involving long multiplication and division.	Discuss each question and strategies used.
LESSON 8 +9 • Consolidate all strategies from previous year. • Develop calculator skills and use a calculator effectively. • Choose and use appropriate number operations to solve problems, and appropriate ways of calculating. • Explain methods and reasoning. • Solve mathematical problems or puzzles. • Make and investigate a general statement about familiar numbers or shapes by finding examples that satisfy it.	MULTIPLES OF 10, ADDITION: Adding quickly two multiples of 10, such as 360 + 250.	CONSECUTIVE NUMBERS: Investigating consecutive numbers.	Display and discuss findings.
LESSON 10 • Understand and use the relationships between the four operations. • Use the relationship between multiplication and division. • Use known number facts and place value to consolidate mental multiplication and division. • Develop calculator skills and use calculator effectively	MULTIPLES OF 10, DIFFERENCE: Finding quickly the difference between two multiples of 10.	TAKE FOUR: a game involving estimating the result of dividing a 3-digit number by a 2-digit number.	Discuss strategies used.

ORAL AND MENTAL SKILLS Derive quickly division facts corresponding to tables up to 10 × 10.
Use the relationship between multiplication and division. **Derive quickly** doubles of two-digit numbers.
Use known number facts and place value to consolidate mental addition/subtraction.

Lessons 1, 3, 5, 8 and 10 are shown in full. In each case, Lessons 2, 4, 6 and 9 are extensions of their preceding lesson. Lesson 7 is an extension of what has already been taught and is given in outline.

LESSON 1 + 2

RESOURCES

Stop clock; suitable textbook examples; pencils and paper; calculators.

PREPARATION

Select suitable textbook pages (or invent your own multiplications) involving a 2-digit number being multiplied by another 2-digit number. Write these on the board. For Lesson 2, select examples that involve multiplying by 50 or 100 followed by addition or subtraction, and include 3-digit × 2-digit examples, eg 131 × 18.

LEARNING OUTCOMES

ORAL AND MENTAL STARTER
- **Derive quickly division facts corresponding to tables up to 10 × 10.**

MAIN TEACHING ACTIVITY
- Understand and use the relationships between the four operations, and the principles (not the names) of the arithmetic laws. Use brackets.
- Use related facts and doubling or halving.
- Use factors.
- Use closely related facts.
- Partition.
- Develop calculator skills and use a calculator effectively.

VOCABULARY
Add, subtract, multiply, total, factor.

ORAL AND MENTAL STARTER

AND THE ANSWER IS: Set the stop clock to 10 seconds. Give the children the answer to a division fact, say 9. They must then give as many different facts that have this answer in the time available, eg 63 ÷ 7; 36 ÷ 4 etc.

MAIN TEACHING ACTIVITY

EXPLORING MULTIPLICATION: Write 36 × 18 on the board and ask for estimates: 'About 650, because 36 multiplied by 20 is 720'. Ask if they can think of ways of making the multiplication more manageable, remembering the work that they have done on factors, using brackets and multiplying by 10, 20 etc. Let them work with a partner and allow them several minutes to complete the task before asking them to explain the ways that they have found. Record the various ways given, which may include: (36 × 10) + (36 × 8); (36 × 20) – (36 × 2); (72 × 9) = (72 × 10) – 72; (12 × 54) = (10 × 54) + (2 × 54); (4 × 9) × (2 × 9) = (4 × 2) × (9 × 9) = 8 × 81.

Now ask the class to check each method given to make sure that it is correct. They may use jottings or the memory facility on their calculator. The children then continue working in pairs to find as many different ways to solve each multiplication on the board as they can.

DIFFERENTIATION

More able: Go on to invent multiplications for their partner to solve.
Less able: Work as a group with your help to find various ways before going on to check each method with a partner.

PLENARY

Check the results and discuss various methods and other ways of checking results.

LESSON 2

Use the **Oral and mental starter** from Lesson 1. For the **Main teaching activity,** extend Lesson 1, but use 2-digit × 2-digit examples such as 23 × 51, 17 × 49, 26 × 99 and 3-digit × 2-digit examples such as 131 × 18, 37 × 102, to involve multiplying by 50 or 100 followed by addition or subtraction. The children should not use the calculator when checking their methods.

RESOURCES

Suitable textbook examples or invent your own; pencils and paper.

PREPARATION

Prepare examples of long multiplication of a 3-digit by a 2-digit whole number, eg 219 × 17, 158 × 36, 365 × 24. For the more able, prepare examples of multiplication of decimals with up to two decimal places multiplied by two-digit numbers.

LEARNING OUTCOMES

ORAL AND MENTAL STARTER
● Use the relationship between multiplication and division.

MAIN TEACHING ACTIVITY
● **Extend written methods to long multiplication of a 3-digit by a 2-digit integer.**

VOCABULARY
Multiply, multiplied by.

ORAL AND MENTAL STARTER

BONDS AGAIN: Give the children three numbers and they must tell you the four bonds linking these numbers, using multiplication and division. This time use whole numbers, and include some decimal fractions, eg 0.75, 3 and 4 give 0.75 × 4 = 3; 4 × 0.75 = 3; 3 ÷ 4 = 0.75; 3 ÷ 0.75 = 4. 0.2, 1 and 5 give 0.2 × 5 = 1; 5 × 0.2 = 1; 1 ÷ 5 = 0.2; 1 ÷ 5 = 0.2. The children may need to quickly jot down the three numbers each time.

MAIN TEACHING ACTIVITY

LONG MULTIPLICATION: Write 326 × 28 on the board and ask for estimates; 'About 920, because 300 × 30 is 900 and it is more than that'. Now ask for suggestions of how to tackle the multiplication. These may include; 'We could multiply the 326 by 20 and write down the answer, then multiply 326 by 8, write down the answer then add the two answers together'; 'We could multiply 326 by 30 and write down the answer, then multiply 326 by 2, write down the answer and subtract this from the first answer'. Explain that *Although these ideas are fine, we really need to use only one operation for a written method.* Write the multiplication vertically and invite the class to help. *Let's multiply by 20 first. How can we do that? It's like multiply by 2 followed by multiply by 10, so 326 multiplied by 20 is 652 multiplied by 10, or 6520.* Record this as shown, then ask *What about 326 × 8?* Give the children time to work out the result (2608) – they may need to jot it down. Record this result and ask the class for the total, 9128. Set the class to work on the other examples.

326	
× 28	
6520	326 × 20
2608	326 × 8
9128	

DIFFERENTIATION

More able: Go on to consider 4-digit numbers multiplied by 2- or even 3-digit numbers.
Less able: Work with this group and go through the examples together.

PLENARY

Give answers to the calculations. Discuss when a 3-digit number may be multiplied by a 2-digit number. For example, *A survey of our local car park found that an average of 326 parking tickets a day were issued over 28 days. How many were issued altogether?*

LESSON 4

Repeat the **Oral and mental starter** and **Main teaching activity** from Lesson 3 by giving more practise of long multiplication using whole numbers. Give the more able children examples involving decimals with up to two decimal places multiplied by a whole number, 4.23 × 18 for example. Remind the children to estimate first and also make sure that the decimal points line up under each other. The calculations should be set out as shown (right).

```
      4.23
    ×  18
   ────────
     42.30    4.23 × 10
     33.84    4.23 ×  8
   ────────
     76.14
```

LESSON 5 + 6

RESOURCES

Long multiplication and division questions; pencils and paper.

PREPARATION

Prepare a selection of long multiplication and division questions, with and without remainders, eg 522 ÷ 18, 828 ÷ 36, 775 ÷ 25, 977 ÷ 36 etc.

LEARNING OUTCOMES

ORAL AND MENTAL STARTER
● **Derive quickly** doubles of 2-digit numbers.

MAIN TEACHING ACTIVITY
● **Extend written methods to** division of HTU by TU.

VOCABULARY

Divide, divided by, divisor, remainder.

ORAL AND MENTAL STARTER

DOUBLE DECIMALS: Use the activity from Lesson 5, Unit 2 of Term 2.

MAIN TEACHING ACTIVITY

LONG DIVISION: Write 918 ÷ 27 on the board and ask for estimates; 'Just less than 36, because there are four 25s in 100, so there are 36 in 900 and 27 is a bit more than 25'; 'More than 30, because 30 multiplied by 30 is 900'. Ask the class to help you do the calculation. *Let's try it by using multiples of the divisor. What can you multiply 27 by?* Record their statements, eg 918 ÷ 27:

27 multiplied by 10 is 270, that leaves 648	918 ÷ 27
	− 270
27 multiplied by 10 is 270, that leaves 378	648
	− 270
27 multiplied by 10 is 270, that leaves 108	378
	− 270
27 multiplied by 4 is 108	108
	− 108
Answer: 34	0

```
                468 ÷ 18
    20 × 18    −360
               ─────
                 108
     6 × 18    −108
               ─────
                   0
               ─────
            Answer: 26
```

Suggest that the calculation could have been shortened by multiplying 27 by 30. Ask how they could do this: 'It's 27 multiplied by 3, which is 81, then multiplied by 10, 810'. Say, *Let's try another example and put this sort of information into a different form.* Write 468 ÷ 18 on the board and ask for estimates. Now ask for volunteers to begin the calculation. *There are two 18s in 46 making 36, so there are twenty 18s in 468, making 360.* Record this and ask *How many are left?* (108). Record this and ask, *How many 18s in 108? 6 multiplied by 18 is 108.* Complete the recording as shown (left). Let the children work in pairs on your prepared examples.

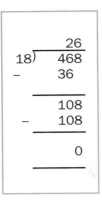

$$
\begin{array}{r}
26 \\
18{\overline{\smash{\big)}\,468}} \\
-36 \\
\hline
108 \\
-108 \\
\hline
0
\end{array}
$$

DIFFERENTIATION

More able: Go on to use the shortened form of long division, as shown on the left.

Less able: These children may need to spend more time on informal written methods and work on simpler examples, such as 182 ÷ 13, 276 ÷ 12 etc.

PLENARY

Give out the answers to the examples set. Discuss the 'remainder' questions, how the children dealt with them and possible 'real life' contexts for these questions.

LESSON 6

Repeat the **Oral and mental starter** from Lesson 5. For the **Main teaching activity,** give the class further practise with both long multiplication and long division examples. Work with less able children, and provide more difficult questions for more able children. In the **Plenary**, try to work out some real life contexts for the questions.

RESOURCES	Copies of photocopiable page 175 ('Multiplication and division problems'); calculators; pencils and paper.
PREPARATION	Photocopy page 175 ('Multiplication and division problems'), one per child.
LEARNING OUTCOMES	**ORAL AND MENTAL STARTER** ● Use known number facts and place value to consolidate mental addition/subtraction. **MAIN TEACHING ACTIVITY** ● **Extend written methods to: long multiplication of a 3-digit by a 2-digit integer;** division of HTU by TU. ● Develop calculator skills and use a calculator effectively.
ORAL AND MENTAL STARTER	AS NEAR AS YOU CAN GET: Repeat the activity from Lesson 3, Unit 8 of Term 1.
MAIN TEACHING ACTIVITY	PROBLEMS: Give out 'Multiplication and division problems'. Read through question 1, and ask the class for estimates and justification of these. They should then work through the problems individually. When they have completed the first four questions they may use a calculator to check these before moving on to questions 5 and 6.
DIFFERENTIATION	More able: Go on to make up some questions of their own. Less able: Let them work in pairs and spend time with them to ensure that they understand the questions.
PLENARY	Discuss each question and the strategies used.

LESSON 8 +9

RESOURCES

A large sheet of card; felt-tipped pens; Multilink cubes or Centicubes; cm squared graph paper; calculators; rulers; pencils and paper.

PREPARATION

Write the following on the large sheet of card, and display it for all to see:

> What's the difference?
> Write down any two consecutive numbers. Now square each one and find the difference between their squares.
> Try other consecutive pairs of numbers in the same way.
> Write down what you found out.
> Using the same rules try numbers that have an initial difference of 2, 3 etc.
> Now try using Multilink cubes to make two squares, one having an edge length 3 and the other an edge length 4. Try other squares with edge lengths differing by 1. What do you notice?
> Can you generalise from your findings?

LEARNING OUTCOMES

ORAL AND MENTAL STARTER

● Use known number facts and place value to consolidate mental addition/subtraction.

MAIN TEACHING ACTIVITY

● Consolidate all strategies from previous year.
● Develop calculator skills and use a calculator effectively.
● Choose and use appropriate number operations to solve problems, and appropriate ways of calculating.
● **Explain methods and reasoning.**
● Solve mathematical problems or puzzles.
● Make and investigate a general statement about familiar numbers or shapes by finding examples that satisfy it.

VOCABULARY

Consecutive, predict, relationship, square number.

ORAL AND MENTAL STARTER

MULTIPLES OF 10, ADDITION: Repeat the activity from Lesson 1, Unit 5 of Term 2.

MAIN TEACHING ACTIVITY

CONSECUTIVE NUMBERS: Explain to the children that they are going to explore consecutive numbers. Ask the class what consecutive means: 'Next to each other like 3, 4 and 5'. Show them the prepared card and read it through, making sure that the children understand what they have to do. Tell them that they should try many different numbers, including decimals, and use their calculators to help them. They may work in pairs to produce a report. This should say a) what they were asked to do, b) how they tackled the investigation, c) any problems they encountered, d) their results and e) their conclusions.

DIFFERENTIATION

More able: May consider cubic numbers and go on to show their ideas spatially or explore what happens with sets of three consecutive numbers when you square the middle number and multiply the two outside numbers.

Less able: May need your help to get started and with their written presentation.

PLENARY

Display the reports and discuss findings. These may include: 'When we used numbers with a difference of 1 and squared them, their difference was the sum of the original numbers'; 'If the original numbers differed by 2, the difference of their squares was twice the sum of the original numbers'; 'We used decimals like 2.1 and 3.1. When squared, their difference was 5.2, the sum of 2.1 and 3.1, so they work!'

RESOURCES
White card; coloured card; calculators; pencils.

PREPARATION
Prepare small squares of white and coloured card, approximately 3cm × 3cm, sufficient for 8 white and 4 coloured squares per pair.

LEARNING OUTCOMES
ORAL AND MENTAL STARTER
● Use known number facts and place value to consolidate mental addition/subtraction.

MAIN TEACHING ACTIVITY
● Understand and use the relationships between the four operations.
● Use the relationship between multiplication and division.
● Use known number facts and place value to consolidate mental multiplication and division.
● Develop calculator skills and use a calculator effectively.

VOCABULARY

Divide, divided by, multiplied by, difference.

ORAL AND MENTAL STARTER
MULTIPLES OF 10, DIFFERENCE: Repeat from Lesson 4, Unit 5 of Term 2.

MAIN TEACHING ACTIVITY
TAKE FOUR: Tell the children that they are going to play a game with their partner involving estimating the result of dividing a large number by a 2-digit number. Give out 8 white and 4 coloured cards to each pair. One of the pair writes any eight 2-digit numbers, one on each of the white cards while the other player writes four 3-digit multiples of 10, up to 300, one on each of the coloured cards. They place their cards face down on the table and take turns to choose one white and one coloured card. For each set of cards turned over, they must give an estimate of the number of times the 2-digit number will divide into the 3-digit number (whole numbers only). If their partner feels that they can better the estimate then he or she must 'challenge', and gives their estimate. They then use multiplication to check the actual result. The player with the nearest answer takes the white card, and the coloured card is placed face down again on the table. For example, if a player selects 27 and 230, and gives an answer of 'about 8', his/her partner might decide to say 'I think it's 9'. They must then use calculators to check both estimations. 27 × 8 = 216, and 27 × 9 = 243. 216 is 14 less, while 243 is 13 over, so 243 is nearest and this player would win the white card. The winner is the first player to collect four white cards. Play a game to demonstrate before the pairs play on their own.

DIFFERENTIATION
More able: Go on to use any 3-digit numbers for the coloured cards.
Less able: Give them single digit numbers on the white cards, and numbers between 100 and 200 for the coloured cards.

PLENARY
Discuss the strategies used.

Multiplication and division problems

1. Bransco United football team is raising money for a local charity. The team pledges 2p for each spectator going through the gates of a home match during the season. There are 14 home matches and the capacity of the ground is 3800. What is the maximum amount they can raise?

2. Parking for the pop concert is a problem. The organiser estimates that he must have space for 1400 cars parked in rows of 32. How many rows will be needed to accommodate all the cars?

3. 26 × [   ] − 7 = 3191

4. Write a number in each circle equal to the product of the numbers in the squares on either side of it

5. Use a calculator to work out the following:

a) (37 × 69) + [   ] = 2600

b) 85 × (92 − 34) = [   ]

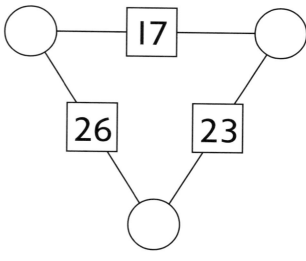

6. Write a number story about: a) 345 × 27 b) 2785 ÷ 16

a)

b)

UNITS 4–5

ORGANISATION (10 LESSONS)

LEARNING OUTCOMES	ORAL AND MENTAL STARTER	MAIN TEACHING ACTIVITY	PLENARY
LESSON 1 ● Change a fraction to the equivalent mixed number and vice-versa. ● Recognise relationships between fractions. ● **Reduce a fraction to its simplest form by cancelling common factors** in the numerator and denominator. ● Order fractions by converting them to fractions with a common denominator.	MIXED PARTS: Giving the number of fractional parts in a mixed number.	CHANGING AND ORDERING: Changing improper fractions to mixed numbers and vice-versa. Find the difference between improper fractions and whole numbers. Reducing fractions to their simplest form. Recognising relationships between fractions.	Mark questions and ask for the meaning of the mathematical words used in the lesson.
LESSON 2 ● Order fractions by converting them to fractions with a common denominator, and position them on a number line. ● Convert a fraction to a decimal using division. ● Recognise the equivalence between the decimal and fraction forms of one half, one quarter... ● Check with an equivalent calculation. ● Develop calculator skills and use a calculator effectively.	DOUBLING, HALVING: Doubling and halving multiples of 10 to 1000.	FRACTION ORDERS: Finding the order of fractions by changing them to fractions with a common denominator. Estimating accurately the position of fractions on a number line. Converting the fractions to decimals and recording them on a line.	Discuss the work and check that they recognise the equivalence between decimal and common fraction forms of simple fractions.
LESSON 3 ● **Solve simple problems involving ratio and proportion.** ● Express a quotient as a fraction.	DOUBLING, HALVING: Doubling and halving multiples of 100 to 10 000.	RATIO, PROPORTION: Solving problems involving ratio and proportion.	Mark the work and clarify any problems that have arisen.
LESSON 4 +5 ● **Understand percentage as the number of parts in every 100.** ● **Find simple percentages of small whole number quantities.** ● **Solve simple problems involving proportion.** ● Develop calculator skills and use a calculator effectively.	FIVE SECOND PERCENTAGES: Answering percentage questions within a five second time limit for each one.	PERCENT: Linking proportion, common factors, decimals and percentages. Solving percentage problems. Introducing the percentage key on the calculator and using it.	Mark the work and create number stories for proportions and percentages.
LESSON 6 ● **Solve simple problems involving proportion.** ● **Understand percentage as the number of parts in every 100.** Express simple fractions as percentages. ● **Solve a problem by representing, extracting and interpreting data in tables, graphs and charts.** ● Develop calculator skills and use a calculator effectively. ● **Solve simple problems involving proportion.**	TEN SECONDS: Answering addition and subtraction questions within a ten second time limit for each one.	SWIM SURVEY: Finding percentages and proportions from data in a survey. Representing them on a 'rectangular graph'.	Discussing the 'rectangular graph'.

	LEARNING OUTCOMES	ORAL AND MENTAL STARTER	MAIN TEACHING ACTIVITY	PLENARY
LESSON 7 +8	• **Understand percentage as the number of parts in every 100.** Express simple fractions as percentages. • **Solve a problem by** representing, **extracting and interpreting data in tables, graphs and charts.** • Consolidate rounding an integer to the nearest 100. • **Use a protractor to measure and** draw **angles to the nearest degree.** • Develop calculator skills and use a calculator effectively.	TEN SECONDS: Answering addition and subtraction questions within a ten second time limit for each one.	PIE CHARTS: Linking rectangular graphs to the introduction of pie charts. Representing, extracting and interpreting data using pie charts. Applying percentages to numbers.	Discuss the pie charts produced.
LESSON 9 +10	• Recognise and extend number sequences and make general statements. • Convert a fraction to a decimal using division. • **Order a mixed set of numbers.** • Give a decimal fraction lying between two others. • Develop calculator skills and use a calculator effectively.	TEN SECONDS: Answering addition and subtraction questions within a ten second time limit for each one.	FIBONACCI: Recognising and extending the Fibonacci sequence. Developing Fibonacci fractions and their decimal equivalents using a calculator. Drawing conclusions.	Explore the decimals generated and position them on a number line. Discuss findings.

ORAL AND MENTAL SKILLS Recognise relationships between fractions. Use known number facts and place value to consolidate mental addition, subtraction, multiplication and division. **Derive quickly** doubles of multiples of 10 to 1000 and doubles of multiples of 100 to 10 000 and their corresponding halves. **Understand percentage as the number of parts in every 100. Find simple percentages of small whole number quantities. Solve simple problems involving proportion. Identify and use appropriate operations (including combinations of operations) to solve word problems involving numbers and quantities** based on 'real life', money or measures (including time).

In Units 4 and 5, Lessons 1, 3, 4, 6, 7 and 9 are shown in full and Lessons 5, 8 and 10 extend the work of the preceding lesson so are shown after it. Lesson 2 is an extension of what has already been taught and is given in outline.

RESOURCES

Copies of photocopiable page 185 ('Changing and ordering'); pencils.

PREPARATION

Photocopy page 185 ('Changing and ordering'), one per child.

LEARNING OUTCOMES

ORAL AND MENTAL STARTER
• Recognise relationships between fractions.

MAIN TEACHING ACTIVITY
• Change a fraction to the equivalent mixed number and vice-versa.
• Recognise relationships between fractions.
• **Reduce a fraction to its simplest form by cancelling common factors**
• Order fractions by converting them to fractions with a common denominator.

ORAL AND MENTAL STARTER

MIXED PARTS: Quick-fire questions asking how many fractional parts in a mixed number, eg *How many sevenths in* $2\frac{1}{7}$*?* (15) or for the more able, *How many sixteenths in* $3\frac{5}{16}$*?* (53).

VOCABULARY

Proper/ improper fraction, mixed number, numerator, denominator, equivalent, reduced to, cancel, strategy.

MAIN TEACHING ACTIVITY

CHANGING AND ORDERING: Ask the children to change some improper fractions to mixed numbers, eg $^{17}/_8$ ($2^1/_8$), $^{29}/_5$ ($5^4/_5$). Ask for the differences between some improper fractions and whole numbers, say between $^{14}/_3$ and 5 ($^1/_3$). *What strategy did you use?* 'I changed the $^{14}/_3$ to $4^2/_3$, and then went up to 5. Try changing some mixed numbers to improper fractions.

Then try reducing fractions to their simplest form by cancelling common factors in the numerator and denominator. The children work individually to complete the 'Changing and ordering' worksheet. Calculators should not be used.

ANSWERS:

1a) $1^3/_4$; b) $5^3/_{10}$; c) $4^3/_8$; d) 7; 2a) $^9/_2$; b) $^{27}/_4$; c) $^{21}/_{16}$; d) $^{35}/_2$; 3a) $^3/_5$; b) $^5/_2$ ($2^1/_2$); c) $^5/_6$; d) $^{19}/_{16}$ ($1^3/_{16}$); 4a) $^3/_4$; b) $^1/_3$; c) $1^4/_5$; d) $4^3/_4$; 5a) $^3/_{100}$; b) $^1/_8$.

DIFFERENTIATION

More able: Could write some further fraction examples for their friends to try.
Less able: May need some help with the vocabulary used on the sheet and, for some questions, the strategies that they should use.

PLENARY

Mark the work with the children and ask for the meanings of some of the words used. For example, *In the fraction $^7/_6$, the numerator is larger than the denominator and can be written as a mixed number: $1^1/_6$.*

RESOURCES	Prepared number line; water-based felt-tipped pen; calculators; pencils; A4 sheets of paper; rulers.
PREPARATION	Make the number line by drawing a line, say 64cm long, on a large sheet of card. Place a '0' at one end and '1' at the other end then cover this with transparent adhesive plastic: Write the following set of fractions on the board: $^1/_2$, $^3/_{16}$, $^1/_4$, $^7/_8$, $^3/_4$. \[0 ——— 1\]
LEARNING OUTCOMES	**ORAL AND MENTAL STARTER** ● Use known number facts and place value to consolidate mental multiplication. ● **Derive quickly** doubles of multiples of 10 to 1000 and the corresponding halves. **MAIN TEACHING ACTIVITY** ● Order fractions by converting them to fractions with a common denominator, and position them on a number line. ● Convert a fraction to a decimal using division. ● Recognise the equivalence between the decimal and fraction forms of one half, one quarter. ● Check with an equivalent calculation. ● Develop calculator skills and use a calculator effectively.
ORAL AND MENTAL STARTER	DOUBLING, HALVING: Ask a mixture of doubling and halving questions for multiples of 10 to, say 1000, eg double 830, half 740.
MAIN TEACHING ACTIVITY	FRACTION ORDERS: Point to the set of fractions on the board. *How could we find their order?* 'We could change them to fractions with a common denominator.' *In this case it would give the fractions* $^8/_{16}$, $^3/_{16}$, $^4/_{16}$, $^{14}/_{16}$, $^{12}/_{16}$, *which could then be placed in order.* Show the number line and ask two children to estimate and mark the position of the fractions $^1/_2$, $^3/_{16}$, $^1/_4$, $^7/_8$, $^3/_4$ on it using a water-based felt-tipped pen. Adjust the positions of the fractions by discussion with the children, perhaps involving

	measurements, eg $^1/_2$ at 32 cm, $^3/_4$ at 48 cm along the line. Now let the children convert the fractions to decimals as a strategy for ordering them, and write these on a line. Give out the A4 paper and ask them to draw a line 20cm long and show the fractions $^4/_5$, $^3/_{10}$, $^7/_{20}$, $^7/_{10}$, $^2/_5$ on the line. Let them calculate the decimal equivalents, either mentally or by using a calculator, and then record these on the line.
	0 $\dfrac{3}{16}$ $\dfrac{1}{4}$ $\dfrac{1}{2}$ $\dfrac{3}{4}$ $\dfrac{7}{8}$ 1 0.1875 0.25 0.5 0.75 0.875
DIFFERENTIATION	More able: Go on to calculate the addition or subtraction of some common fractions and check by adding or subtracting their equivalent decimals and comparing the results, eg $^1/_4 + ^3/_{16} = ^4/_{16} + ^3/_{16} = ^7/_{16}$; 0.25 + 0.1875 = 0.4375, so $^7/_{16}$ is equivalent to 0.4375. Less able: If they finish, let them insert other common fractions on their lines along with their decimal equivalents.
PLENARY	Discuss the work, checking that the children recognise the equivalences between the decimal and common fraction forms of simple fractions such as one half, three-quarters, one-eighth, seven-hundredths etc.

RESOURCES
Prepared ratio and proportion examples; pencils and paper.

PREPARATION
Produce the ratio and proportion questions and write them on the board. Here are some ideas:
1. (see diagram, right, which shows a single tile measuring 3cm by 3cm)

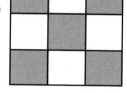

a) What is the ratio of black to white squares in a tile? (5 to 4)
b) What proportion of white squares are there in a tile? (4 in 9, $^4/_9$)
c) How many i) black and ii) white squares would there be if the tiles were used to cover an area measuring 12cm by 12cm? (80 black, 64 white)
2. To make Acifed plant fertiliser, you should mix 150ml of Acifed with every 4.5l of water.
a) What is the ratio of Acifed to water? (1 to 30)
b) How many ml of Acifed for 6l of water? (200ml)
3. There are 7 milk chocolates to every 4 dark in a box of 33 chocolates. How many milk and dark chocolates are in the box? (21 milk, 12 dark)

LEARNING OUTCOMES
ORAL AND MENTAL STARTER
- Use known number facts and place value to consolidate mental multiplication.
- **Derive quickly** doubles of multiples of 100 to 10 000 and their corresponding halves.

MAIN TEACHING ACTIVITY
- **Solve simple problems involving ratio and proportion.**
- Express a quotient as a fraction.

VOCABULARY
Ratio – to every, proportion – in every.

ORAL AND MENTAL STARTER
DOUBLING HALVING: Repeat the activity from Lesson 2, but this time doubling and halving multiples of 100 to 10 000, eg double 4300, halve 9600.

MAIN TEACHING ACTIVITY
RATIO, PROPORTION: Bring seven children to the front, four boys and three girls. Make a line of boy, girl, boy, girl, boy, girl, boy. *What is the ratio of boys to girls?* (4 to 3) *What is the proportion of girls to children?* (3 in 7) *If we had three more lines of boys and girls arranged like this how many boys and girls would there be?* (16 boys and 12 girls) *If there were nine girls, how many boys would there be?* (12) Try some other arrangements of boys

and girls in lines, say girl, boy, girl, girl, boy, girl, girl, boy, girl. Use similar questions to those used before. Remind the children that ratio compares part to part and proportion compares a part to a whole. If, for example, there are eight boys to every one girl in the school football club, the ratio is 8 to 1, while the proportion of girls to the total number of children is 1 to 9 ($^1/_9$); ie in every nine children there is one girl. The children then work individually on the examples on the board.

DIFFERENTIATION

More able: Try making up a number story that could be expressed by the proportion one in every five. For example, *Conkers were shared between Fatima and Serena in the ratio 1 to 4. So Fatima gets one in every five, or one-fifth of the conkers.*
Less able: Discuss the examples with this group.

PLENARY

Mark the children's work with them, clarifying any problems that have arisen.

RESOURCES

Stop clock; prepared proportion and percentage questions; calculators; pencils and paper.

PREPARATION

Prepare questions at two levels of ability, either taken from a textbook or provided by you (the examples on page 33 of 'Supplement of examples: Years 4, 5 and 6' in the NNS *Framework for teaching mathematics* are a helpful guide). Indicate examples that will need a calculator and put these towards the end. Photocopy the examples, enough for one for each child in that group.

LEARNING OUTCOMES

ORAL AND MENTAL STARTER
- **Understand percentage as the number of parts in every 100.**
- **Find simple percentages of small whole number quantities.**
- **Solve simple problems involving proportion.**

MAIN TEACHING ACTIVITY
- **Understand percentage as the number of parts in every 100.**
- **Find simple percentages of small whole number quantities.**
- **Solve simple problems involving proportion.**
- Develop calculator skills and use a calculator effectively.

VOCABULARY
Proportion, in every, out of, percentage, per cent, %.

ORAL AND MENTAL STARTER

FIVE SECOND PERCENTAGES: Ask some 'five second' questions involving percentages, eg *25% of 140; 10 out of 50 is what percentage?* Repeat each question before allowing the children five seconds to answer.

MAIN TEACHING ACTIVITY

PERCENT: Remind the children of the meaning of percent (per = out of, cent = hundred), and of the % symbol (with its suggestion of a fraction and a 1 and two 0s, ie hundredths). Talk about materials used for clothing, such as 100% lambswool or 65% polyester, 35% cotton, giving a total of 100% altogether. Discuss the fact that this information tells us the proportions of what has been used to make the material, *65 parts out of every 100 are polyester (65%) and 35 parts out of every 100 are cotton (35%).* Bring out that 65 out of 100 could be thought of as 0.65 out of 1. *We can say or write 65 out of 100 or $^{65}/_{100}$, or 0.65 out of 1.* Try some others, eg 23 out of 100 = $^{23}/_{100}$ = ? = 23%, moving the position of the blank with each question. Split the class into two ability groups and set them to work on the examples, with which they will continue in the next lesson.

DIFFERENTIATION

More able: Encourage them to answer as many questions as time allows.
Less able: Discuss individual problems as they arise.

PLENARY

Mark the first few questions for each ability group. Ask individuals *Is it a reasonable answer. What makes you say so?*

LESSON 5

Repeat the previous lesson's **Oral and mental starter**. For the **Main teaching activity**, the children continue with the examples they worked on in Lesson 4. Say that this time they will need a calculator for some of the examples. Talk about calculating, say, 40% of £636 (636 × 40 ÷ 100 = £254.40; [6] [3] [6] [×] [4] [0] [÷] [1] [0] [0] [=] £254.40). Introduce the percentage key on the calculator and work it out again; [6] [3] [6] [×] [4] [0] [%] [=] £254.40. Try 15 out of 23: [1] [5] [÷] [2] [3] [=] 0.6521739 out of 1. 0.6521739 × 100 = 65.21739 out of 100, rounded to 65% to the nearest whole number. Use the [%] key; [1] [5] [÷] [2] [3] [%], which once again gives an answer of 65%, rounded to the nearest whole number. The children carry on working through the examples, only using a calculator where indicated. During the **Plenary**, finish the marking and ask for possible stories for a few of the examples that were not already in a particular context, eg 6 out of 9. I scored six penalties out of nine I took this season, which is 2 out of 3, $^2/_3$ or 66.66%.

LESSON 6

RESOURCES

Questions for 'Ten seconds' mental work; Class 6W's swimming survey; a rectangle 1m by 10cm; coloured chalks; pencils and paper.

PREPARATION

Prepare the 'Ten seconds' addition and subtraction questions. Write Class 6W's swimming survey and draw the rectangle on the board.

Class 6W (25 children) Swimming survey levels	Number of children	Proportion of class	Percentage of class
1. Not yet swimming	5		
2. Can swim 25m	7		
3. Can swim 100m	10		
4. Can swim 1000m	2		
5. Can swim more than 1000m	1		

LEARNING OUTCOMES

ORAL AND MENTAL STARTER

● Use known number facts and place value to consolidate mental addition/subtraction.
● **Identify and use appropriate operations (including combinations of operations) to solve word problems involving numbers and quantities** based on 'real life', money or measures (including time).

MAIN TEACHING ACTIVITY

● Solve simple problems involving proportion.
● **Understand percentage as the number of parts in every 100**. Express simple fractions as percentages.
● **Solve a problem by extracting and interpreting data in tables, graphs and charts.**
● Develop calculator skills and use a calculator effectively.

ORAL AND MENTAL STARTER

TEN SECONDS: This activity is the same as 'Five seconds' (Lesson 3, Unit 9 of Term 1), but this time give more difficult questions and allow ten seconds to answer each one.

VOCABULARY

Proportion; in every; out of; percentage;per cent; %; survey; data; table; rectangular graph.

Only use addition and subtraction examples, for example *A train that was due at 8.55 is 17 minutes late. What time did it arrive?; What's the difference between 2.4 and 3.9?*

MAIN TEACHING ACTIVITY

SWIM SURVEY: Tell the children that they are to calculate the proportion and percentage of children in class 6W reaching the swimming levels shown in the table on the board. Work on Level 1 with the class (proportion of class: 1 in 5; 20%), before asking all but the less able to work individually to complete the table and then check that their percentage total is 100. Work with the less able group on this task.

Bring the class back together and complete the table on the board. Next, point out the rectangle on the board and say that you are going to build up a 'rectangular graph' of the swimming survey data. *What is the percentage of children who are at Level 1?* (20%) Measure 20cm along the rectangle to form the first section. Write in both the number of children and the percentage of the class, as shown below. Let individuals come out to measure the other sections using a different colour chalk for each one.

Class 6W – Swimming survey				
5 (20%)	7 (28%)	10 (40%)	2 (8%)	1 (4%)
Levels 1	2	3	4	5
Graph to show the number and percentage of children within the levels they have reached				

Talk about the graph, and that it shows all the data (ie 100%), with the number of children in each swimming level represented both in the correct proportion and to scale (1% being represented by a rectangle of length 1cm along the metre side).

DIFFERENTIATION

More able: as they finish their table of results, they could ask each other questions. eg 'What proportion of the class can swim?' (4 out of 5, 4/5); 'What percentage can swim but cannot yet swim more than 1000m?' (76%).
Less able: Work as a group with you to build up the table of results.

PLENARY

Make sure that the children understand that 'rectangular graphs' are used when there is a need to display the proportions of parts to the whole of a set of data.

LESSON 7 + 8

RESOURCES

Questions for 'Ten seconds' mental work; protractors; calculators; felt-tipped pens of various colours; flip chart or board; pencils; plain and scrap paper.

PREPARATION

Prepare the 'Ten seconds' addition and subtraction questions. Prepare a graph and pie chart on the board. Prepare sets of data for the class to use to produce pie charts.

LEARNING OUTCOMES

ORAL AND MENTAL STARTER
● Use known number facts and place value to consolidate mental addition/subtraction.
● **Identify and use appropriate operations (including combinations of operations) to solve word problems involving numbers and quantities** based on 'real life', money or measures (including time).

MAIN TEACHING ACTIVITY
● **Solve simple problems involving proportion.**
● **Understand percentage as the number of parts in every 100.** Express simple fractions as percentages.

- **Solve problem** by representing, **extracting, interpreting data in tables, graphs and charts.**
- Consolidate rounding an integer to the nearest 100.
- **Use a protractor to measure** and draw **angles to the nearest degree.**
- Develop calculator skills and use a calculator effectively.

<table>
<tr><td>

VOCABULARY

Proportion, in every, out of, percentage, per cent, %, survey, data, table, rectangular graph, pie chart, sector

</td></tr>
</table>

ORAL AND MENTAL STARTER

TEN SECONDS: Repeat the activity from Lesson 6.

MAIN TEACHING ACTIVITY

PIE CHARTS: Explain to the class that you are going to refer to a recent survey on adults smoking (an important health issue that should be discussed by Year 6). On the flip chart or board, draw a large pie chart with $\frac{1}{2}$, $\frac{1}{3}$ and $\frac{1}{6}$ demarcated and a rectangle graph with the same fractions shaded. Discuss the rectangular graph and ask the children to check that the fractional proportions add to 1 by expressing them as sixths, ie $\frac{2}{6}$ smoke, $\frac{3}{6}$ have been smokers but have stopped, $\frac{1}{6}$ have never smoked. Discuss the pie chart. Verify that there are 360° of turn in the circle by showing them that two protractors fit the circle exactly. Talk about how the 'pie' has been cut into 'slices', called sectors. Discuss which sectors represent which smoking habits; *360° represents one (the whole population). Smokers make up $\frac{1}{3}$ of the population, $\frac{1}{3}$ of 360° is 120°; $\frac{1}{2}$ have been smokers but have stopped, which is 180°; $\frac{1}{6}$ have never smoked, which is the final 60°.* In pairs, the children then calculate the percentages for each sector of the pie chart, eg $\frac{1}{3} \times 100 = 33\frac{1}{3}\%$; $\frac{1}{2} = 50\%$, leaving $16\frac{2}{3}\%$ (100% subtract $83\frac{1}{3}\%$, or half of $33\frac{1}{3}\%$ since $\frac{1}{6}$ is half of $\frac{1}{3}$). Enter these on the pie chart, together with suitable labels.

DIFFERENTIATION

More able: could create more pie charts on the class computer.
Less able: work with this group making sure they understand what the questions mean.

PLENARY

Compare the rectangular graph and pie chart, emphasising that they both show the same information, one by dividing the rectangle into smaller rectangles for the proportions, the other by dividing the circle into sectors.

LESSON 8

Recap the **Oral and mental starter** from Lesson 7. For the **Main teaching activity**, start by recapping; discuss the fact that in a pie chart, 10% is represented by 36° and 1% by about 4°. Give the children a set of data. They then work in pairs to show this data in a pie chart, labelling it with relevant percentages. For **Differentiation**, give the ability groups different sets of data (such as cinema attendances or football team results) and ask them to draw pie charts using the data. A calculator may be needed for rounding to whole numbers. In the **Plenary**, discuss the pie charts produced.

LESSON 9 + 10

RESOURCES

Questions for 'Ten seconds' mental work; strip of paper marked with a line, one metre long; calculators; pencils and paper

PREPARATION

Prepare the 'Ten seconds' multiplication and division questions.

LEARNING OUTCOMES

ORAL AND MENTAL STARTER

- Use known number facts and place value to consolidate mental multiplication/division.
- **Identify and use appropriate operations (including combinations of operations) to solve word problems involving numbers and quantities** based on 'real life', money or measures (including time).

VOCABULARY

Sequence,
previous,
consecutive,
decimal place,
numerator,
denominator.

MAIN TEACHING ACTIVITY
- Recognise and extend number sequences and make general statements.
- Convert a fraction to a decimal using division.
- **Order a mixed set of numbers.**
- Give a decimal fraction lying between two others.
- Develop calculator skills and use a calculator effectively.

ORAL AND MENTAL STARTER

TEN SECONDS: Repeat the activity from Lesson 6, but this time using multiplication and division questions, eg *Double 3.75; A square has perimeter 220cm, how long is one side?*

MAIN TEACHING ACTIVITY

FIBONACCI: Say that Leonardo Fibonacci was an Italian mathematician who lived about 800 years ago. *A number sequence was named after him, the Fibonacci sequence, and it went like this: 0, 1, 1, 2, 3, 5, 8.* Write the sequence on the board, ask for the next number (13), and how the sequence is extended (each number is the sum of the previous two numbers).

Ask the children to extend the sequence, working each out in their head, giving 0, 1, 1, 2, 3, 5, 8, 13, 21, 34, 55, 89, 144... *What is the first number above 500?* Let them use their calculators to find the answer. *How many numbers are between 1000 and 2000?* (one, which is 1597) *Between 2000 and 3000?* (none). Make sure that they record the sequence, namely: 0, 1, 1, 2, 3, 5, 8, 13, 21, 34, 55, 89, 144, 233, 377, 610, 987, 1597, 2584, 4181... Next, go on to create some Fibonacci fractions by first writing pairs of consecutive numbers from the sequence; (1, 1), (2, 1), (3, 2), (5, 3), (8, 5), (13, 8) etc. Then, with their help, write the fractions. *The first number of each pair is the numerator and the second the denominator.* Ask them for the fractions: $\frac{1}{1}$, $\frac{2}{1}$, $\frac{3}{2}$, $\frac{5}{3}$, $\frac{8}{5}$, $\frac{13}{8}$... Ask the children to work in pairs to change each common fraction to a decimal and record the result, using a calculator when necessary: $\frac{1}{1} = 1$; $\frac{2}{1} = 2$; $\frac{3}{2} = 1.5$; $\frac{5}{3} = 1.666666$; $\frac{8}{5} = 1.6$; $\frac{13}{8} = 1.625$... Tell them to record all the decimal places that the calculator gives (no rounding) and to record the answers in a column, keeping the decimal digits lined up in their correct places.

DIFFERENTIATION

More able: Should complete more calculations and discuss with others what is happening.
Less able: May benefit by working with teacher guidance.

PLENARY

Start a discussion about the decimal results. They are all between 1 and 2. After the first three, they all seem to round to about 1.6. Display the metre long line and mark 1.5, 1.6666666, 1.6 etc, showing the numbers moving closer and closer to round about 1.6, as suggested in the discussion. Say that they will be investigating this further tomorrow.

LESSON 10

Repeat TEN SECONDS from Lesson 9 as the **Oral and mental starter**. For the **Main teaching activity**, recap and let the children continue where they left off, once again lining up the digits in their correct decimal place; $\frac{21}{13} = 1.6153846$; $\frac{34}{21} = 1.6190476$; $\frac{55}{34} = 1.617647$; $\frac{89}{55} = 1.6181818$; $\frac{144}{89} = 1.6179775$; $\frac{233}{144} = 1.6180555$; $\frac{377}{233} = 1.6180257$; $\frac{610}{377} = 1.6180371$. After about 10 minutes, call everyone together. *What can you say about the results?* 'The numbers are going to just above 1.618'. Let all but the less able children try starting with (2, 2) using the same rule. This gives the sequence 2, 2, 4, 6, 10, 16..., which is double the original sequence and all even numbers. The fractions $\frac{2}{2}$, $\frac{4}{2}$, $\frac{6}{4}$ give a decimal sequence the same as the original. They can then try starting with two different numbers, say (1, 5) using the same rule. This gives the sequence 1, 5, 6, 11, 17, 28, 45, 73, 118, 191, 309... and fractions $\frac{5}{1}$, $\frac{6}{5}$, $\frac{11}{6}$ etc. *What about the decimal sequence?* 'It seems to be going to 1.618'. Discuss the decimals with the less able. Ask them to look at the digits in each decimal place and say if the number is higher or lower each time, eg '1.6 and now 1.625. The 1.6s are the same so 1.625 must be higher.' For the **Plenary**, discuss the children's findings.

Changing and ordering

1. Change these improper fractions to mixed numbers:

a) $\frac{7}{4}$ [ ]

b) $\frac{53}{10}$ [ ]

c) $\frac{35}{8}$ [ ]

d) $\frac{77}{11}$ [ ]

2. Change these mixed numbers to improper fractions:

a) $4\frac{1}{2}$ [ ]

b) $6\frac{3}{4}$ [ ]

c) $1\frac{5}{16}$ [ ]

d) $17\frac{1}{2}$ [ ]

3. Find the difference between:

a) $\frac{17}{5}$ and 4

b) $\frac{5}{2}$ and 5

c) $\frac{43}{6}$ and 8

d) $\frac{29}{16}$ and 3

4. Reduce these fractions to their simplest form:

a) $\frac{6}{8}$ [ ]

b) $\frac{5}{15}$ [ ]

c) $1\frac{8}{10}$ [ ]

d) $4\frac{9}{12}$ [ ]

5. Finish these statements:

a) $\frac{3}{10}$ is ten times

b) _____ is one-quarter of $\frac{1}{2}$

UNIT 6

ORGANISATION (8 LESSONS)

LEARNING OUTCOMES	ORAL AND MENTAL STARTER	MAIN TEACHING ACTIVITY	PLENARY
LESSON 1 +2 ● Use the language associated with probability to discuss events including those with equally likely outcomes.	HALVING MULTIPLES: Giving quickly the result of halving a multiple of 10 or 100.	STEPPING STONES: Playing a probability game.	Discuss the game and analyse the probabilities involved.
LESSON 3 +4 ● **Solve a problem by** representing, **extracting and interpreting data in tables, graphs.** ● **Read and plot co-ordinates in all four quadrants.**	BEAT THE CLOCK, DIFFERENCE: Finding quickly the difference between two numbers.	GRAPHS FROM FACTS: Graphing addition facts.	Discuss and compare the line graphs produced.
LESSON 5 +6 ● **Solve a problem by** representing, **extracting and interpreting data in tables, graphs, charts** and diagrams. ● **Read and plot co-ordinates in all four quadrants.** ● Develop calculator skills and use a calculator effectively.	ADD ON: Adding a string of single digits to a 2- or 3-digit number.	GRAPHS FROM FACTS 2: Graphing multiplication facts.	Discuss the graphs and make general statements.
LESSON 7 +8 ● **Solve a problem by** representing, **extracting and interpreting data in tables, graphs, charts** and diagrams. ● **Read and plot co-ordinates in all four quadrants** ● Develop calculator skills and use a calculator effectively	SQUARE IT:Squaring multiples of 10 to 100.	WHAT'S THE EQUATION?: Exploring $y = x^2$ and other equations.	Discuss findings.

ORAL AND MENTAL SKILLS   Derive quickly: doubles of multiples of 10 to 100; doubles of multiples of 100 to 10 000 and the corresponding halves; squares of multiples of 10 to 100. Use known number facts and place value to consolidate mental addition/subtraction. Consolidate all strategies from previous year, including add several numbers.

In Unit 6, Lessons 1, 3 and 7 are shown in full. Lessons 2, 4 and 8 extend the work of the preceding lesson and are shown after it. Lessons 5 and 6 are an extension of what has already been taught and are given in outline.

RESOURCES

Sheets of card for 'stepping stones'; 7 counters, a different colour per group; cubic dice.

PREPARATION

Cut out sets of 12 'stepping stones', one set per group. Number each set from 1 to 12. Organise the children into mixed ability groups of about 4 or 5 and pair them up with another group. Arrange the 'stepping stones' as shown below, either on the floor or on a large table top, so that two groups will be playing one other.

1	2	3	4	5	6	7	8	9	10	11	12
12	11	10	9	8	7	6	5	4	3	2	1

LEARNING OUTCOMES
ORAL AND MENTAL STARTER
- **Derive quickly:** doubles of multiples of 10 to 100; doubles of multiples of 100 to 10 000 and the corresponding halves.

MAIN TEACHING ACTIVITY
- Use the language associated with probability to discuss events, including those with equally likely outcomes.

ORAL AND MENTAL STARTER
HALVING MULTIPLES: Give the children a multiple of 10 or 100, say 350 or later 4680. Ask them to halve it and quickly give you the answer (175, 2340).

MAIN TEACHING ACTIVITY

STEPPING STONES: Explain that the children are going to play a probability game against the other group. Give each group seven counters and a cubic dice. Explain that the 'stones' are along the banks of a river and the object of the game is to get all the counters across to the other side. They should place the counters as they wish on the 'stones', but no more than 3 counters on one stone. The groups then take turns to roll the two dice and add the numbers shown. If the total is the same as one of their 'stepping stones' with a counter or counters on then they can remove one of the counters and place it on the other side of the river. The winning group is the first to get all their counters across the river.

DIFFERENTIATION

More able: Begin an analysis of the number of ways of making each number.
Less able: Quietly ask them about the reasoning behind the placing of their counters.

PLENARY

Discuss the game, asking questions such as *Why did you decide to place your counters as you did? Where the results as you expected?* Answers may include: 'We decided to put three counters on 7 because there are lots of ways of making 7 with two dice'; 'We didn't put any on 1 because it's impossible'; 'We threw several 11s although there are not many ways of making it!'
  Spend some time analysing the number of ways of making each number and, with the help of the children, build a recording as shown above. Discuss the recording and compare this to what actually happened in each group. You may wish to finish by asking: *I wonder where you would have placed your counters if we had been finding the difference between the numbers on the dice?*

Number	Ways of making the number with 2 dice
1	impossible
2	1,1
3	1,2 2,1
4	1,3 2,2 3,1
5	1,4 2,3 3,2 4,1
6	1,5 2,4 3,3 4,2 5,1

LESSON 2

Repeat the **Oral and mental starter** and **Main teaching activity** from Lesson 1, but this time find the difference between the numbers on the dice when playing the game. Discuss as before in the **Plenary**.

RESOURCES

Number cards 1–99; stop clock; large sheet of cm squared graph paper; large sheet of card; transparent adhesive covering; smaller sheets of cm squared graph paper; water-based pen; wiper; rulers; pencils and paper.

PREPARATION

Prepare the number cards from photocopiable page 13 ('1 to 100 square'). Mount the graph paper on the card and cover it. Using the water-based pen, draw and label two axes as shown on page 188.

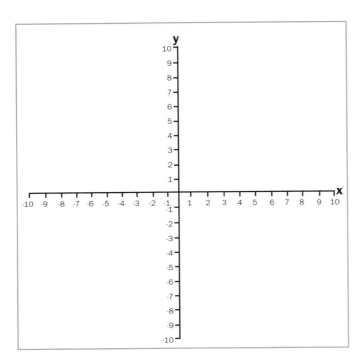

LEARNING OUTCOMES
ORAL AND MENTAL STARTER
● Use known number facts and place value to consolidate mental addition/subtraction.

MAIN TEACHING ACTIVITY
● **Solve a problem by** representing, **extracting and interpreting data in tables, graphs.**
● **Read and plot co-ordinates in all four quadrants.**

ORAL AND MENTAL STARTER

BEAT THE CLOCK, DIFFERENCE: Give out the number cards face down, one to each child. Set the stop clock to 8 minutes. Choose two children to hold up their cards for the class to see. Ask the class to quickly find the difference between the two numbers and tell you the result. See how many the children can do in the time allowed. Ask one child to record the result so that they can try to improve upon their score.

MAIN TEACHING ACTIVITY

GRAPHS FROM FACTS: Ask the children to tell you pairs of whole numbers whose sum is 8. Record these on the board: 0, 8; 1, 7; 2, 6; 3, 5; 4, 4; 5, 3; 6, 2; 7, 1; 8, 0. Tell them that they are going to show these number facts on a line graph. Explain that the axes are called x and y, pointing to each as you say this. *I'm going to plot these ordered pairs as co-ordinates on my graph, using the x axis for the first number and the y axis for the second. I must label the axes 'Values of x' and 'Values of y'.* Using the covered graph, mark one of the pairs with a point, then ask a child to mark another two.

Before proceeding further, ask the class if they can tell you anything about what the finished graph will look like. Answers may include; 'The points will be in a straight line'; 'The line will cut the x and y axis at 8'. Enter the remaining points. Now ask the children what would happen if they went beyond their number facts. *What about negative numbers? Can you find co-ordinates that total 8 when one is negative?* 'Yes (–4, 12), (17, –9)' etc. Plot the extra points given and ask for the children's comments; 'They are still in the same straight line'; 'We can get into the other quadrants'. Discuss whether the points should also be joined to form a line.

Remind the children of work done previously on decimals, that between, say 1 and 2, there are an infinite set of intermediate points such as 1.3, 1.35, 1.352 etc. *So there will be an infinite number of solutions that will satisfy x + y = 8, such as (1.2, 6.8) (7.43, 0.57) (–1.23, 9.23) etc.* Ask the children to give you some more. Tell them that these points are so close that they would make a solid line and therefore we can join the points. Now tell the class that you must give the line a name. Discuss what this could be. *As all the pairs of co-ordinates have a sum of 8, for example (2, 6), (–1, 9), (12, –4) we can call it x + y = 8.* Write this equation along the line. Set the children to work in pairs to draw the graph of x + y = 10.

DIFFERENTIATION

More able: Go on to consider other straight line graphs, such as x + y = 3, x + y = 16.
Less able: Work with this group, discussing in particular the co-ordinates using negative numbers. Ask for co-ordinates in the other quadrants. Discuss what they think the graph of x + y = 10 will look like before letting them continue.

PLENARY

Discuss the graphs produced and begin to make statements about the position of the lines. For example, the lines on each graph are all parallel to each other, the higher the total, the further from the origin, eg x + y = 3 is closer to the origin than x + y = 16, because 3 is less than 16.

VOCABULARY

Origin, maximum, minimum value, range, axes, label, co-ordinates, equation, graph.

LESSON 4

Repeat the **Oral and mental starter** and **Main teaching activity** from Lesson 3, working on different line graphs at a time. Discuss again in the **Plenary.**

RESOURCES	Graph paper; rulers; calculators; pencils.
PREPARATION	Jot down different lists of five single digit numbers, varying the numbers and their order each time.
LEARNING OUTCOMES	**ORAL AND MENTAL STARTER** ● Consolidate all strategies from previous year, including add several numbers. **MAIN TEACHING ACTIVITY** ● **Solve a problem by** representing, **extracting and interpreting data in tables, graphs, charts** and diagrams. ● **Read and plot co-ordinates in all four quadrants.** ● Develop calculator skills and use a calculator effectively.
ORAL AND MENTAL STARTER	ADD ON: Ask one child to tell the class any 2-digit, and later 3-digit number. Tell them to start from this number and add to it the list of single digit numbers that you are going to read out. At the end of the list, ask for the final result. Repeat for other lists and different starting numbers with different children, getting quicker each time.
MAIN TEACHING ACTIVITY	GRAPHS FROM FACTS 2: Ask the children to work individually to draw a line graph of the 3 times table, plotting (1, 3), (2, 6) etc up to (10, 30). Remember to label both the x and y axes. They should then extend the line into the third quadrant, recording some of the co-ordinates. They then write on the equation (name) of the line (y = 3x). On the same sheet they can then go on to draw y = x. For Lesson 6, the children go on to choose other multiplications to graph, eg y = 7x, y = 0.5x, y = –4x. This time they should not label the graph, but give it to a partner to work out the name.
DIFFERENTIATION	More able: Go on to consider the reflection of y = 3x about the y axis and work with their partner to find its equation (y = –3x). They may need a calculator to help with multiplying a negative number by a positive number. Less able: Begin the lesson using the covered graph to discuss with them what the graph will look like and mark some of the points before letting the children work individually
PLENARY	Discuss the graphs and lead the children towards general statements such as: 'They all go through the origin'; 'They are like the sun's rays'; 'The higher the number you multiply by the nearer the y axis'.

RESOURCES

Large sheet of cm squared graph paper; large sheet of card; transparent adhesive covering; smaller sheets of cm squared graph paper; water-based pen; wiper; ruler; calculators with a sign change key; pencils and paper.

PREPARATION

Mount the graph paper on card and cover it. Using the water-based pen, draw and label two axes as shown on page 188 – except that the numbers on the y axis must increase/ decrease in increments of 5.

Plot the following pairs of co-ordinates: (1, 1), (2, 4), (3, 9), (4, 16) and (5, 25). Draw this on a smaller piece of graph paper and photocopy for the class, one per pair.

VOCABULARY

Origin, maximum, minimum value, range, axes, label, co-ordinates, equation, graph.

LEARNING OUTCOMES

ORAL AND MENTAL STARTER
● **Derive quickly** squares of multiples of 10 to 100.

MAIN TEACHING ACTIVITY
● **Solve a problem by** representing, **extracting and interpreting data in tables, graphs, charts** and diagrams.
● **Read and plot co-ordinates in all four quadrants.**
● Develop calculator skills and use a calculator effectively.

ORAL AND MENTAL STARTER

SQUARE IT: Give the children a multiple of 10 to 100, for example 60, and ask them to give you quickly the result of squaring the number. (3600)

MAIN TEACHING ACTIVITY

WHAT'S THE EQUATION?: Draw the children's attention to the graph and explain that five pairs of co-ordinates have been marked on the grid. *What do these co-ordinates have in common? Can anyone tell me another pair?* 'They are square numbers and the next one is 25, then 36...'. Ask them the equation of the graph ($y = x^2$). *What is different about this graph compared with the other graphs that you have drawn?* Answers may include, 'It's much steeper'; 'I don't think we can draw a straight line'. Distribute the copies of the graph and set the children to work plotting the points and extending the graph in the first quadrant. When they have completed this, refer them back to 1^2 being 1 and then 0^2 being 0. *I wonder where the graph will go now? What do we need to square to get the next value?* Hopefully, replies will include; 'Negative 1 squared'. Ask the children if they can use their calculators to help find the result of multiplying a negative number by itself, if they do not already know the result. 'You put in the number press the sign change key then multiply followed by the number again and the sign change key then equals' They then continue the graph in this quadrant.

DIFFERENTIATION

More able: Go on to draw a graph of cubic numbers ($y = x^3$).
Less able: Should only plot with your help, and draw the positive square numbers.

PLENARY

Discuss findings such as multiplying two negative numbers appears to give a positive result and the graph is curved.

LESSON 8

Repeat the **Oral and mental starter** as for Lesson 7, but for the **Main teaching activity**, give the children other equations to graph, such as $y = x + 4$; $y = 6 - x$ or $y = \frac{1}{3}x$. Before they start, ask them what they think the graph will look like; 'I think $y = x + 4$ will be a straight line and when x is 0 then y is 4, every y value is 4 more than the x value'. Ask the children to begin by making a table showing some positive values of x and the corresponding y values, for example the equation $y = 6 - x$ would give:

x	0	1	2	3	4	5	6	7	8
y	6	5	4	3	2	1	0	?	?

Let them use the calculator when negative numbers are involved. When they have calculated about 10 values, they can then draw the graph. Ask the more able children to extend the graph into other quadrants, predicting the position of the line and verifying the co-ordinates using a calculator. Discuss more complex lines in the **Plenary**.

UNIT 7: Assess & Review

Choose from these activities. During the group activities, some children can be completing assessment sheets 5a and 5b, while others work with you on practical tasks. The specific criteria for the assessment sheets are to be found at the bottom of each sheet.

RESOURCES

Questions for 'Ten seconds'; prepared graph; copies of photocopiable page 192 ('Tiles and populations') and page 193 ('Sunday lunch'), assessment sheets 5a and 5b; felt-tipped pens; wiper; metre rule; protractors; calculators; pencils.

PREPARATION

Prepare two sets of questions for 'Ten seconds', one set for addition and subtraction, another for multiplication and division. Draw on a large sheet of graph paper the graph of $y = x$ (on four quadrants), but do not label it. Photocopy page 192 ('Tiles and populations') and page 193 ('Sunday lunch'), one of each per child. Photocopy assessment sheets 5a and 5b, one of each per child.

ORAL AND MENTAL STARTER

ASSESSMENT

Can the children:
● Derive quickly division facts corresponding to tables up to 10×10? Identify and use appropriate operations (including combinations of operations) to solve word problems involving numbers and quantities?

AND THE ANSWER IS: Repeat as for Lesson 1, Unit 2.
TEN SECONDS: Repeat from Lesson 6, Unit 5. Use addition and subtraction examples for the first lesson, and multiplication and division examples for the second. For example, *What's the difference between 1.7 and 3.2? Which number multiplied by 4 gives 0.28?*

GROUP ACTIVITIES

ASSESSMENT

Can the children:
● Solve simple problems involving ratio and proportion? Understand percentage as the number of parts in every 100? Use a protractor to measure angles to the nearest degree? Solve a problem by extracting and interpreting data in tables, graphs, charts and diagrams?

TILES: Give out Part A of 'Tiles and populations'. *Here is a tile decorated with 1cm black and white squares to form a pattern.* Ask the children to find, for example, the ratio of black to white squares. Now ask them to consider, for example, covering a rectangular area measuring 18cm by 12cm with the tiles. *How many black and white squares will there be?* Let them try other rectangles formed by using the tiles.
POPULATIONS: Give out Part B of 'Tiles and populations' and ask them to do the task.
SUNDAY LUNCH: Give out 'Sunday lunch'. Ask the class to use the information given to calculate the time that Mum must put the turkey in the oven and the vegetable bake in the microwave in order to have lunch ready by 1.15pm. Ensure that the children appreciate that Mum is using an 800 watt microwave.
ANSWERS:
Assessment 5a: 13 050; 22 650; 12 231; 3753; 2502; 4698. **Assessment 5b:** 1a) $3^3/_4$; b) $4^1/_5$; c) $5^1/_4$; d) $6^3/_4$; 2a) £12.90; b) £3.12; c) £4.50; d) £9.45; 3a) 12.88; b) 6.12; c) £3.15; d) £1.87; 4a) 1.608956, 1.8, 1.6428571, 1.6216216; b) 1.61, 1.8, 1.64, 1.62; 1.61, 1.62, 1.64, 1.8.

Tiles and populations

UNIT 7

Part A
Tiles

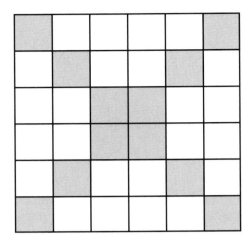

Part B
Populations

This pie chart shows information about heights in the adult population using grouped data.

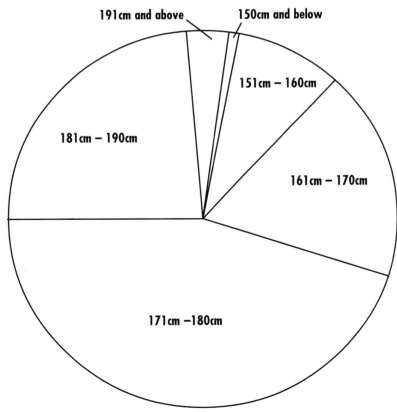

On this pie chart, 3.6° represents 1% and 36° represents 10%. Find and insert the missing percentages, using a calculator to help you.

Sunday lunch

Use the information given below to calculate the time that Mum must put the turkey in the oven and the vegetable bake in the microwave in order to have lunch ready by 1.15pm, if the turkey weighs 5.6 kg.

Cooking times for turkeys:

3.6 – 4.5kg: 30 mins at 220°, 3 hrs at 170°, 30 mins at 200°

5.5 – 6.3kg: 40 mins at 220°, 3hrs 30 mins at 170°, 45 mins at 200°

6.75 – 9kg: 45 mins at 220°, 4 hrs 45 mins at 170°, 30 mins at 200°

Always leave the turkey to stand for 30 mins before serving.

Recipe for Microwave Vegetable Bake:

(The timings given for recipes are for a 650 watt oven, followed in brackets by timings for a 750–800 watt oven.)

Combine onion and margarine, cover and cook on high power for 3 [2] minutes. Stir in flour, blend in the milk gradually. Cook uncovered on high power for 3 [2] minutes. Stir well until thickened.

Stir in seasoning, nutmeg, cream, potatoes, mushrooms and celery. Turn into an oven-proof dish, sprinkle with grated cheese and breadcrumbs.

Cook on high power for 16 [12] minutes. Leave to stand for 5 minutes.

Assessment sheet 5a

Write a number in each rectangle that is the product of the two circle numbers that lie either side of it. One product, 261 × 50 = 13 050, has already been written for you.

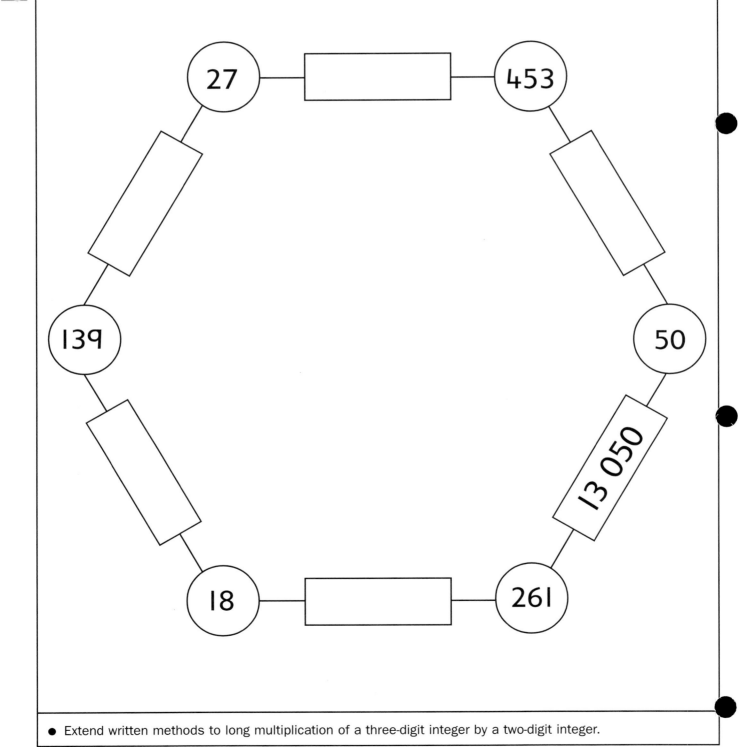

- Extend written methods to long multiplication of a three-digit integer by a two-digit integer.

Name

Assessment sheet 5b

1. Reduce these fractions to their simplest form:

a) $3\frac{15}{20}$ [ ]

b) $4\frac{20}{100}$ [ ]

c) $5\frac{8}{32}$ [ ]

d) $6\frac{48}{64}$ [ ]

2. Find the following percentages without using a calculator:

a) 15% of £86

b) 12% of £26

c) 30% of £15

d) 45% of £21

3. Use a calculator to find the following percentages:

a) 23% of 56

b) 17% of 36

c) $17\frac{1}{2}$ % of £18

d) 8.5% of £22

4.a) Use a calculator to change these fractions to decimals:

$\frac{37}{23}$ _____ $\frac{9}{5}$ _____ $\frac{23}{14}$ _____ $\frac{60}{37}$ _____

b) Rewrite the decimals to 2 decimal places and put them in order with the smallest first.

- Reduce a fraction to its simplest form by cancelling common factors.
- Find simple percentages of small whole number quantities.
- Order a mixed set of numbers with decimal places.

UNITS 8-10

ORGANISATION (15 LESSONS)

LEARNING OUTCOMES	ORAL AND MENTAL STARTER	MAIN TEACHING ACTIVITY	PLENARY
LESSON 1 +2 ● Make shapes with increasing accuracy. ● **Use a protractor to measure and draw acute and obtuse angles to the nearest degree.** ● Solve mathematical problems, recognise and explain patterns and relationships, generalise and predict. Suggest extensions.	PRIME FACTORS: Given a number, respond with its prime factors.	GROWING SHAPES: Look at how many polygons it is possible to build around a single polygon.	Discuss and display the results of the investigation.
LESSON 3, 4+5 ● Recognise where a shape will be after a rotation through 90° about one of its vertices. ● **Use a protractor to measure and draw acute and obtuse angles to the nearest degree.**	TELL ME THE OTHER: Giving one of two angles on a straight line. ANGLES AT A POINT: Finding the difference between angles and 360°.	ROTATING SHAPES: Rotating polygons about a vertex.	Discuss other possible centres of rotation and rotations through different angles.
LESSON 6 ● Recognise where a shape will be after a rotation. ● Recognise where a shape will be after two translations.	WHAT'S THE CHANGE?: Giving change from £5.	TRANSLATIONS: Describing and inventing patterns involving rotation and translation.	Display patterns and ask others to analyse these.
LESSON 7 +8 ● Recognise where a shape will be after two translations. ● **Read and plot co-ordinates in all four quadrants.**	ANGLES AT A POINT: Finding the difference between angles and 360°. WHAT'S THE CHANGE?: Change from £10.	TRANSLATIONS AGAIN: Describing and creating translations using co-ordinates.	Discuss strategies used and display translations.
LESSON 9 +10 ● Explain methods and reasoning. ● Make and investigate a general statement about familiar numbers or shapes by finding examples that satisfy it. Develop from explaining a generalised relationship in words to expressing it in a formula using letters as symbols.	DIVISION MIX: Answering division questions.	CIRCLES AND POLYGONS: Investigating rolling a circle around a polygon and observing its path.	Discuss and display results.
LESSON 11 +12 ● Use, read and write centimetres including their abbreviation cm. ● Record estimates and readings from scales to a suitable degree of accuracy. ● **Solve a problem by** representing, **extracting and interpreting data in tables, graphs and charts**; frequency tables and bar charts with grouped discrete data. ● Develop calculator skills and use a calculator effectively.	ALL CHANGE: Converting metric measurements to smaller or larger units.	HOW TALL?: Estimating and measuring children's heights. Finding the mean, mode and median. Compiling a frequency table and drawing a bar chart.	Consider the class sample of heights Discuss the effect of using different grouped data intervals.
LESSON 13 ● **Calculate the perimeter and area of simple shapes.** ● Express a generalised relationship in a formula using letters as symbols. ● Investigate a general statement about familiar shapes by finding examples that satisfy it. ● **Solve a problem by** representing, **extracting and interpreting data in tables and diagrams.**	PERIMETERS AND AREAS: Answering questions involving perimeters and areas.	FIX THE AREA: Investigating the perimeters of rectangles with the same area.	Draw together the results and make conclusions.
LESSON 14 ● Calculate the perimeter and area of simple shapes. ● Express a generalised relationship in a formula using letters as symbols. ● Investigate a general statement about familiar shapes by finding examples that satisfy it. ● **Solve a problem by** representing, **extracting and interpreting data in tables and diagrams.**	PERIMETERS AND AREAS: Answering questions involving perimeters and areas.	FIX THE PERIMETER: Investigating the areas of rectangles with the same perimeter.	Draw together the results and make conclusions.

LESSON 15	● Appreciate different times around the world.	METRIC TO IMPERIAL: Changing mass and capacity units from metric to imperial and vice-versa using rough equivalents	TIME ZONES: Finding and comparing times around the world.	Mark the work; introduce British Summer Time and the International Date Line.

ORAL AND MENTAL SKILLS Recognise prime numbers to at least 20. Factorise numbers to 100 into prime factors. Calculate angles in a triangle or around a point. Use known number facts and place value to consolidate mental addition/subtraction. **Derive quickly division facts corresponding to tables up to 10 x 10.** Convert smaller to larger units (eg m to km, cm to mm to m, g to kg, ml to l) and vice-versa. **Calculate the perimeter and area of simple shapes.** Know rough equivalents (metric to imperial).

In Units 8–10, Lessons 1, 3, 6, 7, 9, 11, 13 and 15 are shown in full. Lessons 2, 4, 5, 8, 10 and 12 extend the work of the preceding lesson and are shown after it. Lesson 14 is an extension of what has already been taught and is shown in outline.

LESSON 1 +2

RESOURCES

Lists of 2-digit numbers; sets of regular polygons; large sheets of paper; rulers; pencils.

PREPARATION

Make two lists, one for each lesson, of 2-digit numbers for the **Oral and mental starter**. Divide the class into mixed ability groups of about 4 or 5. Make sure the sets of polygons include one of the following shapes for each group; triangle, square, pentagon, hexagon, and octagon. For the less able children, prepare shape templates for 9, 10, 11 and 12-sided regular polygons.

LEARNING OUTCOMES

ORAL AND MENTAL STARTER
● Recognise prime numbers to at least 20. Factorise numbers to 100 into prime factors.

MAIN TEACHING ACTIVITY
● Make shapes with increasing accuracy.
● **Use a protractor to measure** and draw **acute and obtuse angles to the nearest degree.**
● Solve mathematical problems, recognise and explain patterns and relationships, generalise and predict. Suggest extensions asking What if...?

VOCABULARY

Pattern, multiple of, polygon, regular, heptagon, nonagon, decagon, dodecagon.

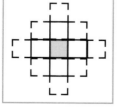

ORAL AND MENTAL STARTER

PRIME FACTORS: Give the children a number and ask them to quickly tell you only the prime factors of that number. For example, 42 gives 2, 3 and 7 only; 6 is not allowed as it is not a prime number.

MAIN TEACHING ACTIVITY

GROWING SHAPES: Give each group a set of polygons and some large sheets of paper. Ask one member from each group to place the square on one of the large sheets of paper and using it as a template, draw round it. Now ask, *If you now draw squares around your starter square so that each square in this first layer shares one side with the starter, no overlapping, how many will you need to draw? Try it and see.* (4) Tell each group to predict how many squares there will be in the second layer (8) and then go on and draw them. Ask the class about the other shapes, *I wonder how many triangles we will need to make the first layer?* 'I think it will be three and it will go up like the three times table'. *What about the octagon?* 'That will be eight!' Select one child from each group to continue to build up the square layers and record how many in each layer.

Others should use the other available polygons as templates and draw their own layers, recording the number in each layer. After the groups have been working for some time and have begun to make statements such as, 'Pentagons go up in 5s and hexagons in 6s but our octagon only goes up in 4s'; 'We can't get more than 4 around the starter octagon because they would overlap', ask *I wonder what happens with a 10-sided polygon, a decagon. What about 12 sides, a dodecagon? 7 sides, a heptagon? 9 sided, a nonagon? 11 sided, a unidecagon?* Leave each group to work on these. They may decide to construct templates of each of the polygons.

DIFFERENTIATION

More able: Let them use their protractor to construct the more complicated polygons.
Less able: Give them a template of the more complicated polygons shapes.

PLENARY

Discuss the work so far.

LESSON 2

Repeat the **Oral and mental starter** from Lesson 1. For the **Main teaching activity,** the children carry on and complete their investigation. In the **Plenary**, discuss each group's recordings and results. Ask them what they found out. Replies may include; 'The 10-sided polygon went up in 5s and the 12-sided one went up in 6s like the pentagon and hexagon'; 'We couldn't find one which had a starter layer of more than 6'; 'The 7-sided polygon was hard. The first layer was 4 then the second was 10. 9 was like that too'. Go on to ask the children if they can make some general statements about how the shapes grow. For example; 'If the polygon has a number of sides which is a multiple of 5 then it will grow in 5s each time, so if we start with a 35-sided polygon we will be able to put five 35-sided polygons around it'; 'The highest number of polygons we can put around the starter is 6'. Finally, give out the circles and tell the class to imagine that this is a polygon with an infinite number of sides. *Let's see how many circles we can fit around it. 6!*

RESOURCES

Large equilateral triangle; large sheet of paper; felt-tipped pen; small rectangles for the less able; protractors; set squares; rulers; tracing paper; polygons, two or three polygons for each pair; flip chart or board; pencils and paper; Logo.

PREPARATION

Draw a large equilateral triangle on the flip chart or board. Provide the class with paper.

LEARNING OUTCOMES

ORAL AND MENTAL STARTER
● Calculate angles in a triangle or around a point.

MAIN TEACHING ACTIVITY
● Recognise where a shape will be after a rotation through 90° about one of its vertices.
● **Use a protractor to measure** and draw **acute and obtuse angles to the nearest degree.**

ORAL AND MENTAL STARTER

TELL ME THE OTHER: Repeat the activity from Lesson 2, Unit 8, Term 1.

MAIN TEACHING ACTIVITY

ROTATING SHAPES: Remind the children of the work done earlier on simple translation of shapes and last term on reflections. Say that in this lesson they are going to look at rotating shapes. Ask if they can tell you what this might mean. Show them the equilateral triangle on the flip chart or board and explain that the triangle could be rotated about one of its vertices, about a point on one of its edges or about any point inside or outside its shape. *We call this point the centre of rotation.* To rotate the shape about one of its vertices, first mark this vertex with a letter, P. Ask one child to rotate the triangle through 90° anti-clockwise about this vertex while the other children give advice. 'All the sides have to move through 90°'; 'Put your finger on the vertex and slowly turn the triangle until it looks as if it's moved through 90°'. Tell the children that this is only approximate – as the shape is moved we lose its exact original position. Ask for ideas to overcome this problem; 'We could draw round the shape first and then move it through 90°'. Let a child try this. Ask the class to predict where this new position, called the image, will be. Emphasise

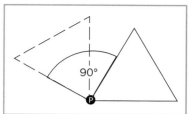

once more that this new position is again only approximate and ask how the drawing could be made more accurate; 'If we used a protractor and ruler we could measure 90° from one of the sides at the point P and draw a line the same length as the sides of the triangle then go to the other side which touches P and do the same. If we join these lines then we will have an image of the original triangle'.

The children work in pairs. They should accurately draw a rectangle 5cm × 3cm on their paper, label any vertex P, and construct the image of the rectangle rotated anti-clockwise through 90°. They then rotate it through another 90° and draw another image. They continue rotating and drawing until the image is back to its original position.

DIFFERENTIATION

More able: Go on to choose their own angle of rotation and observe the results.
Less able: Work with this group initially. If they find constructing the rectangle difficult, then give them a rectangle to use as a template and tracing paper to help with the rotation.

PLENARY

Discuss the images. *Can some of them be expressed as rotations through other angles, eg 180°? How many rotations of 90° were possible before the image was in the position of the original?* Remind them about the equilateral triangle. *How many images would there have been if we had continued to rotate through 90°? What about other shapes?*

LESSON 4

For the **Oral and mental starter**, use the activity ANGLES AT A POINT: Remind the children that the sum of angles at a point is 360°. Give them one angle and ask them to give you its complement. For example, if you give 76°, they should give you 284° (360° – 76°). For the **Main teaching activity** the children work in pairs to rotate a polygon continually through 90° about a vertex. They may then go on to try other polygons, rotating through 90° or other angles. Ask the more able children to try rotating their polygon through 90° about a point on a side or about a point outside the polygon. Each pair should be ready to tell the class what they did and show their results. Some children may also go on to draw a simple shape like a square using Logo then explore ways of continually rotating this about one of its vertices through, say 90° using the 'repeat' procedure. They may then go on to draw more complicated designs of their own choice.

LESSON 5

Repeat the **Oral and mental starter** from Lesson 4. For the **Main teaching activity**, the children should rotate polygons continually through angles that you provide (eg, 45°, 60°, 120°) Work with less able children. In the **Plenary** discuss and compare answers.

RESOURCES

Two large sheets of paper; felt-tipped pens; rulers; pencils.

PREPARATION

On one large sheet of paper draw a simple shape and colour it red. Now translate this shape and colour the image blue. On the other large sheet of paper draw the umbrella pattern shown overleaf.

LEARNING OUTCOMES
ORAL AND MENTAL STARTER
● Use known number facts and place value to consolidate mental addition/subtraction.

MAIN TEACHING ACTIVITY
● Recognise where a shape will be after a rotation.
● Recognise where a shape will be after two translations.

VOCABULARY

Translate, rotate, clockwise, anti-clockwise.

ORAL AND MENTAL STARTER

WHAT'S THE CHANGE?: Tell the children that you will give them a sum of money spent and they must quickly tell you the change from £5. So, if you say £3.56, they must reply £1.44.

MAIN TEACHING ACTIVITY

TRANSLATIONS: Tell the children that they are going to explore another type of movement. Show them your illustration and ask if they can describe how the blue shape can be obtained; 'You just slide the red shape along, you don't rotate it at all'. Remind the children that this type of movement is called a translation. Show them the umbrella pattern (above), and ask how it was started; 'By rotating it through 90° about T'. Now ask the children how the pattern was continued. Replies may include; 'The shaded shape and its image are given repeated equal translations to the right along the strip'. Set the children the task of making their own pattern using rotations and translations. Have tracing paper available for those who need it.

DIFFERENTIATION

More able: Go on to use rotations other than 90°.
Less able: Help them with their patterns and instructions for movement.

PLENARY

Display the patterns and ask children to say how they think some of the more interesting individual patterns have been made.

LESSON 7 + 8

RESOURCES

Large sheet of 1cm graph paper or laminated graph made previously; felt-tipped pens; rulers; pencils; small sheets of graph paper.

PREPARATION

Label the axes of your graph 'First number of the pair' (x axis) and 'Second number of the pair' (y axis). Draw a triangle with co-ordinates (3, 2), (4, 6), (1, 5), colour this red and label it A, B, C. Now draw another triangle (7, 5), (8, 9), (5, 8), colour this green and label it E, F, G. Make sure that the graph is large enough for the children to be able to see it.

LEARNING OUTCOMES

ORAL AND MENTAL STARTER
● Calculate angles in a triangle or around a point.

MAIN TEACHING ACTIVITY
● Recognise where a shape will be after two translations.
● **Read and plot co-ordinates in all four quadrants.**

VOCABULARY

Translate, rotate, image, co-ordinates.

ORAL AND MENTAL STARTER

ANGLES AT A POINT: Repeat the activity from Lesson 4.

MAIN TEACHING ACTIVITY

TRANSLATIONS AGAIN: Show the children your graph and tell them that the green triangle is an image of the red triangle after a translation. Tell them to write down the co-ordinates of A (3, 2) and its image, E, (7, 5). Now ask them to repeat this, writing down the co-ordinates of B and F, and finally C and G. Ask if anyone can see a relationship between the two sets of co-ordinates. They may suggest; 'You must add 4 to the first number in A, B and C to get E, F and G'; 'The second number in A, B and C has 3 added to it to get E, F and G'. Give a sheet of graph paper to each child and tell them to draw and label axes with values from 0 to 10. Ask them to draw a square with co-ordinates (2, 1), (6, 2), (5, 6), (1, 5) for its vertices. Tell them that the square is translated so that the image of the point (2, 1) becomes the point (4, 7). Ask them to draw the image of the square, write down its co-ordinates and find the relationship between the co-ordinates of the original square and its image (The first number of the pair has 2 added, the second has 6 added).

Working with a partner, let each child draw another shape, translate it and then ask their partner to guess the relationship. Alternatively, they could draw one shape and give a relationship that will allow their partner to go on and draw the image. For example, having drawn a parallelogram with co-ordinates (3, 2), (6, 5), (5, 6), (2, 3) they may instruct their partner to draw its image when the first number of each pair has 3 added to it and the second number has 1 subtracted from it.

DIFFERENTIATION

More able: Go on to use four quadrants and two translations.
Less able: Remind them that the x co-ordinate always comes first and encourage them to verbalise the relationship between the co-ordinates.

PLENARY

Discuss and display the translations and strategies used.

LESSON 8

For the **Oral and mental starter** use the activity 'What's the change?' from Lesson 6, but this time ask for change from £10. For the **Main teaching activity**, ask each child to draw a shape, translate it twice and draw the resultant image, making sure their partner does not see it. Their partner must give the possible translations. For example: The triangle A,B,C, may have been translated by adding 5 to each value of x to make the first image (in quadrant 1), followed by subtracting 4 from each y value to give the image P, Q R. Triangle A, B, C could also have been translated by subtracting 4 from each y value to make the first image (in quadrant 3), followed by adding 5 to each x value, once again giving the image P, Q, R. Let the less able work with you as a group. The more able children could go on to combine translations and rotations. Discuss strategies and display transitions in the **Plenary**.

RESOURCES

Lists of division facts; copies of photocopiable page 207 ('Circles and polygons'); large sheets of rough paper; large sheets of cartridge paper; circles of various sizes with a hole at the centre; squares of various sizes; polygons, both regular and irregular; felt-tipped pens; metre rules; rulers; pencils.

PREPARATION

Make two lists of facts associated with division, for example, $64 \div 8 = ?$; $? \div 9 = 5$; $48 \div ? = 6$. Photocopy page 207 ('Circles and polygons'), one per group of 4 or 5 children. Organise the children into ability groups. Collect or make a selection of circles – these will be needed as templates so should be made from thick card or plastic. Make a hole at the centre of each. Collect a selection of squares of different sizes – Dienes flats will be useful here. Have ready a selection of polygons for each group.

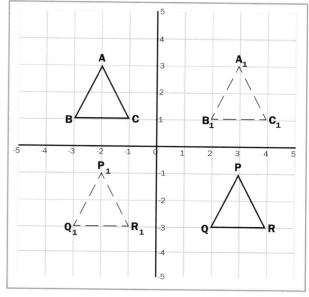

LEARNING OUTCOMES
ORAL AND MENTAL WORK
- **Derive quickly division facts corresponding to tables up to 10 × 10.**

MAIN TEACHING ACTIVITY
- Explain methods and reasoning, orally and in writing.
- Make and investigate a general statement about familiar numbers or shapes by finding examples that satisfy it. Develop from explaining a generalised relationship in words to expressing it in a formula using letters as symbols.

ORAL AND MENTAL STARTER
DIVISION MIX: Ask each child one of the prepared division questions and expect a quick reply. If this is not forthcoming or the answer is incorrect then open it to the rest of the class. See how many correct answers can be given in the time allowed.

MAIN TEACHING ACTIVITY
CIRCLES AND POLYGONS: Explain that for the next two lessons, they are all going to look at an investigation about circles and polygons. During the first lesson there will be time to explore the investigation and make rough drawings and notes. In the second lesson, you want each group to produce a report, including drawings, for display. Tell them that their report should describe what they were asked to do, how they tackled the investigation, any problems they encountered, their results and their conclusions. Give out 'Circles and polygons', and ask them to read the first paragraph. Then ask what they think. Expect replies such as; 'I think the path will be a square but larger than the square that has been drawn round'; 'I think that the corners will be curves!' Without more discussion, set the groups to work. Discuss the investigation with each group individually.

DIFFERENTIATION
More able: Go on to explore for other irregular polygons.
Less able: Give them help getting started.

PLENARY
Discuss any initial problems encountered and ways to overcome these.

LESSON 10
Follow Lesson 9's **Oral and mental starter**. For the **Main teaching activity,** the groups complete the investigation they began in Lesson 9 and prepare their reports for discussion. More able children could explore whether it is possible to express the length of the path of the circle as a formula. The less able may need help to express their findings. For the **Plenary,** display the reports and discuss the various groups' findings. For example; 'We found out that the path made by the centre of the circle was like a square with curved corners'; 'The length of the path is the perimeter of the square plus the circumference of the circle'; 'It didn't matter how large or small the circle and squares were, the path was still a square with curved corners and it was the always the perimeter of the square added to the circumference of the circle'; 'It doesn't matter what shape the polygon is, the length of the path is always the sum of the perimeter of the polygon and the circumference of the circle'; 'The formula is $p = s + c$, where p is the path, s is the perimeter of the shape and c is the circumference of the circle'.

RESOURCES
Height measuring equipment; prepared 'Class Height' charts; felt-tipped pens; calculators; large sheets of paper and 1 cm graph paper for Lesson 12; pencils and paper.

How tall? (to the nearest cm)		
Name	My estimate	Measured height
James	148	142
Amelia	155	154

PREPARATION

Provide height measuring equipment. Prepare two Class Height charts large enough to accommodate all the children's names with the first column headed 'Name' and the second column 'Height in cm'. Write the children's names on one of these charts and display it. Draw the 'How tall?' table on the board (see bottom of previous page). Arrange the children into four groups of mixed ability.

LEARNING OUTCOMES

ORAL AND MENTAL STARTER
● Convert smaller to larger units (eg m to km, cm to mm to m, g to kg, ml to l) and vice-versa.

MAIN TEACHING ACTIVITY
● Use, read and write centimetres including their abbreviation cm.
● Record estimates and readings from scales to a suitable degree of accuracy.
● **Solve a problem by** representing, **extracting and interpreting data in charts, tables and graphs**; frequency tables and bar charts with grouped discrete data.
● Develop calculator skills and use a calculator effectively.

ORAL AND MENTAL STARTER

ALL CHANGE: Give the children metric measurements and ask them to convert them to smaller or larger units. Include length, mass and capacity. For example, convert 250ml to l, 1.7km to m, 125cl to l, 3250g to kg.

MAIN TEACHING ACTIVITY

HOW TALL?: Tell the children that they are going to estimate and then measure to the nearest centimetre their heights. Show them the layout of the table on the board and ask each child to prepare a similar table to show their estimates and the actual heights of the children in their group. They should record their estimates in felt-tipped pen to avoid 'alterations'. Once they have recorded the actual height measurements, discuss how good their estimates were. Select one child from each group to record their group's actual heights on the displayed 'Class Heights' chart. When this is complete, consider the range of the heights. Then ask the children, in pairs, to calculate the average (mean) height of the class using their calculators. Emphasise inputting the numbers carefully and the use of the 'clear entry' [CE] key. Compare the mean with the range, asking, for example, *Is it exactly in the middle of the range? Why not?*

DIFFERENTIATION

More able: Encourage them to help the less able with their work but discourage them from simply telling and allowing copying.
Less able: Work with this group to help them find the mean.

PLENARY

Extend the work by asking whether we could use the data in any other way. *We could use our sample to make statements about Year 6 children's heights in the country but I expect that the range would be greater. We would find some shorter and some taller children. I expect our mean average wouldn't be too bad but really we needed a bigger sample to make sure that the data is accurate.*

LESSON 12

Play the **Oral and mental starter** from Lesson 11, and for the **Main teaching activity,** display the completed Class Heights chart from Lesson 11 alongside a new blank chart. Together build the new chart placing the height readings in

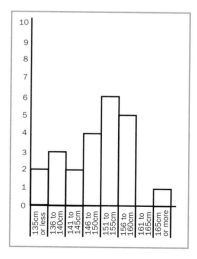

order, shortest to tallest. Find the mode and then the median on the new chart, and discuss the mean, mode and median readings. In pairs, ask the children to make a frequency table using grouped data, eg 135cm or less, 136 to 140cm, 141 to 145cm and so on, up to 165cm or more. Give out the graph paper and ask them to show the data as a bar chart (see previous page). Help the less able children with constructing the frequency table and the graph. More able children could go on to consider what a graph would look like with data grouped in 10cm intervals. In the **Plenary** session, bring up any points that have arisen and discuss them. For example, if the able children have produced the '10 centimetre intervals' graph, compare this with the 'five centimetre intervals' graph.

LESSON 13

RESOURCES

Prepared oblong; 1cm graph paper; felt-tipped pens; pencils and paper.

PREPARATION

Draw an oblong on graph paper measuring 2cm by 18cm. Draw a blank results table as shown below on the board.

Table to show perimeters of rectangles with a fixed area of 36 cm²		
Length (cm)	Breadth (cm)	Perimeter (cm)
18	2	40

LEARNING OUTCOMES

ORAL AND MENTAL STARTER
● **Calculate the perimeter and area of simple shapes.**

MAIN TEACHING ACTIVITY
● **Calculate the perimeter and area of simple shapes.**
● Express a generalised relationship in a formula using letters as symbols.
● Investigate a general statement about familiar shapes by finding examples that satisfy it.
● **Solve a problem by** representing, **extracting and interpreting data in tables and diagrams.**

VOCABULARY

Area, perimeter, formula.

ORAL AND MENTAL STARTER

PERIMETERS AND AREAS: Ask a selection of perimeter and area questions. For example, *What's the length of side of a regular heptagon, which has a perimeter of 42cm? If the area of a rectangle is 32cm² and the long side is 8cm, how long is the short side? If the long side of a rectangle measures 20cm and each of the short sides are half of this, what is the area?*

MAIN TEACHING ACTIVITY

FIX THE AREA: Tell the children that they are going to investigate whether different rectangles with the same area will all have the same perimeter. Say, *Let's fix the area to 36cm² and try one.* Show an oblong measuring 18cm by 2cm and, using a = l × b, verify that its area is 36cm. Now find the perimeter using p = 2l + 2b, giving 36 + 4 = 40. Record the result on your table on the board, leaving space in the columns above and below it. Give out the graph paper and let the children work in pairs to try other whole number measurements for the lengths and breadths of a rectangle of area 36cm². They draw up a table of results. To check their answers, they should then draw each rectangle on graph paper (36 × 1, 18 × 2, 12 × 3, 9 × 4, 6 × 6) and write the lengths, breadths and perimeters involved.

DIFFERENTIATION

More able: Consider narrowing the breadths of the rectangles by halving, giving length 72cm, breadth 0.5cm, perimeter 145cm; length 144cm, breadth 0.25cm, perimeter 288.5cm etc. This should lead to the conclusion that the perimeters increase and nearly double each time. *At the mathematical limit the rectangle's length of edge would be infinity and the breadth zero.* Work with them and discuss these ideas.

Less able: If they are experiencing difficulty with the calculations, move them quickly on to drawing the rectangles and writing down what they have to do.

PLENARY

As a check on the children's results, insert the correct answers to your table on the board, namely for 36 × 1, p = 74; 18 × 2, p = 40; 12 × 3, p = 30 etc. Draw conclusions together, leading to; 'For rectangles with a fixed area many different perimeters are possible with the least given by a square, in this case 6 × 6, with its perimeter 24cm'.

LESSON 14

RESOURCES	Prepared oblong; 1cm graph paper; felt-tipped pens; pencils and paper.
PREPARATION	Draw an oblong on graph paper measuring 11cm by 1cm. Draw this results table on the board:
LEARNING OUTCOMES	**ORAL AND MENTAL STARTER** ● **Calculate the perimeter and area of simple shapes.** **MAIN TEACHING ACTIVITY** ● **Calculate the perimeter and area of simple shapes.** ● Express a generalised relationship in a formula using letters as symbols. Investigate a general statement about familiar shapes by finding examples that satisfy it. ● **Solve a problem by** representing, **extracting and interpreting data in tables and diagrams.**
ORAL AND MENTAL STARTER	PERIMETERS AND AREAS: Use the activity from Lesson 13, extending, for the most able, to questions such as *What's the smallest perimeter you can make from a rectangle with an area of 9cm²?* (a square with length of edge 3cm and a perimeter of 12cm).
MAIN TEACHING ACTIVITY	FIX THE PERIMETER: Remind the children of the work covered in Lesson 13. Tell them that now we are going to fix the perimeter of a rectangle and explore the possible areas. Show them the 11cm by 1cm oblong and ask for its perimeter (24cm). Ask them to find areas for rectangles where each length of side is a whole number of centimetres and the perimeter is 24. Ask them to copy the results table shown on the board and use it to record their results. As before, they should check their answers by drawing the rectangles on graph paper (11 × 1, 10 × 2, 9 × 3, 8 × 4, 7 × 5, 6 × 6) and writing the lengths, breadths and areas of each.
DIFFERENTIATION	More able: Go on to try lengths of edge above 11cm that are not whole numbers, say 11.1 × 0.9 giving an area of 9.99cm², while 11.9 × 0.1 gives 1.19cm². This should lead to *For a fixed perimeter, as the length of edge increases the area decreases.* Less able: Work with this group, developing ideas as they arise.
PLENARY	Write up the table of results on the board or flip chart as shown opposite: Discuss findings. 'As the length of the rectangle decreases the breadths increase and a greater area is covered, with the square producing the largest area.' Point out that you cannot have a rectangle with a length of side of 12cm and a perimeter of 24cm. Let children who tried lengths of side between 11cm and 12cm to report their findings (see **Differentiation**). Now try a fixed perimeter of, say 16cm, giving results of 7 × 1 = 7cm²; 6 × 2 = 12cm²; 5 × 3 = 15cm², 4 × 4 = 16cm²: a square and the largest area again.

Table to show areas of rectangles with fixed perimeters of 24 cm²

Length (cm)	Breadth (cm)	Area (cm²)

Table to show areas of rectangles with fixed perimeters of 24 cm²

Length (cm)	Breadth (cm)	Area (cm²)
11	1	11
10	2	20
9	3	27
8	4	32
7	5	35
6	6	36

RESOURCES

Copies of photocopiable page 208 ('Time zones'); world atlas; a globe; calculator; telephone directories; pencils and paper.

PREPARATION

Write on the board '1oz is about 28g, 1lb is about 450g, 1kg is about 2.2lbs, 1 gallon is about 4.5l, 1l is about 0.22 gallons'. Prepare mass and capacity questions involving rough equivalents of metric units and vice-versa, eg How many pounds is 1350g? (3); 22 pounds is how many kg? (10); How many litres in 4 gallons? (18); Photocopy page 208 ('Time zones'), one per child. Provide some telephone directories. Give out the atlases.

LEARNING OUTCOMES

ORAL AND MENTAL STARTER

● Know rough equivalents (metric to imperial).

MAIN TEACHING ACTIVITY

● Appreciate different times around the world.

VOCABULARY

Time zones, Greenwich Mean Time, British Summer Time, BST, International Date Line, degree, 24-hour clock, table, range.

ORAL AND MENTAL STARTER

METRIC TO IMPERIAL: Point out the equivalences on the board and give the children your mass and capacity questions. Allow some thinking time before asking for the answer.

MAIN TEACHING ACTIVITY

TIME ZONES: Use the globe to explain that the Earth rotates through 360° in 24 hours, so each hour it turns through 15° (360 ÷ 24 = 15). Let one child do the division using a calculator. *The surface of the earth is divided into time zones. There are 24, each of 15° of longitude or 1 hour of time. The zones run north to south and, generally speaking, the time is the same within each zone.* Show them the zones on the globe and on a world map in their atlases. Mention that some countries adjust their times to suit their boundaries.

Introduce the idea of Greenwich Mean Time (GMT), and say that all places in the world are a number of hours ahead or behind it. *For example, Washington DC is 5 hours behind and so is Lima in Peru, which is much further south but in the same time zone.* Distribute the photocopies and discuss the table. Work out the time for Greece with the children and then let them continue with the sheet.

DIFFERENTIATION

More able: Should reach more difficult examples you provide.
Less able: Talk through the early examples before they work as individuals.

PLENARY

Mark the work, asking individual children to describe the strategies they used. For question 4, expect answers such as; 'The USA is a large country with several time zones and times'. For question 5, they may say that Portugal is south of Great Britain, and South Africa is south of Greece. Highlight question 3 for this. Introduce the idea of British Summer Time (BST), saying that in Britain, it is in operation between spring and autumn, while GMT is used between autumn and spring. Discuss the effect that moving the clock forward when moving to BST has on the difference between time in Great Britain and, say, Argentina (GMT 3 hours behind; BST 4 hours behind). Try South Africa (GMT 2 hours ahead; BST 1 hour ahead). Give a brief mention to the International Date Line. This is in the Pacific Ocean, 180° away from Greenwich on the other side of the World. Use a World map to show that, using GMT, if it is noon on Friday in Great Britain, it will be midnight in New Zealand and one second later it will be Saturday. In Samoa, however, it will be 01.00 on Friday at this time. If you travel from New Zealand to Samoa, crossing the International Date Line you will move from Saturday back to Friday and vice-versa.

Circles and polygons

The dotted line shows the beginning of the path being marked out by the centre of the circle as it rolls around the square. What can you say about the complete path? How long is it?

Try this and see if you were correct in your thinking. If the sizes of the shapes are varied does this change your thinking?

Now try rolling circles around other regular shapes.

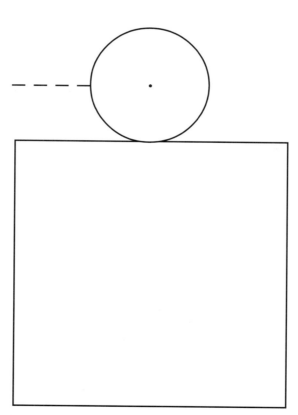

Time zones

Here is a table showing some places in the world and the number of hours they are ahead of (+) or behind (–) Greenwich Mean Time.

Country	Number of hours ahead of or behind GMT	Time (24 hour clock) when it is noon in Britain
Great Britain	**0**	
Greece	**+2**	
Portugal	**0**	
USA: New York	**– 5**	
USA: Los Angeles	**– 8**	
USA: Alaska	**– 10 or 11**	
South Africa	**+2**	
Argentina	**– 3**	
Samoa	**– 11**	
New Zealand	**+ 12**	

1. Work out the times for the third column.

2. If the time in Great Britain is 14.00 hours, what time is it in:

a) New York?

b) South Africa?

c) New Zealand?

3. When it is 06.30 hours in Samoa what time is it in:

a) Great Britain?

b) Argentina?

4. What can you say about times in the USA?

5. Why is the time in Portugal the same as in Great Britain? Use an atlas to check that you were right. What about times in Greece and South Africa?

Use a telephone directory's International Codes section to find other time differences. Make up some questions for your friends to try.

UNIT 11

ORGANISATION (5 LESSONS)

	LEARNING OUTCOMES	ORAL AND MENTAL STARTER	MAIN TEACHING ACTIVITY	PLENARY
LESSON 1	● Use known number facts and place value to consolidate mental addition and subtraction. ● Use informal pencil and paper methods to support, record or explain additions and subtractions. ● Develop calculator skills and use a calculator effectively.	IT!: Doubling, halving or squaring given numbers.	LEMON MERINGUE PIE: Converting imperial units to metric units in a recipe. Drawing a conversion graph for oven temperature from gas marks to degrees Fahrenheit.	Children explain their subtraction methods and how they were sure that they had found all the possible calculations.
LESSON 2	● **Identify and use appropriate operations (including combinations of operations) to solve word problems** based on 'real life', money, using one or more steps and calculating percentages such as VAT and discounts.	IT!: Doubling, halving or squaring given numbers then changing common fractions to decimal fractions, percentages to common fractions and vice-versa.	HOW MANY WAYS?: Finding how many different addition and then subtraction calculations can be produced using four decimal numbers. The results calculated either mentally or by informal pencil and paper methods.	Marking the work and discussing any problems that have arisen.
LESSON 3	● **Explain methods and reasoning.** ● Develop calculator skills and use a calculator effectively.	MONEY PERCENTAGES: Finding simple percentages involving money.	INVOICES: Calculating invoice totals including VAT and discounts.	Asking the children for the solution of Lord Nelson's message. Talking about the Battle of Trafalgar and the flag code.
LESSON 4 +5	● Recognise and extend number sequences. ● Solve mathematical problems or puzzles, recognise and explain patterns and relationships.	DISCOUNTS: Finding percentage discounts.	Danny's secret code: solving and creating number codes. Mark the work and discuss aspects which need clarification.	

ORAL AND MENTAL SKILLS Derive quickly: squares of multiples of 10 to 100; doubles of 2-digit numbers; doubles of multiples of 10 to 1000 and 100 to 10 000 and the corresponding halves. Recognise the equivalence between the decimal and fraction forms. Express simple fractions as percentages (and vice-versa). **Find simple percentages of small whole number quantities.**

In Unit 11, Lessons 1, 2, 3 and 4 are shown in full. Lesson 5 extends the work of Lesson 4 and is shown after it.

RESOURCES
Copies of photocopiable page 214 ('Lemon meringue pie'); large sheet of cm graph paper; felt-tipped pens; pencils and scrap paper.

PREPARATION
Photocopy page 214 ('Lemon meringue pie'), one per child.

LEARNING OUTCOMES
ORAL AND MENTAL STARTER
Derive quickly: squares of multiples of 10 to 100; doubles of 2-digit numbers; doubles of multiples of 10 to 1000 and 100 to 10 000; and the corresponding halves.

MAIN TEACHING ACTIVITY

● **Identify and use appropriate operations to solve word problems involving quantities** based on measures.

● Know (and use) equivalents (of oz and lbs to g, pints to ml tablespoons to millilitres, inches to cm, °F to °C).

● Express a generalised relationship in a formula using letters as symbols.

● Round a decimal number to the nearest whole number or ten.

● **Solve a problem** by representing, **extracting and interpreting data in tables and graphs** eg a conversion graph.

ORAL AND MENTAL STARTER

IT!: Tell the children that you are going to give them a number and an instruction, either double it, halve it or square it. Use the type of numbers specified in the learning outcomes above.

MAIN TEACHING ACTIVITY

LEMON MERINGUE PIE: Give out copies of 'Lemon meringue pie' and say that they are going to use the fish curry recipe information in order to work out the pie's ingredients when using metric units. Talk through the sheet and set the children to work. Encourage as much mental work as possible, and when a pencil and paper procedure is needed let them work on scrap paper before inserting their answers on the sheet. Do not allow calculators.

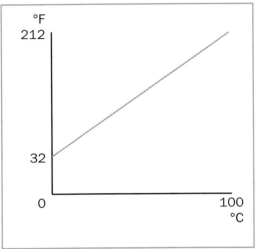

DIFFERENTIATION

More able: Go on to consider how they might draw a conversion graph from oven temperature in °F to/from °C (see above). Work with them to complete the graph.
Less able: May need your help, but encourage as much work as they can without you.

PLENARY

Mark the work with the class and discuss any aspects that need clarification. For example, if necessary work through the formula step by step.

RESOURCES

Pencils; scrap paper and neat paper; calculators.

PREPARATION

Write four decimal numbers (up to 2 decimal places) randomly on the board.

LEARNING OUTCOMES

ORAL AND MENTAL STARTER

● **Derive quickly:** squares of multiples of 10 to 100; doubles of 2-digit numbers, doubles of multiples of 10 to 1000 and 100 to 10 000 and the corresponding halves.

● Recognise the equivalence between the decimal and fraction forms.

● Express simple fractions as percentages (and vice-versa).

MAIN TEACHING ACTIVITY

● Use known number facts and place value to consolidate mental addition and subtraction.

● Use informal pencil and paper methods to support, record or explain additions and subtractions.

● Develop calculator skills and use a calculator effectively.

ORAL AND MENTAL STARTER

IT!: Use the activity from Lesson 1, and introduce examples with 'Change it to'. Say, give them a common fraction and ask them to change it to a decimal fraction, or give a percentage and ask them to change it to a common fraction in its simplest form.

MAIN TEACHING ACTIVITY

HOW MANY WAYS?: Point out the four decimal numbers on the board. Ask the children to add any two of them mentally and record their responses. For example, for 0.4, 0.39, 0.27 and 1.01 they could calculate $0.4 + 0.27 = 0.67$ or $0.4 + 0.39 = 0.79$ etc. When they have correctly recorded all six possibilities, ask for the additions of any three and then all four numbers, giving 11 possibilities altogether. Now give them another set of numbers for them to work on in pairs. They should record their results and be ready to explain the strategies they used for each calculation. Some children may wish to use scrap paper, but no column additions should be allowed. So, 3.2, 7.6, 24, 2.8 as the four numbers might lead children, when adding 7.6 and 24, to write $24 + 7 = 31$; $31 + 0.6 = 31.6$.

When, say, four pairs think they have finished, stop the class and record, searching for 11 additions once more. Ask the children to explain their methods. Now let the children play against each other in pairs, roughly matched by ability. Each pair writes down four decimal numbers and when everyone is ready, they record as before. After, say, six minutes, stop the children. They can check their results using a calculator, and the person in each pair who recorded the most correct addition statements is the winner. Play another addition round before trying subtractions using four decimal numbers placed in ascending order at the start. Here, no negative answers should be allowed.

DIFFERENTIATION

More able: Encourage them to stretch each other with the numbers they use.
Less able: Check that they are not using too difficult numbers and if they are modify them before each round starts.

PLENARY

Let the children explain their subtraction methods. Ask them how many possible subtractions there are, and how they can be sure: 'If the numbers a, b, c and d are placed in ascending order, possible subtractions are $d - c$, $d - b$, $d - a$, $c - b$, $c - a$ and $b - a$'.

RESOURCES

Prepared invoice questions; calculators; pencils and paper.

PREPARATION

Write the invoice questions including discounts, deposits and VAT for two levels of ability. Eg for the lower ability group:

2 Michelin Classic Tyres at £65 each (including VAT)	£
Discount 10%	£
Amount due	£

For the rest of the children, examples such as:

3 Bosch Electric Screwdrivers at £15.50 each	£
VAT at 17.5%	£
Deposit paid	£ 15.00
Amount due	£

Make it clear when they are allowed to use calculators. Photocopy enough for each group.

LEARNING OUTCOMES

ORAL AND MENTAL STARTER
● **Find simple percentages of small whole number quantities.**

MAIN TEACHING ACTIVITY
● **Identify and use appropriate operations (including combinations of operations) to solve word problems** based on 'real life', money, using one or more steps and calculating percentages such as VAT and discounts.
● **Explain methods and reasoning.**
● Develop calculator skills and use a calculator effectively.

VOCABULARY

Amount, percentage, %, VAT, invoice.

ORAL AND MENTAL STARTER

MONEY PERCENTAGES: Ask the children to find simple percentages involving money, say find 10% of £80; 60% of £200; 15% of £500.

MAIN TEACHING ACTIVITY

INVOICES: Talk about the meaning of invoice and write a simple example on the board:

Fit new oven temperature sensor and test	£57.02
VAT at 17.5%	£ 9.98
Total	£67.00

Explain VAT, and let the children work out the example above using the percentage key and memory functions on their calculators: [5] [7] [.] [0] [2] [×] [1] [7] [.] [5] [%] [M+] [5] [7] [.] [0] [2] [M+] [MR]. Round the answer 66.9985 to the nearest penny, giving £67.00 before pressing the appropriate clear keys. Remind the children about discounts (such as '10% off'), and try one or two simple examples mentally. Then give them your prepared examples to work on individually.

DIFFERENTIATION

More able: Let them create some invoice questions for others to try.
Less able: Discuss the early examples with them as a group.

PLENARY

Mark the children's work, asking them to explain their methods and reasoning. Discuss any difficulties that may have arisen, including calculator use.

RESOURCES

Copies of photocopiable page 215 ('Danny's secret codes'); pencils and paper.

PREPARATION

Photocopy page 215 ('Danny's secret codes'), one per pair. Write on the board:

12, 15, 1, 54	21, 54, 15, 21		
		39, 15, 15, 60 39, 15 3, 60	
42, 27, 42, 15 45, ' 9, 36, 45, 9, 33 45, 42 57, 3, 60, 63, 54, 12, 3, 75			
6, 75 12, 15, 66, 27, 36, ' 57 45, 3, 33			
	12, 3, 42, 42, 75		

and also:

a	b	c	d	e	f	g	h	i	j	k	l	m	n	o
1	2	3	4	5	6	7	8	9	10	11	12	13	14	15
p	q	r	s	t	u	v	w	x	y	z				
16	17	18	19	20	21	22	23	24	25	26				

LEARNING OUTCOMES

ORAL AND MENTAL STARTER
● **Find simple percentages of small whole number quantities.**

MAIN TEACHING ACTIVITY
● Recognise and extend number sequences.
● Solve mathematical problems or puzzles, recognise and explain patterns and relationships.

ORAL AND MENTAL STARTER

DISCOUNTS: Ask the children to find discounts of sums of money with the discounts quoted as percentages, eg *How much off if there is 10% discount on £10, £50, £2.30? How much do I pay if there is 20% discount on £5, £60, £75?*

MAIN TEACHING ACTIVITY

DANNY'S SECRET CODES: Say that Danny has started a craze of inventing and using secret codes. Say that a message using the code has been sent to Greg and is written on the board. Ask for ideas on how to 'crack' the code; 'It could start 'Dear Greg', so let's write the numbers under the alphabet letters, 'e' is 15 etc'; 'They're all multiples of 3 in sequence'. Write in all the numbers under the correct letters with their help:

a	b	c	d	...	y	z
1	2	3	4		25	26
3	6	9	12	...	75	78

Then ask them to decipher the message. Next, ask the children to write their name in Danny's code. Talk about how; *If we know the number of a letter 1 to 26, we can simply multiply by 3 to find its code number. Conversely, if a message is to be decoded we simply divide each number by 3, by using the inverse function.* Danny's message to Greg reads:

> Dear Greg
> Meet me at nine o'clock on Saturday by Devil's Oak.
>   Danny

Let them work in pairs and ask each child to write a sentence using Danny's code of no more than 10 words and give it to their partner to decipher. They then start work on the questions on 'Danny's secret codes'.

DIFFERENTIATION

More able: Go on to invent a secret number code of their own.
Less able: Work with this group to decipher the message in question 1 together. Discuss question 2a with them before letting them work on b, c and d, assisting if necessary.

PLENARY

Ask the children to tell you the famous message in question 1: 'England expects that every man will do his duty', from Lord Nelson. Talk about the battle of Trafalgar and tell them that the message was given to the Fleet using a flag code; a string of flags with each one standing for a letter of the alphabet.

LESSON 5

Repeat the **Oral and mental starter** from the previous lesson. For the **Main teaching activity**, remind the children about yesterday's deciphering exercise, and emphasise the importance of a careful layout for each line of the deciphering in question 3. Let them continue working through the questions. Give help to the less able children when necessary. Those who complete the sheet can continue with their own codes and write short messages in them for their partners to decipher. Do not let their codes become too difficult, say using three functions or very high numbers. In the **Plenary**, write the first two lines of Charlotte's poem on the board, ask individuals for their suggested next two lines.

> The pebbles on the seashore
> All clattering about ...

Lemon meringue pie

Here are some of the ingredients used for a fish curry recipe. Use this information to give you the lemon meringue pie's ingredients in metric units.

Fish curry recipe: $\frac{1}{2}$ oz (14g) butter, 2 tablespoons (30ml) mild curry powder, 1lb (450g) white fish fillet, skinned and cubed, $\frac{3}{4}$ pint (450ml) fresh milk

Fill in the boxes to help you:

1 oz = [ ] g   1 tablespoon = [ ] ml   1 pint = [ ] ml

Now complete the lemon meringue pie recipe's ingredients and cooking information:

Lemon meringue pie recipe:

For the pastry: 4oz plain flour   (_____ g)

1 oz margarine (_____ g)

1 oz lard   (_____ g)

For the filling:

4 level tablespoons cornflour (_____ ml)

1$\frac{1}{2}$ oz butter   (_____ g)

2 large egg yolks

2 large lemons

$\frac{1}{2}$ pint cold water (_____ ml)

2 oz caster sugar   (_____ g)

For the meringue:

2 large egg whites

4 oz caster sugar   (_____ g)

You will also need a deep enamel pie plate with sloping sides and a rim, measuring 6 inches (_____ cm) diameter at the base and 8 inches (_____ cm) diameter at the top.

Preheat the oven to 380°F (_____ °C to the nearest 10 degrees).

Note: 1 inch is equivalent to 2.5cm.
Formula to convert °Fahrenheit to °Celsius: °C = (°F – 32) × 5 ÷ 9.

Danny's secret code

1. Use Danny's code to decipher this famous message:

15, 42, 21, 36, 3, 42, 12   15, 72, 48, 15, 9, 60, 57   60, 24, 3, 60

15, 66, 15, 54, 75   39, 3, 42   69, 27, 36, 36   12, 45

24, 27, 57   12, 63, 60, 75

36, 45, 54, 12   42, 15, 36, 57, 45, 42

2. Here are some calculations using Danny's code. Try them, writing the answer as a number. The first one is done for you.

a) l + r = 90

b) m – g = ☐

c) s × c = ☐

d) x ÷ f = ☐

3. Charlotte makes a new code. She uses two functions to help her:

[+2] followed by [×5]

She writes the first two lines of a poem she has written in her code:

110, 50, 35   90, 35, 20, 20, 70, 35, 105   85, 80   110, 50, 35

105, 35, 15, 105, 50, 85, 100, 35   15, 70, 70

25, 70, 15, 110, 110, 35, 100, 55, 80, 45   15, 20, 85, 115, 110

Decipher Charlotte's code below:

a	b	c	d	e	f	g	h	i	j	k	l	m
n	o	p	q	r	s	t	u	v	w	x	y	z

Write the first two lines of her poem.

Write the last two lines yourself and then write it using the code. Let your partner work out how your poem ends.

UNIT 12

ORGANISATION (5 LESSONS)

	LEARNING OUTCOMES	ORAL AND MENTAL STARTER	MAIN TEACHING ACTIVITY	PLENARY
LESSON 1	● Find simple common multiples. ● **Solve a problem by** representing and **interpreting data** in diagrams.	KEEP DOUBLING: Repeatedly doubling, starting from a single digit number.	COMMON MULTIPLES: Finding common multiples using Venn diagrams. Finding the lowest common multiples.	Mark work and explain strategies.
LESSON 2 +3	● Recognise and extend number sequences, such as the sequence of square numbers or the sequence of triangular numbers. ● Make and investigate a general statement about familiar numbers. ● Develop calculator skills and use a calculator effectively.	KEEP DOUBLING: Repeatedly doubling, starting from a 2-digit number less than 30. KEEP HALVING: Repeatedly halving, starting from a 2-digit number.	STEPS: Investigating number sequences from triangular layouts, including summing the numbers in each row and generalising about the sequence generated.	Children report back on their discoveries.
LESSON 4	● Recognise and extend number sequences, such as the sequence of square numbers or the sequence of triangular numbers. ● Make and investigate a general statement about familiar numbers. ● Develop calculator skills and use a calculator effectively.	KEEP HALVING: Repeatedly halving, starting from a multiple of 10 to 1000.	CUBES: Generating cubic numbers first by using cubes and then in numerical terms.	Check results and discuss them.
LESSON 5	● Recognise and extend number sequences, such as the sequence of square numbers or the sequence of triangular numbers. ● Make and investigate a general statement about familiar numbers. ● Develop calculator skills and use a calculator effectively. ● Develop from explaining a generalised relationship in words to expressing it in a formula using letters as symbols.	SEQUENCE TEASERS: Extending sequences.	HOLLOW CUBES: Building hollow cubes and investigating their relationships with cubic numbers.	Bring together practical and numerical results.

ORAL AND MENTAL SKILLS Derive quickly: doubles of 2- and 3-digit numbers and the corresponding halves; doubles of multiples of 10 to 1000 and the corresponding halves. Recognise and extend number sequences.

In Unit 12, Lessons 1, 2 and 4 are shown in full. Lesson 3 extends the work of Lesson 2 and is shown after it. Lesson 5 is an extension of what has been taught and is shown in outline.

RESOURCES

Venn diagrams; pencils and paper.

PREPARATION

Draw a two-attribute Venn diagram on the board labelled as shown opposite. Draw a two-attribute blank Venn diagram on A4 paper then photocopy enough copies for at least 3 per child.

LEARNING OUTCOMES

ORAL AND MENTAL STARTER
● **Derive quickly:** doubles of 2- and 3-digit numbers.

MAIN TEACHING ACTIVITY
● Find simple common multiples.
● **Solve a problem by** representing and **interpreting data in diagrams.**

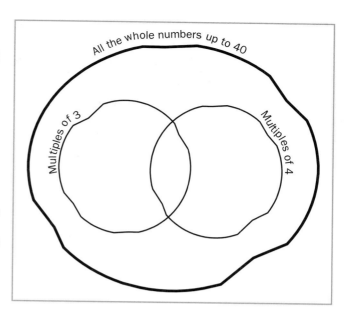

VOCABULARY

Multiple of, common multiple, lowest common multiple.

ORAL AND MENTAL STARTER

KEEP DOUBLING: Start with a single digit number and let the children repeatedly double it until no-one can successfully produce an answer, eg 3, 6, 12, 24, 48, 96, 192, 384, 768... Differentiate by asking the less able the first few doublings.

MAIN TEACHING ACTIVITY

COMMON MULTIPLES: Point out the Venn diagram on the board, based on multiples of 3 and multiples of 4. With the children's help, insert each of the numbers 1 to 40 into the correct region, dealing with each number in order. Ask for the description of each region; multiples of both 3 and 4, multiples of 3 but not 4, multiples of 4 but not 3, neither multiples of 3 nor 4. Emphasise that the numbers in the centre region, multiples of both 3 and 4, are called common multiples of 3 and 4.

Working in pairs, the children then create other Venn diagrams for the set of whole numbers 1 to 40, eg multiples of 4 and 8, multiples of 3 and 5. Discuss what they found out. 'In the multiples of 4 and 8 there were no numbers in the multiples of 8 but not 4 region, as all multiples of 8 are also multiples of 4. In the multiples of 3 and 5, the first common multiple was 3 × 5, 15, the next 15 × 2, 30, the next would be 15 × 3 and so on'. Ask questions such as *Write down three common multiples of 3 and 7, greater than 50,* which the children can work on in pairs or individually. Introduce the term 'lowest common multiple', the smallest number that is a common multiple of two numbers. Ask questions such as: *Find the lowest common multiple of 2 and 7 (14), 8 and 12 (24), 10 and 12 (60), 12 and 16 (48).*

DIFFERENTIATION

More able: Find the lowest common multiples for higher pairs of numbers and go on to work with three numbers.
Less able: Give them simple numbers to work with, but make sure that they know how to tackle the questions.

PLENARY

Mark the work and ask individuals to describe their strategies. 'In the 2 and 7 question I just multiplied 2 by 7 giving 14, but it didn't work for 8 and 12 because 24 is the answer'; 'I just took the larger number and saw if it was a multiple of the smaller number. If it wasn't I doubled the larger number and tried again, then I trebled and so on'. Show this for 10 and 12, giving 12, no; 24, no; 36, no; 48, no; 60, yes.

RESOURCES
Large sheets of paper; felt-tipped pens; calculators; pencils and paper.

PREPARATION
Write 'Steps' on the board as follows:

```
1
2   3
3   5   6
4   7   9   10
5   9   12  14  15
6   11  15  18      21
                        28
                            36
```

LEARNING OUTCOMES

ORAL AND MENTAL STARTER
● **Derive quickly:** doubles of 2- and 3-digit numbers and (for Lesson 3) the corresponding halves.

MAIN TEACHING ACTIVITY
● Recognise and extend number sequences, such as the sequence of square numbers or the sequence of triangular numbers.
● Make and investigate a general statement about familiar numbers.
● Develop calculator skills and use a calculator effectively.

VOCABULARY

Sequence, consecutive, pattern, square number, triangular number, difference pattern.

ORAL AND MENTAL STARTER
KEEP DOUBLING: Repeat the activity from Lesson 1, but this time start with a 2-digit number less than 30.

MAIN TEACHING ACTIVITY
STEPS: Ask the children what they can say about the numbers in 'steps 1' on the board. 'The first column goes up in 1s. The second column is odd numbers starting from 3. The third column goes up in 3s starting from 6. The fourth column goes up in 4s, starting from 10'. Let the children work in pairs, first copying and then extending the sequences mentally. They should then record their results on scrap paper. When they are confident that they are correct, they copy their results on to a large sheet of paper using a felt-tipped pen. When they have finished up to, say the eighth row, write in the numbers on the board. Ask them to look at each row's numbers and their differences. *What do you notice?* 'The differences decrease by 1 between each pair of numbers'. Ask about the number sequence that runs down the diagonal, ie 1, 3, 6, 10 etc. 'They are the triangular numbers.' Now write up Steps 2 for them to copy and continue:

```
1
2   2
3   4   3
4   6   6   4
5   8   9   8   5
6   10  12  .   .   .
```

DIFFERENTIATION
More able: Encourage them to write as many comments as possible.
Less able: You may wish to work with these children as a group.

PLENARY
Write in the numbers for 'steps 2' on the board and ask what they discovered; 'The columns are the tables'; 'All the rows had symmetry, sometimes around a single number and sometimes around two'; 'We found that it was every other row for 'one number symmetry' with the rows in-between having 'two number symmetry''.

LESSON 3

For the **Oral and mental starter**, use the activity KEEP HALVING: Start with a 2-digit number and let the children repeatedly halve it until no one can successfully produce an answer, eg 64, 32, 16, 8, 4, 2, 1, 0.5, 0.25, 0.125... For the **Main teaching activity**, remind the children of the work done in Lesson 2, then ask them to work in pairs to sum the numbers in each row of 'steps 1'. They can use calculators when necessary depending on ability. Ask them how they could express each total, using square numbers to help the description (1 is 1^2, 5 is $1^2 + 2^2$, 14 is $1^2 + 2^2 + 3^2$ etc). The more able children could express this as; 'The 4th row's total is the sum of the first 4 square numbers', or 'The nth row's total is the sum of the first n square numbers'. Now let them try summing 'steps 2's rows and then expressing the totals in triangular number terms; '1 is the first triangular number, 4 is the sum of the first two triangular numbers, 10 the sum of the first three...'. 'The nth row's total is the sum of the first n triangular numbers'. Let them continue both sequences, find the total in each row and check by using their generalisations. During the **Plenary**, let the children explain what they found out.

LESSON 4

RESOURCES

Multilink cubes; calculators; pencils and paper.

PREPARATION

Make up cubes of different colours, made from one, eight and 27 Multilink cubes.

LEARNING OUTCOMES

ORAL AND MENTAL STARTER
- **Derive quickly:** doubles of multiples of 10 to 1000 and the corresponding halves.

MAIN TEACHING ACTIVITY
- Recognise and extend number sequences, such as the sequence of square numbers or the sequence of triangular numbers.
- Make and investigate a general statement about familiar numbers.
- Develop calculator skills and use a calculator effectively.

VOCABULARY
Sequence, pattern, cubic number, cubed (^{3}), difference, difference pattern.

ORAL AND MENTAL STARTER

KEEP HALVING: Repeat the activity from Lesson 3, this time starting with a multiple of 10 up to 1000.

MAIN TEACHING ACTIVITY

CUBES: Show the cubes to the children and ask *How many Multilink cubes are there in each? How do you know?* 'For the eight cube, there are 4 in the bottom layer and 2 layers, so there are 8'; 'I just said for the 27 cube that it's $3 \times 3 \times 3$ making 27'. Write the sequence 1, 8, 27, on the board and, using the last comment say, *Oh I see its $1 \times 1 \times 1$ making 1, $2 \times 2 \times 2$ making 8 and $3 \times 3 \times 3$ making 27.* Say that these numbers are called cubic numbers. Ask for the next cubic number in the sequence ($4 \times 4 \times 4$, making 64). *The number 64 is a cubic number made from $4 \times 4 \times 4$, or $4^2 \times 4$. This can be written as 4^3, which is four cubed.* Ask the children to use their calculators to find 5^3, 6^3, 7^3. Record their answers on the board, making the sequence: 1, 8, 27, 64, 125, 216. They should then work individually to copy and continue the cubic number sequence: 1^3, 2^3, 3^3, 4^3, 5^3, 6^3...

DIFFERENTIATION

More able: *What is the first cubic number above 1000?* (1131, or 11^3) *Are there any between 3000 and 4000?* (3375, or 15^3) *What's the first above 10 000?* (10 640, or 22^3) *What's the highest cubic number the calculator will display?* (99 897 344, or 464^3). Trial and improvement strategies are needed here. *What's the highest square number it will display?* (99 980 001, or 9999^2). Here the square root key may help.
Less able: Work on through the sequence.

PLENARY
Make sure that the sequences produced by the children are correct, and let everyone use their calculators to check the more able children's results before discussing them.

RESOURCES	Prepared sequence examples; Multilink cubes; pegboard with pegs showing the first two hollow squares in the sequence; calculators; pencils and paper.
PREPARATION	Make up the pegboard as shown, using a different colour for each hollow square: Build the first hollow cube with a liftable lid made from Multilink cubes: Write some sequence questions, bearing in mind differentiation, eg 2, 4, 8... (16, 32, 64); 3, 7, 12... (18, 25, 33); 13, 12, 10, 7... (3, –2, –8); 324, 108, 36... (12, 4, 1 $\frac{1}{3}$).
LEARNING OUTCOMES	**ORAL AND MENTAL STARTER** ● Recognise and extend number sequences. **MAIN TEACHING ACTIVITY** ● Recognise and extend number sequences, such as the sequence of square numbers or the sequence of triangular numbers. ● Make and investigate a general statement about familiar numbers. ● Develop calculator skills and use a calculator effectively. ● Develop from explaining a generalised relationship in words to expressing it in a formula using letters as symbols.
ORAL AND MENTAL STARTER	SEQUENCE TEASERS: Ask the children to give the next number in a sequence, and the next, and the next, and so on. Repeat each sequence as a class slowly and try other sequences.
MAIN TEACHING ACTIVITY	HOLLOW CUBES: Remind the children about the hollow square and hollow triangle work previously covered (Lesson 4, Unit 12, Term 1) by showing and discussing the hollow squares on the pegboard and the number of pegs used to create each one. Ask how the numbers in each would continue and write the sequence on the board: 8, 12, 16, 20... 'They are consecutive multiples of 4, starting with 8'. Next, show the hollow cube and ask how many Multilink cubes were used to make it (26). *That's $3^3 – 1$.* Make sure that the children appreciate that this is the first hollow cube that can be made. Split the class into mixed ability groups of about 6 children and let them organise the building of consecutive hollow cubes, giving a number sequence of 26, 56, 98...
DIFFERENTIATION	More able: Children could think about developing a formula, where Number of Multilink cubes = (term number + 2) cubed – term number cubed, or $n = (t + 2)^3 – t^3$, where n is the number of Multilink cubes and t the term number. Less able: Continue their work with the cubes, other children may start to think about: 1st cube: $3^3 – 1^3$ (26) 2nd cube: $4^3 – 2^3$ (56) 3rd cube: $5^3 – 3^3$ (98) They could verify this theory with solid cubes that fit in the hollows. Let them use calculators to develop the sequence further.
PLENARY	Bring the lesson together, linking the building of the hollow cubes, the number of cubes that will fill the hollow being subtracted from the solid cube and the generalisations using cubic numbers without the need to build.

UNIT 13: Assess & Review

Choose from these activities. During the group activities, some children can be completing assessment worksheets 6a and 6b, which assess their skills with solving word problems involving numbers and quantities, including calculating percentages such as VAT, and solving a problem by using tables and graphs, while others work with you on practical tasks. The specific criteria for the assessment sheets are to be found at the bottom of each sheet.

RESOURCES

A list of divisions for the **Oral and mental starter**, including division facts and divisions based on facts, eg 360 ÷ 6, and percentage questions for money percentages; the shape shown, right, drawn on to a large sheet of paper; a large sheet of graph paper with a four-quadrant grid having values tracing −10 to +10 marked on each axis (or use the laminated graph from Lesson 3, Unit 6) and with a rectangle having co-ordinates (2, 3), (2, 1), (5, 1) and (5, 3) drawn – do not label these; paper; felt-tipped pens; wiper; paper; protractors; rulers; graph paper; assessment sheets 6a and 6b, one for each child.

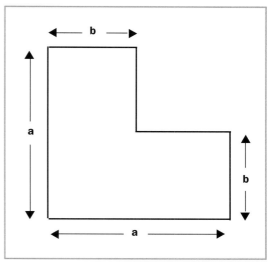

ORAL AND MENTAL STARTER

ASSESSMENT

Can the children:
- Derive quickly division facts corresponding to tables up to 10 × 10?
- Find simple percentages of small whole number quantities?

SQUARE THE ANSWER: Give a division from your first list and ask the children to give the answer to the division, followed by the result of squaring the answer, eg 270 ÷ 9 gives 30, squared 900.

MONEY PERCENTAGES: Repeat the activity from Lesson 3, Unit 11.

GROUP ACTIVITIES

ASSESSMENT

Can the children:
- Calculate the perimeter and area of simple compound shapes that can be split into rectangles?
- Read and plot co-ordinates in all four quadrants?
- Use a protractor to measure and draw acute and obtuse angles to the nearest degree?

PERIMETER FIX: Show the shape to the children and tell them that the sides marked 'a' are of the same length and the sides marked 'b' are also the same length. If the perimeter of the shape is 40cm, what can the children say about the lengths 'a' and 'b'? (a = 10, b = 5) Let them find the area of the shape if 'a' is 10cm and 'b' is 5cm (75cm²), and then consider other values of 'b', say 8 cm. What is the area now? (96cm²)

ROTATIONS: Give the children protractors and rulers, and ask them how they would go about constructing a regular hexagon with side length 6cm (angles 120°). Let them do this.

Now ask them to tell you about the image when the hexagon is rotated anti-clockwise through 90° about a chosen vertex. Let them try the rotation.

TRANSFORMATIONS: Give the children the graph and ask for the co-ordinates of the rectangle. Label the co-ordinates and ask transformation questions like: *If we rotate the rectangle through 90° clockwise about the vertex (2, 1), what will the co-ordinates of the image be?* [(2, 1), (4, 1), (4, −2), (2, −2)]. Translate the rectangle so that the image of the vertex (5, 1) is at (−4, 1). *What are the other co-ordinates? If you reflect the shape about the x axis, what are the co-ordinates of the image?* Later, you may wish to ask questions about combining reflections, translations and rotations, for example: *What transformations are needed to give an image with co-ordinates (−1, −3), (2, 3), (2, −5), (−1, −5)?* [Rotating 180° clockwise through (2, 1), giving [(2, 1), (−1, 1), (−1, −1), (2, −1)], followed by translate 'subtracting 4' from each value of y.] Some children may need tracing paper to help with this activity.

ANSWERS:
Assessment 6a: 1a) £5.25; b) £6.98; c) £19.20; d) £9.60; e) £20.40; 2a) £7.20; b) £252; c) £21.60; d) £3.20; e) £740; 3a) £20.00; b) £66.25; c) £1.95; d) £270; e) £237.50; 4) DIY store £75.53 (Wednesday); Dad's friend £78.14.
Assessment 6b:

Model	VAT @ 17.5%	Total cost
Mini 33	£148.58	£ 997.58
Mini 44	£157.33	£1,056.33
Maxi 500	£167.83	£1,126.83
Power 400	£173.08	£1,162.08
Super power	£201.08	£1,350.08
Executive	£209.83	£1,526.33

Assessment sheet 6a

Do not use a calculator for these questions.

I. Find 15% of:
a) £35   b) £46.50   c) £128   d) £64   e) £136

2. If 5% is:
a) 36p   b) £12.60   c) £1.08 d) 16p   e) £37
what is 100% of each amount?

3. If 40% is:
a) £8.00 b) £26.50   c) 78p   d) £108 e) £95
what is 100% of each amount?

You may use a calculator for this question.

4. Dad wants to paint the outside of the house this year. He estimates that he will need seven 5-litre tins of masonry paint and it's going to be expensive. We went to the DIY store and the paint costs £11.99 a tin, with 10% off on Wednesdays. Dad's friend is a builder and he says that at his wholesalers the same paint costs £9.50 excluding VAT (17.5%). Where will the paint be cheapest and what will the total cost of seven tins be? Make sure that your working is clear.

Show your working here.

● Identify and use appropriate operations (including combinations of operations) to solve word problems involving numbers and quantities based on 'real life' and calculating percentages such as VAT.

UNIT 13

Assessment sheet 6b

You may use calculators.

Criterion computer model	Cost excluding VAT	VAT@17.5%	Total cost
Mini 33	£ 849		
Mini 44	£ 899		
Maxi 500	£ 959		
Power 400	£ 989		
Super power	£1,149		
Executive	£1,299		

Sales of Criterion Computers for week commencing 7th September			
	Bristol branch	Cardiff branch	Birmingham branch
Mini 333	23	19	28
Mini 440	17	26	26
Maxi 500	15	6	16
Power 400	12	18	28
Super power	26	32	19
Executive	12	37	53

Draw a bar chart using grouped data to show the number of computers sold in each of the following price ranges:
Below £1,000
£1,001–£1,100
£1,101–£1,200
above £1,200.

● Solve a problem by representing, extracting and interpreting data in tables and graphs.
● Explain methods and reasoning.